THE INTEMPERATE AUCTIONEER

THE INTEMPERATE AUCTIONEER

John Hurste

The Book Guild Ltd
Sussex, England

First published in Great Britain in 2002 by
The Book Guild Ltd
25 High Street
Lewes, East Sussex
BN7 2LU

Typesetting in Times by
IML Typographers, Birkenhead, Merseyside

Printed in Great Britain by
Bookcraft (Bath) Ltd, Avon

A catalogue record for this book is available from
The British Library.

ISBN 1 85776 676 8

Intemperate

1) Given to or characterised by immoderate indulgence
   in intoxicating liquor.
2) Excessive indulgence of a natural appetite or passion.

From *Webster's Encyclopaedia and Dictionary*

CONTENTS

FOREWORD

This narrative is a humble attempt to recount and remember the life and times of John Francis Bowers (1890–1984). His lifestyle was so far removed from the present day as to appear unreal.

Frank – as he was known throughout most of his long and fruitful life – following early heartbreak became a successful farmer, a keen fox-hunting man, a horse-buyer for the Army in two World Wars, a much sought-after horse judge and a successful exhibitor of top quality horseflesh. He outlived almost all of his true friends. Acquaintances and customers, of which there were many, have described him thus:

> 'Often a bit too sharp for his own good, particularly with "hoss deals".'
> 'Seldom went 'ome same day as he set off.'
> 'A man's man.'
> 'A hard drinking womaniser who managed to get away with it.'
> 'Could charm the clothes off your back if it suited him.'
> 'They don't make 'em like that fellow any more.'

The author persuaded Frank in his latter years to record on tape the many facets of his varied and interesting life. Almost without exception, every chapter is based on true facts as he remembered them.

1

First Selling Experience

Frank was fortunate to find his true vocation in life, almost by accident, at the tender age of seventeen. It all started when he visited the Auction Mart in his home town of Walshford. He was anxious to submit a claim against one of his neighbours for damage caused by trespassing poultry and intended asking Joe Falshaw, the local valuer, to act for him. Frank was in his second year at Farrick House; a large arable farm in the plain of York. He was still learning his trade, ably assisted by his late father's foreman. He'd called next door, at Terry Foster's run-down holding, soon after he'd arrived at the family farm.

'He's still away at yon Walshford market,' his harassed wife had informed him. 'Nivver gets home afore dark yance he sets off – allus gits stopped, drinkin' and sich like.'

Frank had been amazed at the number of children running around the untidy farmyard – barefooted and scantily clothed.

'Are these all yours, Mrs Foster?' he asked politely.

'Aye lad, seventeen of 'em,' she replied proudly, cradling the youngest in her arms. 'This 'ere's gan to be last if I've aught to do with it – yon medic's tell't him there baint be ony more on accounts of me 'ealth, like.'

'And your husband agreed, I trust?'

'Nah, Terry nobbut grinned as he allus does, wi' his flat cap o'er his left lug and tell't him seventeen were nowt! He tell't him his old father sired twenty-one – twice o'er!'

'Looks as if he's tryin' to emulate his father's prowess,' grinned Frank.

'Nah! he were nobbut 'aving him on; twenty-first were born dead, and then they got Terry, like – best if they'd nivver bothered.'

It was close to harvest and Frank was particularly proud of a field of wheat close by the Foster homestead; he decided one morning to ride out to where the men were working, to make a final inspection. As he trotted closer he realised that they had all stopped work. Most of them were doubled up with laughter.

I hope they're not laughing at this old pony of mine, he thought to himself – his father had bought him Topsy almost ten years previously and Frank had long since outgrown her.

'What's so funny?' he enquired of his foreman, who simply pointed in the direction of the nearby farmhouse and then proceeded to stagger along gasping for breath between fits of laughter. All Frank could see was a long line full of washing, as befits such a large family. Then he spotted, in the middle of the line with a stiffish breeze howling through it, a voluminous pair of knee-length pink bloomers.

'She's just put 'em out,' he heard his foreman gasp. The pantaloons tried hard to take off as a kite might do.

Obviously not new, thought Frank, and then he caught sight of the true reason for the uncontrolled merriment, the entire rear of the pants had been patched with a Saxa Salt bag. 'I bet that sort of linen is a bit rough on the backside,' Frank said aloud, only to put his men back into convulsions.

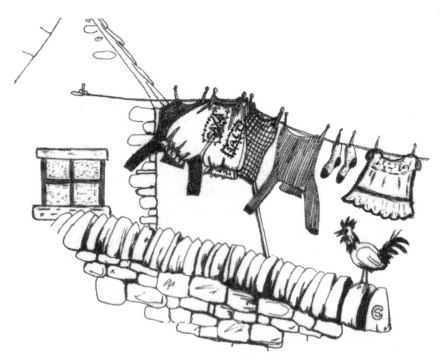

Pink Bloomers – 'I'll bet that sort of linen is a bit rough on the backside'

2

'I don't suppose she'll notice now, at her age,' one of them remarked.

'I suppose Terry needs a bit of salt on it these days,' quipped the foreman, sending his men once more into hysterics.

At this point Frank was somewhat alarmed to see arranged in a straight line close by the boundary fence, twelve mobile chicken arks. He was aware that each hut was capable of containing around fifty birds. Six hundred pullets ready for a go at my wheat, he thought. As he rode around the headland and drew closer he got the impression that his field was sprouting mushrooms; then he realised the chickens were white – and they were already attacking his crop in hundreds.

'Get your bloody poultry away from my wheat field!' he yelled at the unfortunate Mr Foster who happened to be dismounting from his pony in the yard as Frank galloped up. He was half out of the saddle when his young pony bolted. 'Whoa!' he shouted, 'whoa!' only to find himself deposited within seconds head first into a large slimy pond, full of very smelly, highly viscous, green fluid. It all happened so quickly that the older man had no idea quite where he was. As the truth slowly dawned on him, words of invective flowed endlessly from this half-submerged, diminutive, figure. His family quickly gathered around, pointing, laughing and dancing with glee; Frank roared with laughter and, as old Terry rose unsteadily to his feet still not certain what had hit him, Frank introduced himself.

'I know who you are,' snapped Terry. 'What does t'want?'

Frank quickly withdrew his proffered hand as he realised that one twice the size of his own and covered with mud was about to grasp it. 'Your poultry,' Frank said.

'Well, what about 'em?' was the reply.

'You'd better keep them out of my wheat from now on,' said Frank in as firm a voice as he could muster. 'I shall be asking Joe Falshaw to make out a claim for damages and you'll be hearing from him shortly.' With that, trying to look as dignified as possible, he rode slowly out of the yard.

Frank was at the Auction Mart next morning: it was housed to the rear of a substantial red sandstone Queen Anne residence in the centre of the small town of Walshford; off to one side was a large uncovered yard divided by row upon row of wattle hurdles. The new sheep market I've heard so much about, thought Frank. This was a new venture by Joe Falshaw; at this time all cattle, horses and pigs were usually sold privately in the main street, but because more and more stock were coming forward and virtually blocking the road to traffic, Joe had started one of the first Auction

Markets in the country. Commission was small, one penny in the pound, but the farmers were beginning to see the sense of having their sheep penned and sold for them; besides, they could leave their flock in somebody else's care and spend the rest of the day in one of the four market taverns close by. This led to some very uproarious days and nights, but as yet Frank remained aloof from such goings-on. He was soon to be pitched headlong into it but at the moment he was having difficulty in finding Joe Falshaw's office.

He walked straight into someone who gasped at the impact. The passageway was dark but Frank could make out a pretty girl, even taller than himself, 'and probably a little older than me,' Frank thought.

'I do apologise,' she said. 'I'm always dashing about and bumping into people.' What a marvellous deep, cultured, voice, thought Frank. 'Can I help you?' the girl enquired.

'Well, I'm looking for Mr Falshaw.'

'Ah, yes, he's in his office. I'll show you, he's my Uncle, you know. I'm Evelyn Coverdale, just here on a short holiday.'

Little did Frank know then, but he had just met his future wife, though it would be twelve years before he slipped the ring on her finger. A great deal would happen in the meantime, including the First World War.

'A young man to see you Uncle,' she said as she ushered Frank into a rather dingy office. With that she smiled and was gone.

'Ah, you've met my niece have you?' the man said as he offered an out-stretched hand. 'Lovely girl, comes from near Malton you know; my brother-in-law farms over there.'

Umm, thought Frank, farmer's daughter, eh? and nice with it. Frank then found himself staring with admiration at the immaculately-dressed erect man who confronted him. His waistcoat in particular caught his eye, bright yellow with black and red squares.

'Well, what can I do for you, young fellow?'

'Ah, yes. I want to make a claim against one of my neighbours. My name is Frank Bowers and I come from Farrick House.'

'Knew your father well, splendid chap, particular friend of mine. I heard you'd been pitched in at the deep end when he passed away. How's your mother taking it, settled down yet?'

'Yes, she seems to have recovered,' Frank said, 'though she was heart-broken at first having to leave Bolton Grange.'

'Have you still got that ghost, or whatever it is?'

'Yes sir, but we've come to accept it.'

'Which neighbour, and what's it about?' he fired.

4

'Well, it's Terry Foster.'

'Ah, that old rogue – never sober you know, worst horses and implements in the district, only good for one thing they tell me.'

'Yes, well he's moved over five hundred pullets close by my boundary, next to a field of wheat, and they've already done quite a lot of damage.'

'Right, I'll be out first thing in the morning. You've never been here before have you?'

'No,' said Frank.

'Let me show you around.'

The next hour was pure magic for Frank as he became aware of the many interesting facets of an auctioneer's life. He was shown the produce market, where all types of produce, poultry, fruit and bric-a-brac were offered for sale. He saw the sheep market and warmed to his host's enthusiasm and listened intently to his plans for sale rings for sheep, cattle and pigs. All too soon Joe had to excuse himself, 'Farm sale well north of here this afternoon, near Ripon,' he said. 'Quite a long bumpy journey in a small dog cart, you know. I'll be with you quite early in the morning.' And with that he was gone.

Frank thought long and hard that evening about his experience of the morning, 'pity my father wasn't an auctioneer' he mused, little realising he was already hooked and his future was being shaped for him. Joe Falshaw had already decided Frank would be a likely successor if he could somehow be persuaded to come in with him, and Frank was to be drawn back to Walshford like a moth to a flame.

As promised, Joe was in the yard at Farrick House early next morning. Together he and Frank examined the damage to the wheat field; the poultry had not been moved. 'Hundreds of them,' said Frank.

'I'll shift him,' said Joe. 'A claim for ten pounds with my fee of two guineas should make him sit up. Leave it with me.'

'Have you ever thought that your schooling could be put to better use than farming, Frank?' Joe asked as they sat down to breakfast. The home-cured fatty bacon and fresh eggs with dripping bread soon disappeared.

'Marvellous breakfast, Mrs Bowers,' Joe said. 'I've been asking your son if he ever thought he might make an auctioneer.'

'Well Joe, he's a farmer because his father wanted it. I thought maybe a doctor or solicitor, but as you know he had to leave school early.'

'I have an opening for him in my firm if he's interested.'

'Thanks, Joe,' she said, 'but I need him here.'

5

'Ah well, it seemed a good idea; if ever you change your mind, Frank, let me know.'

Terry Foster reluctantly agreed to move his poultry and paid over the ten pounds Joe was asking. However, he flatly refused to pay the two guineas costs.

'Leave me to sort that out with young Bowers,' was as near as Joe could get to a full settlement. 'I'll pop round and see him personally. He got me dumped in the mud – ruined a good pair of breeches.'

It was to be a month before Terry Foster arrived in the stackyard. 'We must talk about this 'ere two guineas.'

'Good, have you come to pay?' said Frank.

'Nay, you employed yon auctioneer, so you can pay his fee.'

'Pay up inside a week, or else!' replied Frank curtly.

'How about sharing it then, I'll pay one pund, you pay t'other.'

'Forty-two shillings and not a penny less, you old skinflint, and think on you pay Joe Falshaw next time you go to Walshford.'

A few days later Frank made the excuse that he needed a saddle he had seen advertised for sale at the market and made straight for Joe Falshaw's office.

'I was looking for your niece, Mr Falshaw, thought she might like to come out to the farm for a game of tennis.'

'She's gone home, Frank, doesn't come over here very often either. Buying furniture?' Joe asked.

'No,' said Frank, 'but there's a good saddle to sell, lot 350.'

'Yes, that's an ex-cavalry saddle, seen active service so I'm told.'

'I may stay for that, if it's going cheap look out for me,' said Frank.

'Right, I'd better get on – be pushed to get through all this lot before two-thirty – most pressing appointment this afternoon, could do with an assistant, you know.'

That afternoon at the auction Frank was dozing on one of the easy chairs three rows back from the rostrum. He vaguely heard Joe Falshaw declare 'Well, ladies, gentlemen, I have to leave you for a most pressing appointment; however, in the audience here is a young man who has designs on becoming an auctioneer. Not many of you know him, his name's Frank Bowers and he comes from Farrick House.' Frank sat bolt upright. 'Right young man, up you come and here's your hammer and don't rush it, if a buyer wants anything he'll bid. Look after him, folks, and see you next week.' With that he hurried from the room and a slightly

6

dazed young man peered nervously at the curious faces arranged before him.

'Lot 251, sir,' he heard a porter shout out, 'up there on the balcony at the back, needs slight repair and one leg missing.'

The saleroom was, in fact, a disused chapel. Most of the wooden benches had been taken out to make room for furniture and audience participation; around the auditorium was a balcony. The building had been built into the side of a hill and was split-level. Conveniently, Joe Falshaw, who had bought the chapel for £100, had been able to fit rear double access doors so that large items such as wardrobes, beds and pianos, could easily be wheeled in and displayed around the balcony.

'Lot 251, ladies and gentlemen, a grand piano. How much am I bid?' Frank found that the hand holding the gavel was shaking. 'Ten pounds? Eight then, anybody start me off? I'll take five.' At that moment one of the regulars, a certain Sidney Jesuiter whose lifestyle was as far removed from his ecclesiastical name as chalk is from cheese, shouted, 'Hang on boss, let's have a peep!'

Sidney never paid more than a pound for any lot and he usually managed to fill his cart with items bought for between one shilling and half a crown. He moved towards the piano, lifted the lid and then let it fall with a resounding crash. That was all it needed to unbalance the piano – the books holding up one side crumpled in a heap. Lot 251 tilted on its side, went through the balcony rail and crashed upside down to the floor below. Fortunately there was nobody underneath, but ivory keys, lengths of wire and splintered wood were splayed around the room, one black note actually bounced off the wall and landed on the rostrum.

'I'll give you a bob, guv'nor,' Sidney declared, realising he had put the young trainee in a tight spot. 'Only trying to help,' he said meekly as he saw the steely look in Frank's eye and the set of his jaw. 'Not my fault you know, your men put it too close to the edge, in my opinion,' said Sidney, whereupon the two porters started to move menacingly towards him.

'All right,' said Frank, 'let's leave it. Lot 252 please,' referring to his notes, 'quantity of books.' Oh my God, thought Frank, same books that were holding the thing up!

'Sixpence,' shouted Sidney.

'Anybody give me a shilling?' queried Frank. 'Ninepence, then. No advance on sixpence?' – bang – 'sold to the gentleman up above for sixpence plus piano, charge him one and a tanner. Name please?'

'Jesuiter, Sid Jesuiter.'

'And very aptly named,' Frank quipped, a remark which brought hearty

'Your men put it too close to the edge'

laughter and a ripple of applause from his audience. I'm going to enjoy this, thought Frank, and so a new career opened up for the young farmer's son.

'Can I take you up on your offer, Mr Falshaw?' Frank asked as Joe returned.

'Yes, lad, I thought you might like it. Salary of a hundred pounds a year, if that's all right, with a chance of a partnership, and then it'll be yours

8

when I retire.' The two men shook hands on the deal. 'By the way, what happened to the piano I saw Sidney loading on his cart?'

'Ah!' said Frank, 'a slight accident.'

'Never mind,' said Joe. 'He tells me you dropped him in for a split kettledrum at sixpence and a harp with only three strings for a shilling – he thinks he can patch up the piano; reckons you sold him a three piece orchestra for half a crown!'

'Three shillings to be exact,' said Frank.

2

Formative Years

John Francis Bowers was born in the year 1890. He was the long-awaited son of a successful, hard-working farmer, anxious for a male heir. Three previous births, one stillborn, had produced only girls, who formed little part in their father's plans for the expansion of his farming enterprise.

It was nearly dawn on a wild, gale-swept March morning when Francis was born; his mother, a refined, large-framed, handsome woman, was already thirty-eight years of age when this lusty 9lb boy came into the world. The local doctor, summoned at midnight, had arrived by pony and trap with only twenty minutes to spare; the journey from York, some ten miles away, having taken twice the normal time, because a fallen tree blocking the road had meant a wide detour.

'A fine pair of lungs,' Doctor Shaw remarked to Francis's father as he consumed his fourth large glass of whisky before sitting down to breakfast. 'That lad could make an auctioneer one day,' he prophesied, little knowing how true these words were to prove.

'No, he's last of the line,' his father remarked, 'so he'll have to take over from me when the time comes.'

In fact, Francis's family had farmed Farrick House since 1640 when it was won in a game of cards by a noted gambling ancestor; before that they had been yeoman farmers of unbroken lineage dating back to 1290, when the earliest recorded ancestor had taken a 'vaccary' or breeding farm – one of the thirteen left vacant in the Bowland Forest area of Lancashire, following the inquisition avenging the murder of Henry de Lacy.

Francis's mother had other ideas for her son. She was well-educated, a clergyman's daughter, and envisaged a professional career for him.

'Maybe he'll make a lawyer, or even a doctor,' she whispered weakly to the doctor as he left the nursery, assuring her the child was one of the strongest he'd ever delivered.

Francis was going to need a strong constitution. He became a successful farmer; a much respected agricultural auctioneer, one of the best known men in the hunting field, not only in his native Yorkshire but many surrounding counties; a top showman and judge of horses. He was to serve his country as a horse-buyer in two World Wars; and retained all his faculties, including his wonderful memory and his zest for life, until he died peacefully in his sleep at the age of ninety-four.

Although Francis always had an eye for the ladies, he was basically a man's man; he always enjoyed the company of young people and it was perhaps the only regret in his full and active life that his wife – he married at the age of twenty-nine – refused to have any children. She was heard to declare in confidence: 'Frank is not a family man; he has too many outside interests, he is hardly ever at home, either away fox-hunting or working, and rarely comes home the same day that he sets off.'

Francis's first, formative years were sheltered and comfortable. His life was dominated by his mother who started his education. The two elder sisters already had a tutor; a room in the rambling farmhouse had been turned into a schoolroom and it was here that Francis learned discipline and the good manners that were to be with him all his life.

It was shortly after his sixth birthday that Francis's father decided his son was having too soft an upbringing and it was time to start work on the farm. He had recently acquired the tenancy of Bolton Grange, near Catterick, and moved his family there. The Grange was basically an arable unit. A large stable of shires, the heavy work horse, were needed to work this 350-acre unit. It was clear that Francis showed a keen interest in these horses since he could toddle around the farmyard, and the foreman, a man called Jim Boynton, with one son of his own, nurtured this interest. It was undoubtedly his influence that was to give Francis his lifelong love of horses of whatever shape and size.

The shire-horses were bred on the farm; they were broken to harness and the plough, and it was here that Francis was given early tuition in the handling of young horses. He was to derive great pleasure for most of his life in producing young, unbroken, hunters from scratch, either for showing or for 'the gentry' to purchase. He often remarked in later life that when farming was in the doldrums in the late twenties and most of the thirties, the extra income from the sale of young horses 'kept the ship afloat.'

When Francis was eight, the perpetual tug-of-war between his parents as to his future came to a head.

'You'll kill that boy if you work him much harder,' his mother remarked.

'I intend making a man of him,' was the reply.

'Then he must be sent away to school,' she declared, and so it was decided. Reluctantly his father agreed to allow his handsome young son to be packed off to a small private kindergarten school run by a worthy Miss Masters, a plump unhappy woman, humiliated by her father as a young girl and separated from the mother she loved by her untimely death from breast cancer at the age of thirty-six. With a great hatred of sex, she derived some happiness from teaching other people's children how to prepare themselves for adult life.

Great store was placed on religion, which irritated Francis somewhat, but it ensured he was to remain a religious man for the remainder of his long life. The pupils, from both sexes, remained at the school until the age of twelve; although they shared the same classroom, sleeping arrangements in separate dormitories was very much the order of the day.

Francis was ten when, encouraged by a forward young maid, barely sixteen, he was caught 'red-handed' in her arms around midnight, in the walk-in linen cupboard. He was packed off home immediately with a note suggesting he be sent forthwith to a school 'for boys only'. Mother was shocked, father was secretly amused and delighted – he could now untie his son from his mother's apron strings; it was therefore hastily arranged that Francis would be admitted as a full boarder at Feversham Grammar School, overlooking the River Swale in North Yorkshire.

Discipline at the school was harsh and life for the younger boys particularly trying. Francis progressed to the Middle School and was at last beginning to enjoy himself. He was ill-prepared for the summons to attend the headmaster's study one cold December morning.

'Francis,' said the headmaster gently, laying a comforting arm around his shoulders, 'we have just been informed that your father died suddenly late last night from a heart attack. You are to leave school immediately; your place is at home now, at your mother's side. She needs you to run the farms in his place.'

It was fortunate in one way that during school holidays Francis's father had always kept his son's nose to the grindstone. On the coach journey home into the Vale of Mowbray, the young, heartbroken boy thought wistfully about his taskmaster father. He was beginning to realise why this firm parent had tried so fiercely to instil into him the need for hard work – it was the only way to succeed. With livestock prices at a very low ebb there was to be no place in farming for slackers.

He remembered with pride how, at the age of twelve, he and the son of the farm foreman were given the task of driving a herd of cattle from the rented farm near Catterick to Farrick House, some 35 miles away, in part along the Great North Road, but for most of the way by a green lane, the old drovers' route stretching from Scotland to the south of England. The boys had one horse which they rode in turn, and one dog. The journey normally took two days. Unfortunately at the first overnight halt on a farm near Bedale a bitch on heat escaped and, as so often happens with dogs, Francis awakened at dawn the next morning to find that his dog had taken to the surrounding countryside and was nowhere to be found.

Meanwhile his father, fuming at the end of the second day and unaware what had happened, sent a telegram to Farrick House, 'Get back soonest – Urgent' it read. Although it was by now teatime on the gruelling third day, the boys, without having had any rest, both jumped on the horse and galloped almost non-stop straight home. They arrived travel-weary and dust-stained around 9.00 p.m.

'What's happened father?' Francis enquired as he stumbled into the kitchen.

'Nothing,' his father replied, 'I wanted you back here yesterday – yon long thirty-acres field by the river needs ploughing afore it rains, you'd better start first thing in the morning.'

And now he was gone! How can I manage to look after two big farms? Francis thought. His reunion with his mother and sisters was a tearful display; the funeral even more so. There was the largest gathering of farming folk mixed with gentry ever seen at the local parish church. Francis suddenly realised how popular and respected his father had been. He received many offers of help that day, and knew then that if things were to go wrong in the future there were neighbours prepared to help him out.

Things did not go well. The first blow was, of course, the loss of the tenancy of Bolton Grange. Following a decent interval, the local land-owner and his agent arrived in the yard, unannounced, demanding to see Mrs Bowers. The squire was sympathetic but firm; he was not prepared to let a 14-year-old boy straight from school take over the tenancy of the Grange, particularly when the family had a perfectly good property near Wetherby to fall back on.

And so Francis had to organise a move for all the live and dead stock down to Farrick House. His mother was heartbroken,, for she did not relish living in such a large, draughty, farmhouse – she had gone there as a young bride and hated every minute of it. However, needs must, and so the traumatic move began. The only mode of transport was either by foot, by horse, or by train. Apart from four young horses who would probably have

13

proved too much of a handful on the road and so were moved by rail, everything else had to be pulled or driven the 35-mile journey south.

Eventually the move was complete. Francis was exhausted; his mother never really got over the sudden shock of the loss of her husband and her beautiful home in such quick succession. His elder sisters went their separate ways and kept a discreet distance; Francis really was on his own.

It was his second night at Farrick when strange noises in the next room startled him. He and his mother were sitting quietly by the large open log fire in the kitchen, the room was dimly lit by two oil lamps and one flickering candle. He saw his mother sit bolt upright and watched fascinated as her hands holding her knitting started to tremble.

'What's that noise?' he demanded.

'That's our family poltergeist,' she whispered.

'Our what?' Francis said.

'Our ghost,' she replied. 'I was hoping it would have gone away. That's why I persuaded your father to rent Bolton Grange when you were away at school; it seems your presence in this house triggers off a reaction from the spirits.'

Francis laughed. 'Rubbish,' he said as he rose and moved towards the door.

'You must not go in,' his mother pleaded, 'not until it goes away.'

'But I can hear sobbing, as if a girl is crying,' Francis said. Just then he heard something hit the other side of the door with a thud and fall to the floor. He moved to the fireplace, grabbed the twelve-bore shotgun which he had fixed there that very morning and, full of youthful bravado, burst into the room. It was empty. The sobbing ceased immediately. At his feet lay a brass candlestick, one of a pair which he had watched his mother place on the chest of drawers at the other side of the room the previous day. The other candlestick was still in place. He was amazed to find a mark, in the form of a cut, on the inside of the door where obviously the base of the candlestick had hit. Francis stood transfixed as each of the ancient brass handles of the chest of drawers suddenly rattled in rotation. He turned and dashed out of the room slamming the door behind him.

'Is that why nobody wants to live here?' he said.

'Yes, son, but I suppose we must try and live with it, you and I.'

'But where does the sobbing come from?' Francis asked his mother, trying to be brave.

'Legend has it that Robert Bowers, one of your ancestors, fought for the king at Marston Moor. He returned home maimed and died six months after the battle. His only daughter fell in love with an Irish groom employed in the stables here, and she became pregnant; the youth was horse-whipped and sent back to Ireland, the unfortunate girl was hidden away in this house. When she had safely given birth to a boy child, the infant was immediately taken from her and placed in foster care. It may well be that you were the next boy child to be born here – when we took you away from this place I had hoped that would be the end of it.'

But that was not the end of it. On many occasions disturbing noises and the unaccounted-for movement of various objects continued at intervals until eventually Francis and his mother grew to accept the spirit within the house. The main difficulty was in convincing the servants that 'the being' was harmless. After one or two maidservants had been driven out by the ghost, Mary Bowers turned in some desperation to a relative in southern Ireland who obtained for her the services of a big buxom maid named Brigitte, aged 18.

In no way could Brigitte be considered a maiden – she was a pretty girl bursting with health, a good worker, ill-educated in all but the ways of the flesh. She immediately became infatuated with the tall, good-mannered young master of the house – his quiet, polite behaviour was a revelation to her. Accordingly she set out to ensnare him. On the pretence that she wished him to look at a nest of kittens in the hayloft, she led Francis into the barn. Brigitte climbed the ladder first and then swooned in his arms. Francis, just sixteen, soon caught on that he had been led into a trap. His first fumbling attempts at lovemaking exasperated his eager partner, and gradually she took command. Eager to please but not exactly certain what was expected of him, Francis allowed himself to be taken along in a mounting wave of pleasure.

Much later, Francis had almost reached the bottom of the ladder with Brigitte a few rungs above him, when the foreman entered the barn. He saw the young man's knees give way slightly as he touched the floor, he observed two flushed faces and a certain disarray of the maid's attire – he gave his young boss a quizzical look and noticed the look of triumph on his face.

'Beg pardon sir!' he said diplomatically. 'Shall you want the men to start riddling potatoes first thing in the morning?'

'Yes, er ... yes, good idea, Jim. Will you see to it then?'

'Yes sir, no need for you to be there.'

'Right,' said Francis. 'Oh, by the way Jim, this name my parents gave me – Francis.'

'Yes sir.'

'Well, I think it sounds a bit feminine. I wish to be known as Frank in future.'

'Very good, sir,' said Jim giving Miss Brigitte a knowing wink. 'I think perhaps you're right – now you've proved yourself an all, I'll see to it the men know. Oh, and don't worry, I won't be telling them about anything else.'

3

Buying His First Hunter

Frank was lucky with his principal; fortunately they shared an innate and long-lasting love affair with horses. Joe was often heard to remark, 'Mustn't let a day's hunting come before work' and Frank took no encouraging to hold him to that philosophy.

Until now a few chance days as a boy with the Bedale Hunt on the old family pony was all that Frank had managed, enough to whet his appetite. Farrick House came within the York and Ainsty country. Both hunt areas were vast and were hunted at least three days a week, and very often four. And so there was Monday country, Wednesday country and Friday country. With no motorised transport as yet, it was the usual practice for hounds to be taken to the meet the previous day, and housed overnight at some suitable hostelry or farm to be ready for an early start the next morning. It was possible occasionally to use the local railway system but invariably hunt members would hack to the meet; journeys in the early morn of up to 25 miles would be commonplace.

It was the time of the annual Horse Fairs, first Appleby, then Brough Hill close to the Westmorland border, followed closely in North Yorkshire by Topcliffe Fair and finally the largest sale of all, Barnaby Fair at Boroughbridge. The date for these sales was traditionally the same every year. Scores of 'travelling people', many of them true Romanies, were on the move long before the sale dates. A major part of their lifestyle consisted, and still does to this day, of rearing young horses on suitable grass verges as they moved about before taking them to the horse sales; and then spending the whole day buying and selling, at the same time consuming vast quantities of ale and spirits. This invariably led to uproarious evenings with many fights and arguments. The movement of many Romany families through Wetherby on the tortuous journey north inspired Frank to go along to Barnaby Fair in search of his first hunter.

The morning dawned with every prospect of a fine warm day. Frank had

17

asked his principal to drive him there in the pony and trap – hoping to fall back on his expertise should he find a suitable horse. Joe promised to take him and introduce him to Jim Ruddick, one of a handful of horse-traders who could be relied on, but thereafter he would be on his own. Joe was driving north to carry out a long overdue valuation.

The sight which met the two men as their Dales pony, with his extravagant knee action, trotted imperiously down the Great North Road into Boroughbridge, was to stay with Frank for the remainder of his life. Every road in the town was lined with horses of all ages and colours, workhorses, hunters, hackneys, vanners – piebald and skewbald – ponies, fell ponies, packhorses, shetlands; they were all there.

'You're going to be spoilt for choice, young man,' said Joe as he drove into the large yard to the rear of the main hostelry in town, the Crown Hotel.

'You can always find Jim Ruddick here,' said Joe, 'he's probably in one of the stables, he usually has about eighty young horses at this sale. He brings a lot of good quality horses from the East Riding, usually hackney/thoroughbred cross; try and buy one of that sort if you can.

'Ah, there he is. Jim, meet a young assistant of mine, looking for his first hunter. As you can see he's a tall lad, so nothing under sixteen hands, perhaps a five-year-old if you have one.' And with that Frank was left in the care of one of the leading horse-dealers in the north of England.

It was a fortuitous meeting; the rapport between the two men was instantaneous and resulted in many a profitable transaction on both sides in later years. They had no idea, for instance, that Frank was to become a horse-buyer for the Army, and that their friendship would last until 1940 when Jim Ruddick was tragically drowned at sea. At the age of sixty-five he had finally decided to retire to a small cottage on the east coast, but had persuaded the authorities to allow him to accompany a consignment of horses bound for Norway by ship from Newcastle. He and Frank had gathered up eighty 'remounts' from the Thirsk area, but, unfortunately, the ship was dive-bombed in Stavanger Harbour and Jim went down with his horses. But that was in the future.

'Right, Frank,' said Ruddick, 'come and have a look at this.' Frank found himself inspecting a superb dark brown gelding. 'By a good thoroughbred horse called Convermore out of a half-bred mare, four year old and just been broken in. Best youngster I've owned for many years.'

Frank tried hard not to be taken in by the sales patter.

'What height is he?' Frank asked, trying to show his indifference.

'Sixteen two; quiet temperament, just like an old tup.'

18

'Has he seen hounds?' Frank enquired.

'Shouldn't think so! Found him on a farm, top end of Wensleydale.'

'How much?' said Frank.

'As a special favour to you – forty guineas.'

'I've really only got about thirty pounds to spend.'

'Give me your hand,' said Jim.

Frank held his hand out; Jim Ruddick gave it a hearty slap. 'Thirty-five pounds and he's yours.'

Frank handed over seven five-pound notes.

'How do you intend getting him home?' Jim asked.

'I thought if I could borrow a saddle and bridle, I'd ride him home.'

'No problem,' said Jim, 'but I don't suppose he's seen much on the roads, so take care.'

'I'll have a look around and come back in about an hour.' said Frank. When he returned the horse was being ridden around the stable yard by a young gypsy, no more than ten years old, thought Frank.

'Lovely mover,' said Ruddick as he bustled up to Frank, 'can be ridden by a child, as you can see. I'll call at the office for the tack in a week or two.'

Frank mounted his new purchase with trepidation – he'd never been on a horse of this size before. Once clear of the town he allowed him to trot on at his own pace. The journey was uneventful until close to the outskirts of Wetherby. He had been watching a cloud of dust approaching for some time; too late he realised it was a 'horseless carriage'. It happened to be the local squire – a somewhat short-sighted man in any event – intent on finding out how fast his new purchase, a 1907 Silver Ghost Rolls Royce (the first to be sold in the north of England) could go on a decent straight road.

So engrossed was he in watching the speedometer needle move through the twenties, to thirty-five miles per hour, that he never saw Frank on his young horse.

The result was electrifying. As the car bounced over the ruts it backfired twice in quick succession; the horse whipped round; 'it was a miracle I stayed on,' said Frank later. Completely terrified it took its hapless rider straight over the roadside hedge, scattering a gang of Irishmen engaged in mowing grass with long-bladed scythes, and galloped off. Frank was never in charge of his speeding mount as, followed by shouts of encouragement from the Irish onlookers, he simply clung on hoping for the best. Farmer Gyles Nicholson and his womenfolk scattered in alarm as Frank thundered past.

At the far end of the field loomed a formidable thorn hedge. It had originally been cut and laid but then the top had been allowed to grow, so although whippy, from a few yards out it appeared very solid indeed. Frank realised he had 'no brakes' and very little 'steering' because, as can often happen with a young horse, it had managed to get its tongue over the bit. He therefore resigned himself to being 'carted' over the fast-approaching obstacle.

It was not to be. At the very last second the horse ducked its head into the bottom of the hedge and swerved violently to one side. It was impossible to stay with the animal. Frank catapulted out of the saddle, went easily through the top of the 'bullfinch' and, he recalled, had plenty of time to realise he was heading for a huge pile of steaming, strawy manure, removed that very day from the cattle sheds ready for spreading on the land.

The impact winded him temporarily but as he moved each arm in turn, then his legs, he realised he was unhurt. Amazed to find himself still clutching the bridle he was still gathering his wits when a cultured voice said, 'I thought he was going to jump it.' It was Gyles Nicholson, his face beaming as he looked at Frank.

'So did I,' Frank retorted.

'You went over very easily, if you don't mind me saying so. Good job we moved that muck out this morning, though.'

Frank climbed down. 'Yes, I suppose so. Where's the driver of that bloody motor car?'

'Careful, young man. That's my landlord, daft as a scuttle but a powerful man nevertheless – here he comes down the field now. You're lucky, he doesn't usually stop.'

'Good-day, Squire,' Gyles said touching his cap, 'this here's young Bowers, a new auctioneer in these parts.'

'Dashed sorry, young man,' said Colonel North. 'Never saw you. Mighty fine animal you were riding, had him long?'

'No sir, only bought him this morning, haven't got him home yet,' replied Frank.

'Know a bit about them, you know, cavalry officer and all that,' said the Colonel; 'is he good to catch?'

'No idea. It might not be too easy – I've still got his bridle!'

All attempts at getting anywhere near the horse failed dismally. The Colonel, who normally sported a florid complexion, went purple as he dashed about in his deerstalker hat and ankle-length overcoat. The Irishmen, happy for a break in their day-long toil, cursed profusely as the horse continually eluded their grasp.

'Never mind,' gasped the Colonel. 'Nicholson, you bring one of your own horses over and let him follow you back to the farm. I'll run this young chap into Wetherby and he can come for him in the morning.'

And so Frank had his first ride in a motor car. He was hooked immediately. The firm could do with one of these, he thought, I'll have to suggest it to Joe. However Frank was nearly twenty-three before he finally persuaded the senior man to invest in a car. He was to hold a driving licence until well into his ninety-first year when finally his eyesight started to let him down. The bonnet, from about 1926 onwards, always sported a running fox. The same mascot was left to the author by Frank on his death, together with a pair of solid silver boot hooks.

In later years Frank often boasted that he had followed 'Charlie' (a hunting man's affectionate name for his quarry) home late at night many a time. He'd let him down only once, he said – that was when, having imbibed too much gin, he ran slap bang into the back of a bus – full of policemen!

When Frank finally arrived home, he tried hard to explain to his mother what had happened. Yes, he had bought a horse, but no, he hadn't got it home, he had to go for it in the morning. Dick Boynton, Francis's foreman, hooted with laughter when Frank told him his story.

'It takes seven falls to make a rider; is that the first?' he asked Frank.

'Well, er, yes,' said Frank, 'I never came off old Topsy.'

'I'm not surprised, she had a back like a table top,' Dick remarked. 'Don't forget when you go for him, if this young horse is as green as it would appear, mount him in the box and walk him quietly around a few times before you bring him out.'

Frank had to walk next morning, a distance of some eight miles. He found his horse munching hay in a large box.

Gyles was in the yard – 'Caught him with no trouble after he followed me into the yard, seems a very quiet sort if you treat him right.'

'Thanks,' said Frank, 'How much do I owe you?'

'Nothing,' Gyles said, 'Happy to do you a favour, may ask you for one in return some day.'

The horse stood perfectly still as the saddle and bridle were fitted. 'I'd like a leg up,' said Frank.

'What? In here? Not a very high roof, you know,' said Gyles.

'Best way with a young horse,' said Frank, airing his knowledge, 'Don't want him bucking me off or anything like that in the yard.'

'Just as you say; up you go,' said Gyles helping a slightly nervous young man to get astride. Frank clicked his tongue and touched him lightly with his spurs … Bang! – the next thing he knew his head was through the loft floor. Even more amazing, so was the head of his new purchase – about a yard in front of him.

What had happened, although Frank failed to realise it at the time, was that the horse had taken a sudden plunge forwards and upwards; both front legs were firmly planted in the cast iron manger to which he had been tethered a short while ago.

'Are you all right?' shouted Gyles, safely outside.

'I think so,' said Frank. 'Lucky the floor was rotten. I'll climb through and come down the stairs, you get hold of the horse's head and try to get him down.'

'Not likely!' said Gyles. 'You can do that; I'm keeping well away from this fella; somebody will get laid out before he's finished.'

It took some time to extricate the horse from his lofty perch, fortunately he remained calm. Most horses would have panicked, thought Frank, striving hard to find some attribute for his recent purchase. More rotten floorboards were quickly removed and finally the horse was coaxed backwards until he dropped with all four legs onto the ground.

Strangely enough, that horse never reared again. He had apparently made quite a name for himself in Upper Wensleydale as a three-year-old and had been known to come over backwards more than once; Frank was of course unaware of this at the time. (Never were the Latin words *caveat emptor* [buyer beware] more true than in horse fair transactions.)

Apart from a small graze over one eye, the horse was still unblemished. For how much longer? Frank mused.

'Have you a mounting block in the yard?' he asked.

'Yes,' replied Gyles.

'Right, you hold his head whilst I get on again, and hang on until I get out into the lane.'

Apart from a couple of playful bucks as they moved off, the journey to the main road was uneventful.

'Reckon he's got a cold back,' shouted Gyles as Frank rode away. In his inexperience Frank had little idea what he was talking about. It came to him in a flash, however, why the horse was already saddled and being ridden around the Crown Hotel stable yard on his return the day before. In future he always insisted on seeing the tack put on and asked to see the horse ridden before making up his mind to purchase.

Disasters often run in threes, thought Frank as he made his untroubled way the next couple of miles to the outskirts of Wetherby. 'Wonder what else can happen before I get this chap home.'

His thoughts were rudely interrupted by the sound of a post-horn behind him, he was alarmed to see a column of dust fast approaching from the north; Oh Lord! he thought, the Yellow Earl. With that he pushed his horse into full gallop and dashed for the safety of the town. He quickly dismounted in the first side street and took a firm grip of his horse's head. Do him good to see this lot, thought Frank as he turned the horse's head towards the main road.

The Earl of Lonsdale, plus entourage, was on his way from Lowther Castle in Penrith towards London. Various staging posts with fresh horses were always laid on. Nothing less than full gallop between stages satisfied his Lordship, as far as he was concerned anything or anybody en route had better get out of the way. Having changed horses at Boroughbridge, it was full speed ahead to Doncaster, thence to Grantham, and so on.

Frank counted seven coaches and one wagon, all painted yellow, as they thundered past. The notes from the post-horn rang out from the leading coach, warning the townsfolk to beware. Within seconds all that was left was a cloud of dust, a couple of barking dogs, and a startled horse trying its best to break away from Frank's restraining grip.

Finally they made it home to Farrick.

'Nice horse,' said Dick Boynton as he led him away to the stable block.

'Inclined to be a bit skittish,' replied Frank. 'He's got a cold back.'

'Oh, we'll soon have him over those problems,' said the youngster. 'Let me have him for a week, I'll straighten him out.'

Next day Frank noticed with pleasure that young Dick had the 'breaking tackle' on the horse; the following day he had him working well in 'long reins' and two days later had him pulling the plough.

'I'll not work him too hard, boss,' said Dick, 'but a bit of field work will do wonders for him.'

And so it proved. Within a couple of months Frank had him cub-hunting. It was an early meet, six-thirty in the morning, twelve miles away and pretty close to the old Harrier Kennels. Having doffed his cap to the Master and introduced himself, Frank set about finding out what he should do.

Little did he realise as he listened to the Huntsman, that this man telling him what to do was to become one of the most famous hunt servants of all time. It was, in fact, the legendary Frank Freeman; destined at the end of that season to leave the Bedale to make his name with the Pytchley and other famous hunts.

'We think there is a vixen and four well-grown cubs in this first covert,' he heard Freeman say. 'For those new to cub-hunting, we are trying to teach a young "entry" of hounds to hunt the fox; we are also hoping to teach the young fox all about hounds. We hope to catch the weakest in the litter, then next time we come here, hunting proper, they'll know to get the hell out of it.'

The next few hours were pure magic for Frank. His young horse settled down nicely after the first hour; hounds dashing past in full cry just inside the covert upset him at the start, but he took all the strange sights and sounds in his stride, and finally gave Frank one of the most enjoyable mornings of his life.

The quiet ride back in mid-morning brought home to Frank just how valuable young Dick could be in helping to 'make' young horses – he decided to offer him the job as farm foreman next year when his father retired.

'Joe Falshaw wants you back in the office as soon as you can make it,' his mother remarked as he entered the house. 'I think he wants you to go with him into Nidderdale; he warned me you would probably both be late back!!'

4

Wilstrop Hall Estate

Next morning Frank caught the horse-drawn charabanc into town, a new service operating between York and Wetherby; there seemed to be no set time-table but usually one came along about every two hours. The stage coach was always hopelessly full and not to be relied on.

Joe was waiting. 'Hello Frank, how's that young horse coming along? Your mother tells me you both had your first day's cub-hunting this morning.'

'Great fun,' replied Frank, 'Steady as a rock always, never an anxious moment.'

'Good. Now, we've been asked to take over the management of a Wilstrop Hall Estate, towards the top end of Nidderdale. Here's the letter from a firm of London solicitors. Seems everything is a mess. We'll take the pony and trap. I want you to take over the running of the place eventually; it may mean living over there from time to time. The first priority is to prepare an "Inventory and Schedule of Repairs". Apparently the resident agent has ceased to attend to correspondence – I gather he's on the bottle. The owner, a Major Marmaduke Spencer, is suffering from dementia, his wife has obtained a court order certifying the old boy as insane, unfit to manage his affairs. Local gossip has it she brought the resident agent back from Germany about twenty years ago and they've been lovers ever since.

'I'm told that in the early days she cleared off twice back to Bavaria and arrived home each time with a newly-born daughter. The older girl left home some time ago, to become a nun; the younger daughter, now aged twenty-five, is still around; she stands to inherit the estate and we're being called in on her behalf to try and sort things out.'

'Sounds interesting,' said Frank.

'I warned your mother you might be late back,' said Joe. 'We'll call at the Whitwell Hotel on the way up the dale, landlord's an old friend of mine, Tom Kilburn, stout fella, he'll know what's going on. His wife serves the best ham and eggs in Yorkshire, so we'll skip lunch and eat when we get there.'

Frank had to agree; he'd never enjoyed ham and eggs as much before – the fresh-baked crusty bread with local butter was a delight in itself. In his usual considerate manner Frank complimented his hostess on her high tea.

'You must have a secret to be able to prepare food like that.'

'Not really,' she replied. 'I suppose it's because everything is home-grown, the hens run around the yard and live off scraps, the pigs we rear and kill ourselves. They almost live off beer slops alone, they go mad for that you know, but give 'em too much and they can soon be rolling around dead drunk. Tom, my husband, cures the hams and the bacon himself; he puts a lot of brown sugar in with the salt, that gives the special flavour, I think. You ought to come and see us on a pigsticking day; we always have a good party in the evening. We have fresh roast spare rib – taken with plenty of rough cider you can have a wonderful time. We have "the shoot" about the same time.'

'Your wife has suggested I come and see you again when you slaughter one of the pigs,' Frank said to his host as he and Joe were leaving.

'Yes, we usually have a good do; we always get the local butcher to come along to do the nasty bit, about the end of October.'

'Right,' said Frank, 'I'll be here, without fail.'

'What happens at "the shoot"?' Frank asked his employer as they proceeded on their way westwards.

'Oh, that's a great day out,' said Joe. 'Haven't been for a few years myself, been too busy, but you'll enjoy it. Best likened to the old-fashioned Fair Day ... kiddies' sports, dancing around a maypole, fell race, hound trail, sheepdog trials and "the shoot" – a hangover from the days of archery I should think, anybody who fancies himself as a shot can enter. They set up targets on the village green, you fire from thirty yards with a twelve-bore, loaded with number five shot, twenty-five points for a pellet in the bull, down to five points for an outer – good fun. It's usually won by a gamekeeper; I came third about five years ago, got a live goose for a prize. The winner, a young newly-married gamekeeper called Tweet Umpleby, won a quart bottle of whisky, proceeded to drink most of it and went missing until next day. Woke up in bed with an ex-girlfriend, just before his wife, suspecting the worst, broke in. Apparently she chased him down the village street wielding an axe, him clutching his breeches to his chest – startled the vicar, making his morning calls, so I'm told, as they dashed past.

26

'I think she soon forgave him. Once she saw the look on the parson's face watching her husband's bare backside disappear at top speed down the road, she collapsed in a heap laughing. Caused quite a stir in the district at the time, but I understand he's kept his nose clean since.

'You'll probably meet him soon, he's employed part-time up at Wilstrop keeping down a plague of rabbits – quite a character really.'

'Where does he get the nickname Tweet?' asked Frank.

'Oh, he gets that from his habit of standing above a rabbit warren in the breeding season, putting his lips to the centre of the palm of his hand and kissing it with a quick intake of breath, exactly the sound young rabbits make if being attacked by a stoat or weasel; frightens the whole ruddy lot. Any rabbits away from home, particularly breeding does, dash back home and Tweet picks 'em off with his twelve-bore as they come running in.'

Just then Joe turned the hackney left-handed onto the long approach drive to Wilstrop Hall.

'What a beautiful house,' Frank said as they drew nearer the main residence.

'Been here a long time,' said Joe. 'I've been warned it's full of death-watch beetle and dry rot; the trustees want to know the cost to renovate and repair, or whether it will be cheaper to pull it down. There's a very nice dower house close by which could more than accommodate the whole ruddy family. Whoa,' he called to the horse as the trap slowed to a walk and came to rest outside the front door.

'I've already been warned there's a couple of particularly savage guard dogs quite often running loose. Sit quiet for a while; there are no servants left but somebody will have heard us.'

Frank noticed a lace curtain from an upstairs window move slowly aside. 'We're being watched from upstairs, Joe,' he whispered.

'Aye, that's possible! Tom Kilburn told me these folk are believed to sleep all day, and that there's dim lights and movement all night. The solicitors told me there would be no point arriving before five o'clock. What time is it now?'

'Four-thirty,' said Frank.

'All right, we'll sit tight and see what happens.'

Five minutes passed and there was no sound. Frank was fascinated by the impressive chimneys, the soft local limestone, each stone with a herring-bone pattern, the thick, studded oak front door. 'Why do they mark all those stones with such a wonderful pattern?' Frank asked Joe.

'Well, it's a very soft stone when quarried, particularly liable to frost damage; so that herringbone pattern is put on by the stone masons before it leaves the quarry; it helps to get rid of surface water which might freeze and gradually destroy it.'

What a mine of information this chap is, thought Frank; aloud he said, 'I could easily dash across and pull the bell handle.'

'Right,' said Joe, 'but watch out!'

Frank heard the bell ring out deep inside the house, and within seconds he heard the baying of two hounds, then snarling and whimpering behind the door. A sharp command rang out and there was silence; one moment later he heard a man's voice call 'Come here, you two,' an internal door slammed, then the bolts were withdrawn and the heavy main door creaked open.

A tall, silver-haired, slightly dishevelled man moved forward, stared hard at Frank then shifted his gaze to the pony and trap.

'Yes! What can I do for you?'

'Are you Captain Pilkington?' Joe asked.

'Yes sir. Who the devil are you?'

'Joe Falshaw, auctioneer; you should be expecting me. I wrote last week to make an appointment, addressed it to Lady Cecilia.'

'First I've heard of it, what's your business?' the Captain demanded haughtily.

'It's all right, Cecil,' Frank heard a cultured lady's voice and the shuffle of footsteps crossing the hall at the same time. 'These gentlemen have called to see me; they're having tea with Marmaduke and myself. I'll explain later what it's about. Come in gentlemen, come in.'

'Is there anybody to look after the pony and trap?' Joe enquired.

'Not really,' the Captain retorted crossly, 'No staff left, you know.'

'Yes, you can stable the pony, Cecil. I intend to speak with these people alone,' said Lady Cecilia. Follow me young man, we're having tea in front of the fire in the big hall.'

Frank followed a shuffling figure of medium height along the dimly-lit passage into a large hall. Across one end was a minstrels' gallery and below it, stretching from wall to wall, the largest dining table Frank had ever seen. Joe Falshaw joined them and introduced himself.

Frank was at last able to have a good look at Lady Cecilia. He noticed she was wearing leather mocassins of a type he had never seen before, an oriental gown, loose-fitting and of ankle length, and a floral-patterned headscarf.

In later years Frank recalled he never saw her without a headscarf. But it was the perfect features, only slightly lined from age, and the deep-set, almost violet-coloured eyes, which impressed him as he was introduced.

'Gosh, ma'am,' he blurted out, 'you must have been very beautiful as a young girl.'

'Indeed I was, indeed I was. Do you know, young man, that's the nicest compliment I've had for years. You should have seen me when I came here as a young bride so long ago.'

'I wish I had, ma'am,' Frank said, catching a disapproving glance from Joe.

'Mr Falshaw wrote telling me he was going to bring his young assistant along to look after my estate. I think you and I will get along famously.'

He does seem to have a way with the ladies, thought Joe. That niece of mine never ceases to ask how he's going on and what he's doing. Had I said that to her Ladyship she would probably have told me to mind my own damn business!

'Now sit here in front of the fire and I'll go and fetch the Major. I make all the decisions now, you know, but he still likes to think he's in charge.' With that she shuffled out of the room.

Frank stood with his back to the crackling log fire, whilst Joe moved over to look at the table.

'Gosh, everything in here must be as old as the house,' said Frank.

'This table must be,' said Joe, 'there's no way you could get this in or out of the room; the whole place must have been built round it. Come and have a look at this; it's one solid piece of oak, there's the bole of the tree, look, underneath. Probably hundreds of years old when felled, the woodmen had the task of sawing it by hand lengthwise. Somebody then had the job of polishing the flat surface – and what a marvellous end result.'

'Bet you could sit forty or fifty people at one go,' said Frank.

'Oh yes, I'm told they often did. Rumour has it that Mary Queen of Scots lived here under house arrest for a time and that the family were hosts to more than one king of England.'

'Plenty of feasting, music and dancing?' queried Frank.

'Yes,' said Joe as they both moved swiftly back to the fire.

'Here comes the Major,' said Joe. 'Used to be a hell of a fella, they tell me. Ran his own court in the village; he was judge and jury in these parts, not averse to seeking out favours from his tenants' wives and daughters in lieu of rent.'

'Good afternoon, Major,' Joe remarked. 'Nice to meet you again; you may remember me? Joe Falshaw? I acted for one of your tenants many years ago when you evicted him for non-payment of rent.'

'I remember – John Henry Roberts, wasn't it? A drunkard and a scoundrel, battleaxe of a wife, if I recall. Couldn't make much of her, she threatened to knife me, you know.'

'Yes, dear,' his wife murmured. 'I wish you could remember the present as well as you can the past! This young man is Frank Bowers and he's come to look after the estate on behalf of the trustees.' Frank shook the old man's hand warmly.

'Wish I was your age again,' said the Major. 'I wouldn't half make 'em sit up around here.'

'Yes, dear,' said his wife. 'Now sit down and have some tea. I made these sandwiches specially for you, Mr Falshaw, and bought the slab cake from Mrs Stordy at the village shop.'

Frank eyed his sandwich with some dismay. It was almost two inches thick, made of a very dry wholemeal bread; as he munched away he realised the filling was fish paste.

'Special Indian tea,' he heard his hostess say. 'Sorry, the milk has gone off; will you have it with lemon?'

'Yes,' said Frank meekly. Oh for the pub down the road. he thought.

'Now, Frank,' said Lady Cecilia, 'try this fruit cake, it's been hanging around here for ages. My menfolk won't eat it; how fortunate that it keeps for ever.'

'Probably left over from last Christmas,' thought Frank as he forced the stale cake down.

'Well. If we're all finished, I'll show you around the house. You stay here, Marmaduke, where it's warm, whilst I show these nice gentlemen around. When we've finished you must make an appointment with the Captain to meet in the Estate Office; he can show you around the farms. I have to bring him in you know, otherwise he sulks and goes off to the local pub and starts drinking.'

The conducted tour of the house was a revelation to Frank; it was like moving around in a bygone age. He was just beginning to appreciate the magic and value of antiques; here was a house full to the brim with the most wonderful genuine articles.

'You'll probably never again come across such a collection of rare furniture,' said Joe. He was right.

'You can see why they need guard dogs around here, can't you?' Frank whispered to Joe.

'This is a nice room,' he heard his hostess say. 'We used to have breakfast here in the morning years ago; the windows face due east and get the morning sun. I think that carved frieze above the panelling is particularly nice, don't you?'

The entire room was panelled in oak from floor to ceiling; the frieze went all the way round, showing the most intricate carving in relief of hunting dogs, pheasants, wild deer and wild boar among other animals.

'We have to try and save this house for posterity,' Joe said to Frank. 'Perhaps, my lady, we could make a more detailed inspection of the first floor now? The solicitors inform me that thieves have stolen most of the lead from the roof and there's a lot of water getting in.'

'Yes, isn't that naughty! Cecil told me about it last year, I don't think it's been replaced, you know.'

'We'll have to look at that as soon as we can,' said Joe.

'I can smell dry rot!' Frank said, keen to show off his newly-acquired knowledge of these things.

'Perhaps you're right,' said Joe. They were standing in the centre of a large lounge. 'Try the floor over by that window.'

Frank moved to the window and gingerly jumped about a foot in the air. Crash! He went straight through the floor and landed in the cellar. A cloud of yellow dust and splintered wood followed him; he looked up through the dust and saw Joe peering down, grinning from ear to ear.

'I was just about to ask her Ladyship how we would get into the cellars – you beat me to it!'

The Major was fast asleep in front of the fire as the two men bade farewell.

'You will probably have to stay somewhere for a day or two when you return and get the Captain to show you the estate,' Joe remarked as the pony trotted down the drive.

'That Whitwell Hotel will suit me fine; perhaps we could call on the way back and arrange it,' said Frank.

'No. I want to go back over Goat Fell and call at the Moorcock. You can usually find Willie Pratt there early evening. He's a cattle-dealer from Padside, buys a lot of cattle in Scotland. I think if we can convince him to send some to Walshford we can sell 'em for him and make it worth his while.'

The Moorcock Inn was perched near the summit of the fell, on the drovers' route between two dales. The bar was empty. Frank noticed first a delicious smell of newly-baked bread wafting through from a vast farm kitchen behind the bar. Horse brasses gleamed on the old beams, a peat fire (the first Frank had seen) inside a huge, inglenook filled the room with a strange aroma. Smells like incense, Frank thought. Gently simmering, hanging over the fire from a highly-polished crane and reckan, was a large pot full of home-made stew.

'Help yourself,' said Joe handing Frank a bowl.

'Always available for weary travellers, mostly drovers and farmers returning from market. Salt of the earth, these people. Jack Webster runs the farm, his wife looks after the pub, mostly. They lost their only son a few years ago with consumption, ten years old, I think. There's two daughters, both good-looking lasses; the older one, she'll be about eighteen now, probably gone into service somewhere.'

Just then from the kitchen both men heard a tinkling peal of youthful laughter. What a delightful sound, Frank thought. He was busy studying the many polished brass objects surrounding the grate. The gentle glow from the fire gave unusual relief to various objects new to Frank.

'What's that?' he asked Joe.

'That's called a toasting dog in these parts.'

'Never seen one of those before.'

Frank spun round as a girl's voice said, 'Good evening, gentlemen. Can I help you?'

He involuntarily drew in a quick breath as his glance took in a tall beautiful girl, her auburn hair tied back with a large red ribbon, highlighting perfect features. She moved forward gracefully, and Frank, fascinated by two large dangling earrings, then noticed her eyes, set wide apart, green flecked with hazel. Cat's eyes, he thought (and that was to be her nickname until the day Frank lost her). He noticed the tight bodice, the small shapely waist, flowing skirt, the small, neat white apron, the full sensual mouth and lips the colour of the hair ribbon.

'I'm Charlotte Webster. Mother's busy in the kitchen, Father is still out in the shippon milking. Hev you come to stay?'

'No,' said Joe as he introduced himself. 'I'm a friend of your father's. I was hoping to catch Willie Pratt. Does he still call here on his way home from market?'

'Nivver fails, he should be landin' any minute.' Frank heard the lilt in her voice and found himself fascinated by the local dialect. 'I thought you were 'im when th' oss clattered across th' yard; there now, I can hear me dad in't scullery. I'll tell him as how yer here.'

A few minutes later Jack Webster, the landlord, joined them. A tall handsome man, Frank could see he'd stamped his 'get' on his daughter. He shook Frank's hand warmly.

'Time thou had some young blood to help thee,' he said casually to Joe. 'Does t'want to stable th' oss to'neet?'

'No,' said Joe, 'I was hoping to have a quick word with Willie Pratt and then we'll have to get on our way.'

'You mon stay here!' said Jack. 'There's some bad weather closing in, no neet to be making a long journey, I know.'

Frank found himself avidly agreeing to the suggestion. He had already made his mind up he must get to know this lovely daughter of his better.

'I think that's a good idea, Mr Falshaw. (Frank always showed a certain amount of deference to his employer unless they were alone.) 'Give you more time to chat with Willie Pratt.'

'Usually here before now,' said the landlord glancing at the old grandfather clock at the foot of the open staircase. 'You can take rooms one and two, then we'll give you a good breakfast and send you packin' tomorrow. Roast leg of lamb for supper, one of me own, poor little beggar were fast in a rabbit snare for a couple of days afore I fun it, had to slaughter it.'

The clatter of hooves in the yard announced the arrival of Willie Pratt. 'Here's your man,' said Jack, then bending over the bar he said, 'Only chap I know round here who preaches about demon drink every Sunday and nivver refuses an offer to tack one rest o' t' week.'

A large, bearded man entered the bar; he wore a long frock coat unbuttoned to show a bright yellow waistcoat. Frank noticed in particular the gold chain stretching from each fob pocket across his belly, a heavy round pendant dangling from it. He took a large watch from one pocket and checked the time with the grandfather clock.

'He allus has to check with me grandfather clock, tha noows, cos he noows it's allus reet,' said Jack.

The large figure took no notice of the jibe. From the other pocket, also connected to the chain, he extracted a square gold snuffbox, opened it, and placing the snuff on the back of his left hand took two sniffs up both nostrils. With his eyes closed he pulled a large red spotted handkerchief from an inside poacher's pocket, sneezed, then wiped his finely-waxed moustache with it, this time placing it in the breast pocket of his coat. He opened his eyes and surveyed the three men in the room.

'Well bless me!' he said. 'Falshaw, you old rogue! What are you doing here?'

'Come to see you,' said Joe.

'Good, always ready to do business; who's buying drinks, then?'

Willie Pratt was on his third large whisky before he asked, 'Who's this young fella, then?'

'Ah! sorry,' said Joe. 'Frank Bowers, my new assistant.'

'Pleased to meet thee,' boomed out this mountain of a man. 'If tha turns out to be as good as thy boss tha'll do for me!' Turning to Joe he said, 'Now then, what's your business?'

'Come over to the fire and I'll tell you,' said Joe. 'You an' all, Frank. Now, instead of everybody selling their own stock as they do on market days, perhaps standing with 'em all day in the street, I've an idea to start selling 'em in our yard at Walshford. There's a big shed yonder, we could make a ring inside it and folk could bid for stock under cover. We could charge a penny or two commission, but I need fellows like you to support it, send stock regularly, like. We might have to form an Auction Mart Company and appoint a few prominent men like yourself as directors.'

That's clever, thought Frank as he noticed Willie sit up to his full height, he obviously likes the idea of being a company director.

'Aye! sounds a good idea to me,' said Willie. 'I've been wondering how long we could keep filling these market squares wi' cattle and sheep; one of them newfangled motor cars came through t'Hawes t'other day, nivver heard such a racket. Daft beggar went past a line of bulls tethered in front of t'Hare and Hounds at twenty miles an hour, they all broke loose, all t'other stock bolted, two fellas got knocked down, one of me Scottish bullocks finished up inside Metcalfe's grocer's shop. Did five punds' worth of damage afore we got 'im out.'

'Aye,' said Joe, 'well, we're getting much more traffic than you at our end. My solicitor tells me it won't be too difficult to set up a company and sell shares; that way we can get in some brass to pay for setting this thing up. We'll need to build pens to hold stock, a ring to sell 'em in with a rostrum, and an office. I thought of asking eight or ten of you fellas to put up, say, one hundred pounds apiece to start. You're the first I've asked. You'd be a shareholder and we'd pay a dividend on those shares; you could buy more or sell yer shares at any time. Bound to be a good investment, what do you say?'

'I'll have to give it some thought,' said Willie. 'They don't tak' kindly to change, tha knows, these farmers, but there may be some'at in what tha' says. Onyhow because of yon commotion at t'Hawes I nivver sold any of me Scotties. They're turned out on a field nobbut two miles from 'ere; we could slip down and I'll sell 'em to thee cheap. There's twenty of 'em, all well grown bullocks.'

'How much?' said Joe.

'Twelve pund ten shillings apiece,' was the reply.

'Drink up and we'll go have a look,' said Joe. 'Are they on our way home?'

'No, they're back t'other way. We can just as soon walk.'

Frank was about to have his first lesson on hard bargaining. One hour later they were still in the field. Willie had dropped his price to twelve

34

pounds. Joe had upped his original bid from eight guineas to ten; in the meantime they seemed to have discussed every topic under the sun. Here's one man keen to sell and the other keen to buy, they're both putting on a show of indifference, play-acting, thought Frank; it's nothing but bluff and counter-bluff.

'Let's go back to the pub,' said Willie. 'I can't tak' a penny less than twelve pund, tha's nowhere near, not shaping at all.'

The light was just beginning to fail as they arrived back at the Moorcock.

'I think we'd better stay the night,' said Joe, 'your mother won't mind, will she, Frank?'

'Shouldn't think so! You warned her I might be late,' said Frank, keen to renew his contact with the daughter of the house.

'Right then, landlord, we'll take those two rooms and you'll be stopping for supper, Willie? Three for supper and we'll have three whiskies to be going on with.'

Frank could hardly take his eyes from Charlotte as she waited on them during supper. She had become used to the local boys staring at her and making crude advances, but this one's different, she thought. The way he looked at her made her feel strangely uncomfortable. She returned his gaze until she felt herself blushing. She moved hastily away and joined her father behind the bar.

'Away, girl,' said her father. 'Gan clear the table, there'll be nobody else calling now, help your mother wash up. I'll join these fellows playing dominoes.'

So a marathon game of dominoes ensued. 'Three pence a corner, winner of three hands to buy drinks,' said Joe.

No mention whatsoever of the cattle, they must both have decided to call off the deal, thought Frank. He heard the grandfather clock strike twelve, and still the game went on. Frank excused himself; he needed a breath of fresh air. He was trying hard to keep pace with three hardened drinkers, and realised he was going to make himself ill if he carried on.

Joe joined him in the primitive gents' toilet. 'No need to have any more drink, me lad, but I'll tell you what to do – get on the bar and let yon lass get away to bed. Cut my whisky down by half with more water, give Willie Pratt my share. He's hoping I'll get tight, then he can get his price for yon cattle. We'll play him at his own game!'

It was at least three hours later before Willie Pratt decided he ought to be going home.

'What about these cattle?' said Joe. 'Do you want to sell 'em or not?'

'Twelve pund,' said Willie, 'not a penny less.'

'Too much,' said Joe.

'Right,' said Willie, 'sudden death, just you and me with the do's, twelve pund if I win, eleven if you win.'

'If I win you deliver 'em for free,' said Joe.

'By, you're a hard man, Falshaw, all right.'

'And you come in as a shareholder when we get the Auction Mart set up.'

'Very good,' said Willie grudgingly.

Joe beat his opponent handsomely; he chipped out and left him holding double six with two other dominoes.

'Double or quits,' said Willie.

'I'll play you again,' said Joe, 'but for different stakes. Let me pay you now for those cattle. Here you are: two hundred and twenty in fivers.' He counted out the money. 'Now,' he said, 'I shall want some "luck money". Give me a fiver back.'

Willie meekly handed back a fiver with a pained look on his face. 'Frank, don't ever get as tight as this boss of thine, the fella 'as no mercy, no mercy at all.'

'If you catch a weasel asleep, you mon piss in his ear,' Joe said. 'Don't ever feel sorry for these cattledealers, Frank, they can always take care of themselves, they'd soon be out of business otherwise.'

Frank realised that in spite of the insults, both men had a grudging respect for each other.

'Are we playing dominoes or do you want a game of cards?' demanded the landlord.

'Dominoes,' said Willie, 'I'm going to play him fer me cattle back.'

'No, Willie,' said Joe. 'I've got the bullocks and you've got your brass; we're neither of us sober and we might regret it.'

'Aye, maybe you're right. Tell thee what I'll do, fifty pund agin fifty punds' worth of shares in this new company of yours.'

'Right, you're on,' said Joe.

Frank stood behind Joe as he played and watched with some amazement as he let his opponent win. Of course, he thought, a deliberate ploy to get this man in as a shareholder.

'I win,' boomed Willie, as he thumped down the winning domino. 'Landlord, drinks all round. What's that light? There's somebody in the back yard.'

'You daft bat,' said Jack as he drew the curtains back, 'it's the sun, look, almost broad daylight.'

Frank never got to bed that night. The landlord hastily cooked bacon and eggs; Joe fed the hackney, hitched him to the trap and at five-thirty in the morning they were ready to be off.

'I'd like to come and stay for a day or two next week,' said Frank, 'quite a lot of work to do at Wilstrop Hall.'

'You'll be welcome any time, young man,' said Jack Webster. 'I'm sure our Charlotte can look after you.'

Frank failed to see the wink he gave Joe.

They were back in the office soon after nine o'clock. Miss Smith, the secretary, assumed both men had arrived together. Frank quickly swilled the lather off the horse and rubbed him down in the stable; nobody was any the wiser. He was able to ring through and tell his mother he had stayed in town all night; few people had the telephone as yet, but the link to Farrick House had been considered essential.

'I left one of the lamps burning all night,' she told him. 'Dick Boynton needs to have a word, and will you be going to the opening meet, he wants to know.'

'You bet,' said Frank. 'See you about teatime.'

5

Water-Divining

A few days later Frank was back at the Moorcock, a recent chance remark from his mother that she was in need of a companion housekeeper already fermenting in his brain. If possible he had every intention of taking Charlotte back with him.

He hoped to be able to persuade her to go to the Whitwell shoot with him on Saturday; in the meantime he had to prepare a Schedule of Repairs for ten farms and the whole of the village properties. He also had a crisis on his hands – the village water supply had dried up.

Captain Pilkington barely failed to hide his glee as he passed on the news to Frank when he arrived at Wilstrop Hall on Thursday morning.

'I've sent a message to John Blake of Hampsthwaite, a noted water-diviner,' he informed Frank. 'You'll need to find an alternative supply quickly; I reckon he'll be here by lunchtime. Here's a map of the estate, it's my guess you'll need to look for water up above York House Farm, somewhere here,' he said, dabbing his finger on the map.

John Blake was a tall man; he carried the tools of his trade in a cloth bag slung over his shoulder. His attire on such a nice day amused Frank – brown leather leggings over a stout pair of boots; an unusually heavy overcoat of calf-length; a red and white spotted muffler knotted around his neck worn gypsy fashion, with a brown top hat as his crowning glory.

Frank explained the problem whilst the worthy Captain hovered in the background, anxious not to be left out.

'Looks a likely place,' was Blake's only remark when the three men arrived at York House.

'You'll need to find water here in this bottom field so we can dyke it across to the stream which should be supplying the reservoir,' Pilkington remarked.

'There'll be no water theer! As yer can reach, we'll hev to be higher up.'

It was an unusually warm day for early November and Frank, wearing only a light jacket, was perspiring freely as he tried to keep up with this man.

'You'd think that heavy overcoat would slow him down,' he panted, turning to the Captain who was falling even further behind.

'You go on, Bowers, I'll catch up later.'

'Reckon we need to be about 'ere,' he heard John Blake mutter as he eventually caught up with him. Frank watched fascinated as he strode purposefully across the contours of the hillside, in his hand a forked hazel twig, both prongs held lightly; suddenly the twig buckled and bent diagonally towards the ground.

'Uhh!' the man grunted, 'strong signal theer.' He moved on, turned and moved back; down went the point in the same place. He rummaged in his back pocket, took out an ash stake pointed at one end with the bark peeled off at the other, and drove the stake into the ground with a heavy wooden mallet.

'Allus use ash, tha knows,' he said to Frank. 'Stays theer a long time wi'out rotting, and them white tops can allus be seen.'

When the work was finished there were two lines of stakes roughly forming a large cross on the hillside. 'Get your men to sink a shaft weer them two lines cross: in the middle of that there's watter at about six feet down. If there i'nt enough, there's more at about thirty foot.'

Just then Frank caught sight of Lady Cecilia struggling up the hill, leaning on a large shepherd's crook.

'Good heavens, what the devil are you doing here?' said the Captain.

'I've come along to show you how to use that divining rod. I can do it, you know,' panted her Ladyship.

Not surprising, thought Frank, as he observed she was still wearing her moccasins and spotted headscarf, she looks like a witch.

And indeed she had the 'power'; the twig she borrowed from John Blake worked equally well for her as for him. Frank asked to have a go – nothing. Then the Captain tried, with the same negative results.

'There you are, Cecil. I've told you before, it works for me; no need to have employed this fella.'

Good Lord, groaned Frank to himself as he noticed John Blake turn abruptly on his heels and set off towards the village, that's probably going to cost us twice as much.

'Silly old witch,' John Blake muttered as Frank caught up with him. 'What does she know about it?'

'Quite tactless,' said Frank.

'Who wants the bill, Mr Bowers? They tell me these folk nivver open letters or pay their whack.'

'You'd better send it to our new office at Walshford, address it to Joe Falshaw, auctioneer; new regime here now, you know.'

'Not afore time either,' was the reply. 'You'll do well if you can handle 'em, in my opinion. Watch out for yon Pilkington fella; couldn't lie straight in bed they tell me. I wouldn't have come only he tell't me as how there were new fellas in charge. Hev you ony staff laid on to dig a pipeline in?'

'No,' said Frank. 'I'm told there's only one estate worker left.'

'Aye, that'll be Simon Stott, good chap in his younger days, nivver out o' pub these days. Can't think how his missus coped and reared six kids on't meagre bit of brass he took home.'

'Any suggestions?' asked Frank

'Well I'm no pushing it, think on, but we have a newish machine in our yard, me own invention like, a sort of h'excavator, does t' work of three or four men, shovels a trench out like nobody's business. You'll need to borrow a traction engine to drive it like, and pull it uphill, none too safe working t'other way on.'

'Right,' said Frank, 'that's what we'll do. How expensive is it?'

'Five bob a day to hire, then yer steam engine, that'll be extra of course.'

'Good,' said Frank, 'as soon as we hit water we'll get in touch.'

'Tha'll find any amount of water up theer, enough to supply th' entire neighbourhood.'

'That's it, then,' said Frank, 'thanks for all your help.'

It was Saturday morning and Frank had persuaded Charlotte to go with him to the Whitwell shoot on her own; 'just the two of us,' he had pleaded the evening before when she had suggested taking her younger sister with them as a sort of chaperone.

'All right then! – provided my parents have no objection.'

'You'll need to be back early to help me in the bar,' her mother said, 'you know we get very busy wi' folk calling on their way back.'

Charlotte was delighted, she was already falling for this attractive young man who had suddenly come into her life. The thought of a day out with him, entirely on her own, was almost too much to bear.

Frank had wasted no time on the Friday. It was important the village had water at the earliest opportunity; not only was he able to organise the hire of the excavator but he managed to borrow a traction engine and had them both on the site before dark that same evening. He also persuaded Tweet Umpleby to help Simon Stott sink a shaft first thing Saturday morning.

40

It was nine-thirty as Frank and Charlotte rode down the fell road towards the village, Frank on his attractive dark bay horse, Charlotte managing to look lovely in spite of having to ride her father's shaggy black 'fell-pony'.

'I wish you'd wait for me,' she said plaintively.

'We're only walking,' Frank said smugly.

'Yes, and I'm having to trot all the time to keep up.'

Frank reined in and with a sudden impulse leant over as she came alongside and lightly brushed her forehead with his lips. 'I think you are the most beautiful girl I have ever seen,' he said. She blushed instantly and tried to move away.

'Stop it, Frank,' she said unconvincingly, 'someone will see us.'

'I don't care,' said Frank.

'No, but I do, I have to live with these people around here.'

'Not for much longer I hope. I'd like you to come home with me, my mother needs a companion. Can your parents manage without you?'

'How strange you should say that, only t'other day me mum was suggesting it was time I got mysen a job!'

'We'll have to try and improve your vocabulary,' Frank said as he turned away.

'Pardon?'

'Oh nothing,' Frank said. 'I'll ask your parents when we get back.'

The sound of a traction engine hard at work floated across from the other side of the valley as they arrived in the village. 'I hope they haven't started using that digging machine without my permission,' Frank muttered under his breath.

'I just want to leave a note for Captain Pilkington in the office, then we'll call at York House to see if they've found water, and then you and I can enjoy ourselves at the fair.'

'My aunt lives yonder at Pear Tree Cottage; I'll call to see her until you're ready to go on,' said Charlotte.

Frank was halfway up the farm track towards York House when he saw Tweet urgently running towards him.

'There's been an accident, sir,' he gasped. 'We fun a lot of water half hour since, Simon Stott thought we'd better get yon machine to dig a trench, we hadn't been going five minutes when that arm came round, knocking Simon flying, and I reckon he's dead!'

'Damn it,' said Frank. 'Were you working uphill?'

'Naw! We started close to yon shaft, nobody tell't us different. By, there aint half some watter coming out.'

41

'Never mind that, you go back and see if you can do anything for him, I'll go and ring for the doctor.'

'I reckon you'll need yon local bobby an all, and some'at to tak' him away in.'

'What a dreadful start,' Frank groaned, 'I'll have to tell 'em up at the hall.'

Having organised medical assistance, he called at the police house. 'He's gone to the Whitwell Shoot,' his wife informed him. Frank then galloped up to the rear door of the hall.

'Captain Pilkington,' he bellowed out. Eventually an upstairs window swung open.

'What the devil!' said the Captain.

'There's been an accident, it seems Simon Stott's been killed up at the borehole.'

'Good Lord! I'll be there as soon as I can.'

It was fully thirty minutes before the doctor arrived and certified the estate worker dead. Tweet volunteered to take him home on a hay sledge and Frank agreed to call and tell his widow the dreadful news.

'Don't forget we are covered for insurance,' Captain Pilkington said. 'Two thousand per man for workmen if killed whilst working for the estate, less if injured, but there's no doubt Simon has qualified for full payment.'

'Is the premium paid?'

'Certainly,' said the Captain. 'Do it through my own agency, earn a bit of commission that way. She lives in the cottage next to the church.'

Frank knocked tentatively on the door; it opened to reveal a pleasant-faced plump woman, still wiping her hands on her apron.

'Mrs Stott?'

'Yes.'

'I'm Frank Bowers, new agent for the estate.'

'Oh yes, Simon mentioned you this morning, working on a new water supply isn't he? 'Bout time if you ask me.'

'Yes. Can I come in a minute?'

'Of course, come into the best room.'

'Could you sit down, Mrs Stott?'

'Of course. Is anything the matter?'

'Yes, I'm sorry to tell you your husband has been killed. The arm of the excavator struck him from behind. Fortunately he never knew what hit him.'

'Good Lord! and him talking all the time about retiring.'

42

'There will almost certainly be two thousand pounds compensation from our Insurance Company.'

'How much? – two thousand pounds!'

'Yes,' said Frank, 'perhaps that might not be enough.'

'That'll do for me, young sir! I've been married to the blighter for over thirty years, nivver had a penny out of him when he was alive, so I reckon I'll be entitled to a payment like that now he's gone.'

'The estate will pay for funeral expenses, Mrs Stott, they're bringing him down on a sledge.'

'I'll lay him out proper in this room, he allus said we wouldn't have far to carry him to be buried: most likely his two sons and Tweet with three others will carry him there on hay forks. We can get a pitch pine coffin lined with cotton wool and a shroud for three pounds eighteen and sixpence, that's what me mother's coffin cost a month ago, eighty-six she was.'

'I'm very sorry, but I'll have to go now. Don't forget to send me the bill.'

As he left all Frank could hear was Mrs Stott repeating over and over again, 'By gum – two thousand pund eh – two thousand pund.'

It was lunchtime before Frank and Charlotte arrived at the fair. She had been sweetness itself when Frank finally arrived at her aunt's house, apologising for the delay. He deliberately kept the news from her so as not to spoil her day. Happily the children's sports were finished and entries were being taken for the Shoot.

'You must have a go, Frank,' Charlotte said.

'I've never been much good with a twelve-bore shotgun,' he replied, 'prefer a rifle myself. I'll have a go just to please you, but I really want a word with P.C. Roberts; he's supposed to be on duty somewhere around here.'

Slowly but surely, Frank was beginning to blame himself for the accident; there would almost certainly have to be an inquest. It would need a satisfactory coroner's verdict to get Mrs Stott the insurance money. 'I'll just slip into the pub and see if he's there – give me five minutes.'

Frank found his man propping up the small private bar in the rear of the pub. He introduced himself.

'Glad to know we're to have some fresh blood looking after the village,' said the constable. 'As for them up at th' hall, washed me hands on'em – some of the goings-on. You know as how someone's pinched the lead off the roof – well, I have me own suspicions who's behind that little lot, and there's been various other h'irregularities. Anyhow what can I do for yer?'

43

'I hope it won't spoil your day, but Simon Stott's been killed up at York House this morning, a new type of ditching machine; he and Tweet Umpleby decided to use it without my consent. There'll have to be an inquest, the doctor's seen him and Tweet's offered to borrow a sledge and take him home. I thought you should be informed.'

'Quite right, me lad. Quite right. Poor old Simon. Have you been to see Ethel, his wife?'

'Yes,' said Frank.

'Aye, she's a cousin o' mine, had a hard time of it, he allus spent what little brass he earn't on hi'sen. Were she upset?'

'Not really,' said Frank. 'Perked up quite nicely when I told her she stood to gain an insurance payout of two thousand pounds.'

The constable whistled.

'But we do need a verdict of accidental death, I reckon, to be sure of her drawing.'

'Leave it to me, young sir,' said Constable Roberts, drawing himself up to his full height. 'I'll bring all my considerable h'influence to bear on the court. I'd better cycle up theer right away.' He bellowed through to the main bar, 'Landlord, this young man would like to buy two double whiskies, we'll drink this and then I must ask you to accompany me to the scene of the accident. Haven't had a fatal accident round here since young Fred Atkinson went through the ice on the river many years ago.'

Everything worked out well in the end. Charlotte moved higher up in Frank's esteem, for she hid all her disappointment when they had to leave the fairground abruptly, and insisted on calling to console the widow on the way back.

Frank was absolved from all blame. Ethel Stott drew two thousand pounds and moved to a small cottage on the shores of Morecambe Bay. The estate had a plentiful new water supply two days later. Even Tweet's wife was happy, not only because he was safe, but because he was kept away from Whitwell and the 'goings-on' which always occurred.

6

The Opening Meet

The first entry in Frank's hunting diary reads:

> 23rd October, 1908. Opening meet. Easingwold 10.30 a.m. found near Crayke, fox ran due north, went to ground below White Horse at Kilburn; found again in Priory grounds at Coxwold, large ginger dog fox ran south east with Yearsley on the right, swung left as if for Stonegrave into the Howardian Hills, ran the valley between Terrington and Ganthorpe, right again below Bulmer Bank; hounds caught up with him in Sheriff Hutton Park; sixteen miles point, twenty-four miles as hounds ran. Only Master, Hunt servants, myself, William Winspear, Bobbie Dawson, Walter Jackson in at the finish.

Frank's young horse made his mark that day – he was a natural jumper and careful schooling by Dick Boynton over the last few weeks paid off; every obstacle came the same to him. Many experienced hunting men on good horses were left far behind. The Master and Hunt servants had as usual changed to fresh horses following the first run, but they swore that 'Tuffan' (he was given that name on the spur of the moment when the master asked his name) finished freshest of all. Frank had the devil of a job convincing the Master it was Tuffan's first full day's hunting and that he was still only a four-year-old.

It was getting quite dark as the four tired but elated riders bade good-night to the Master and his hounds, as they turned south and headed for the kennels on the outskirts of York. The quartet had to head north west back to Easingwold and then on almost as far again to get to the Wetherby/Boroughbridge area and home.

The hack home became almost as legendary as the run. They managed to get some warm gruel for the horses and had a riotous time at the Green

Man in Farlington, the first village they came to. Next call was at a very small ale house at Stillington. The landlady had just removed a trayful of delicious teacakes from the oven; they bought the lot, Frank recalled. Eaten still hot, with knobs of butter, they tasted superb. Only when the landlord returned home, shaking raindrops from his cloak did they decide to proceed on their way.

'Just as well,' said the landlady; 'you've drunk the pub dry, there's nowt left to sup!'

By the time they reached Easingwold they had decided to visit every hostelry they came across.

'Very ancient settlement, Easingwold,' Bill Winspear had been telling them as they plodded onwards through the dark and rain; 'dates from Anglo-Saxon times you know, used to be occupied by a tribe known as "Easings" before the Vikings and then the Normans came. Belonged to some earl or other from Northumberland originally. Very important place in them days, and since of course; major staging post for the last two hundred years for coaches and the Royal Mail between York and Edinburgh. Hard to realise that nearly everywhere we've been today was within the Forest of Galtres; great royal hunting area until Charles I had most of it cleared.'

They managed to get away with visiting only four public houses in the town. Frank was beginning to wish he'd gone south with the hounds, but Bobbie Dawson had invited him home to Malvern House near Ripon. 'Come and stay the week-end' had been the invitation to Frank, 'then we can both hack to the opening meet of the Bedale on Monday morning.'

Then it was on, further westwards. They said farewell to Bill Winspear near Aldwark and crossed the toll bridge there at a canter; they were over the bridge and away before the startled toll keeper had struggled out of his cottage. Thence to Boroughbridge; they managed to acquire more gruel for the horses and some delicious mulled wine for themselves at the Crown.

'This is where I bought Tuffan,' said Frank, trying hard to focus his eyes onto Walter Jackson's. 'Thirty-five quid, that's all.'

'A bargain, Frank,' said the older man, 'after what I saw him do today. If I were you I'd keep his purchase price a secret, you never know who's listening. If I ever want to disclose a purchase price I usually tell folk he's cost twice as much. Often if that gets about, and they can knock say a fiver off when th' hoss comes up for sale, they think they've got a bargain.'

Frank and Bobbie eventually said goodnight to Walter, and wisely ignoring two more hostelries on the outskirts of the town, headed west once more through Skelton, past Newby Hall, over the tricky ford across the River Ure near Ripon Racecourse; they managed to get their horses to gallop down the Racecourse itself and so to Malvern House.

By the time the horses had been dried off and fed, rugged up and bedded in deep straw, the time was fast approaching midnight. Two tired but happy young men made much of recounting their exploits of this famous day to Bobbie Dawson Snr.; a keen hunting man himself until a bad accident brought about early retirement. He was a knowledgeable listener. 'I reckon Frank has landed himself with one of the best hunters in Yorkshire,' Bobbie told his father. 'You'll like him when you see him in the morning. Plenty of bone, goes all day, jumps like a stag and sensible with it; very fast too, shot past me as if I was standing still soon after we left Coxswold. As far as I can tell, he was in front all the way, heard the Master bellow out "Hold hard" twice at Frank – you were lucky Frank, if anybody gets in front of his hounds they usually get such a cussing they never forget it.'

'I thought he was quite nice, really,' said Frank, 'He had a good look at Tuffan and then asked me what I called him, that was all.'

'Ah! well he'll probably want to buy him then, can't abide to think anybody is better mounted than he is. Think on you ask him plenty if he pesters you, but he's cute enough to send somebody else in his place, so beware.'

Frank enjoyed a relaxing weekend and on Monday morning, quite early, he and Bobbie were on their way to Bedale. Tuffan had had a slight swelling in both forelegs on Sunday morning; quite usual after really hard work, Frank was told by the Dawson's stud groom. 'We'll put the cold water hosepipe on him for half an hour, then pressure bandages. Should be all right for Monday.' He was.

'Look at that,' said Bobbie as Tuffan came out of his box, 'ready for anything. Look at his head, that's what the Arabs call "the look of the Eagle". He knows he's superior and shows it, the eyes have it; the way he carries himself, you don't find many horses with it.'

Although Frank bought and sold or judged many thousands of horses over the years, he never saw another with quite the same presence as Tuffan. (The only horse to come near was Red Rum, the famed Grand National winner, trained as a two-year-old by Robert Renton near Ripon in his last years as a racehorse trainer before he was sold to Ginger McCain.)

The journey to Bedale was uneventful. The two friends caught up with several other riders on their way; by the time they rode into Bedale marketplace they were some twenty strong. There was already a large gathering of mounted followers and a considerable throng of country folk keen to watch this annual spectacle.

It seemed everybody had already heard of the Sheriff Hutton run and the exploits of Tuffan and his young rider. Wherever Frank moved he was aware of close scrutiny and admiring glances.

'I'd like to introduce you to one of the Joint Masters,' Frank heard Bobbie saying. 'Lady Tanfield, this is Frank Bowers, auctioneer from Wetherby.'

'Welcome to our Hunt, Frank; they tell me you showed that York and Ainsty lot a clean pair of heels the other day, good for you! I can't stand their pompous Master at the best of times. If you get chance, both of you, call in at Sleningford on the way home tonight; there's always a decent sort of supper available. By the way, Bobbie, I don't suppose you can spare a sip from your hip flask? I find it a little chilly this morning and I seem to have forgotten mine.'

'Have mine, your Ladyship,' Frank blurted out. 'It's full of brandy and I'm not really keen on it myself. Keep it for the day if you like.'

'You're far too kind, Frank.'

'Not at all, my Lady, only too delighted.'

'Well; perhaps you will call this evening, then, and collect the flask?'

'Certainly, ma'am.' Frank felt ten feet tall.

Little did he know then that her Ladyship's main weakness was 'the drink', that brandy was indeed her favourite tipple, and that her physician had issued stern warnings to all close relatives that her Ladyship was to be banned from partaking until further notice. A few years later when Frank came to reside between Ripon and Thirsk he hunted almost exclusively with the Bedale, with Lady Tanfield as sole Master. By this time he was finding the Hunt horses for her and a large flask of brandy for every meet. Her Ladyship knew to draw up on Frank's right hand side just before hounds moved off.

'Morning, Frank.'

'Good morning, my Lady,' was the stock reply.

'Slightly chilly again this morning,' she would say.

'Yes, my Lady, would you like a little taste of something to warm you up?'

'Well that would be splendid,' she would say. Whereupon Frank would quickly hand over a full flask from his right hand pocket and move away; invariably it was handed back empty soon after the Huntsman blew for home.

As the hounds moved away Tuffan started playing up; he remembered Saturday well and the excitement returned. He gave a couple of playful bucks. Frank decided to pull him to the rear of the mounted field. 'The martingale's broken,' Bobbie shouted to him as he dropped back. By the time Frank had steadied Tuffan and removed the broken martingale he was entirely alone. He noticed the horse prick his ears and lift his head as soon as he was ready to remount.

'Steady boy, whoa, we'll soon catch up,' and then he heard hounds coming towards him in full cry. Suddenly, loping along quite unhurried, and only a field away, was a fox, heading straight back towards the town.

I'll bet someone's dropped a bagman in the first covert, said Frank to himself. He waited until hounds arrived and quietly followed them back down the road quite alone; he was just in time to see the fox enter the garden of Bedale Hall. The hounds had their quarry in view and were closing fast.

Frank stayed on the main road; he had the parish church to the rear, and was easily able to look over the low wall of the hall grounds. He watched with mounting excitement as the hounds crashed around inside a large patch of rhododendron bushes; then suddenly there was 'Charlie'. Frank watched in amazement as the fox dashed across the lawn and took a flying leap at one of the windows of the hall. It turned out the window was closed. The fox bounced back and lay stunned for a couple of seconds; Frank steadied Tuffan who was starting to react to the wonderful 'music' reverberating around the grounds. He saw the fox move unsteadily towards him, and there he was, swaying and still very groggy on the wall top, within four yards – he could almost touch him. The pathetic look on the fox's mask as he stared Frank straight in the eye stifled the 'holloa' he was about to make. He watched almost mesmerised as the fox slowly made his way across the road, over the wall into the churchyard and between the gravestones until he disappeared under a large horizontal stone slab, raised about two feet off the ground with a pedestal at each corner.

Frank quickly looked around. Good, he thought, nobody else has seen him. A few keen foot followers were tumbling out of a couple of pubs down the main street, having heard the racket; three or four pink coats were galloping fast towards him from the direction of the Crakehall covert.

'Have you seen him, young man?' roared J.J. Mowbray.

'Saw him go into the hall gardens, sir.'

'Good show – better go in on foot, Downs,' he said to his Huntsman.

'You two whips get round the back, he's almost certain to want to break out there.'

Hounds were quiet; one or two were feathering their tails on the lawn below the window; just one hound tried to come over the wall near Frank.

'Get away back,' bawled the Master, cracking his whip. Most of the mounted followers had by this time joined Frank. Good, he thought, any scent over the road will be completely destroyed.

'Did you see him, Frank?' asked Lady Tanfield.

'Yes, my Lady, he definitely came into the grounds; seems to have dodged them in those rhododendron bushes.'

After ten minutes fruitless search, a stentorian voice bellowed out: 'Would you please get those bloody dogs out of my garden!'

'That's the owner – retired Major-General and non-hunting man, new to the district,' he heard someone remark.

The Huntsman quickly blew the hounds to him and joined the field on the road.

'Queer do that, sir,' he said to the Master, 'almost as if he's gone into the house through yon window!'

Frank could see the Master still shaking his head as the cavalcade moved away. He wisely kept Tuffan at the back; everybody had gone, all the spectators had walked back down the street as he looked across, and there, under the gravestone, he could just make out a nose and behind it two eyes watching his every move. Frank slowly doffed his cap, gathered up the reins and trotted purposely after the rest of the mounted field.

7

Murder Most Foul

Next day Frank awoke early; he'd slept solidly and felt refreshed – he stretched. 'Ouch!' he moaned, as he reluctantly moved his stiff legs. Apart from two sore buttocks there were no lasting ill effects from two days' hard hunting.

Dick Boynton was already with Tuffan when Frank hurried into his box. He listened intently as his young master enthused about his prowess and the way he'd performed over the weekend.

'Reckon you've gone and bought yourself a good un, boss,' he remarked as he brushed him down. 'No heat in his legs at all – cold as ice, not a mark on 'im; deserves a day off, even if he does look as fresh as a daisy.'

'Shan't need him till next Saturday – you'll hev to exercise him for me, busy week ahead.'

Frank was at the office soon after eight-thirty – as usual Joe was there before him.

'Could you handle a farm sale on your own, Frank? – mostly pigs,' was his opening remark.

'Well, er, I suppose so,' said Frank hesitantly.

'Good. You remember that David Davidson fellow at Sledgate Farm? – his wife disappeared a few months ago? Well, he's been arrested – charged with her murder and the sheriff wants us to sell all his possessions and take over the running of the place.'

'Has she been found?'

'Apparently not – the police have been digging all over the farm for weeks, without trace, but I gather they've found part of a human thigh bone in the sow house. The prosecution must think they have enough proof that he dismembered the body and fed it to the pigs.

'We've been instructed to sell him up, so I suggest you get yourself over there right away. Take Tant Walmsley with you, make out an inventory and get the sale advertised as soon as possible.'

51

'Feels quite eerie in here, boss,' shouted the Auction Mart foreman. The two men were in a filthy sow-farrowing house. The squealing from a host of hungry sows was deafening.

'Doesn't look as if they've been fed for days,' shouted Frank in return.

'Is this where they think he cut her up?' asked Tant as the noise subsided.

'So they say – but they haven't got a body – can't see how they can charge a man with murder if there's no body.'

'Hell of a good preacher, tha' knows,' said Tant wistfully; 'came o'er and preached at our chapel regular like.'

'He's a circuit preacher, I believe,' said Frank.

'Aye! Fancy feeding his wife to this lot: is there nowt left?'

'I understand a few bone fragments have been found, but nothing else.'

'Tall, handsome chap...' said Tant, 'fancied the ladies though – havin' it off with that Alice Taylor what lives next door to me; she's bin runnin' about after him for weeks, reckons to call herself a Sunday School teacher just to be near him.'

'Let's get round the other buildings,' ordered Frank, 'and find out just what we have to sell.'

'Good Lord! This barn's full of half-starved runts.'

'Not fit to look after a cage full of white mice, if you ask me – needs lockin' up, this chap.'

'They have done,' chuckled Frank.

'Not afore time. Criminal – keepin' animals in this state! You'll hev your work cut out sellin' this little lot.'

Back at the office Frank knocked lightly on Joe's office door and walked in.

'How did you get on, young fella?' asked the older man – a smile playing around his lips.

'Never seen such a "muck-hole" – half-starved pigs all over the place. They've even rooted up the flagged floor to one barn searching for food. Most have had their tails chewed off and there's obviously been some cannibalism going on. We've decided to ring all the sows in the snout and turn 'em out in that scrub woodland below the farmhouse. I've sent Tant off to find a load of barley or some sweepings-up at the corn mill; and to see if he can get hold of a cartload of potatoes to keep 'em going. I'll go back tomorrow and see if some local lad can be put on to feed 'em until the sale.'

'Good lad,' said Joe.

'Tant tells me this "preacher man" is noted for being more than friendly with the younger ladies in his flock. Apparently he's been messing around with a Sunday School teacher, name of Alice Taylor, who lives next door to Tant. We found this letter in a girl's handwriting with other correspondence behind the door – the rest are mainly bills. By the looks of it, he owed a fair bit of brass around the place.'

Joe turned the letter over aimlessly in his hand, sniffed at it and held it up to the light.

'Hmmm! Very interesting. Miss Smith!' he called out to his secretary.

'Yes, sir?'

'Boil me a kettle if you please.'

'We can't . . .!'

'Sssh!' said Joe.

'And when it's boiling, steam me open this letter. Now, what are we doing about the sale?'

'I've made out this advert for the papers and another for posters – emphasising we're selling by order of the sheriff's office.'

'Quite right,' exclaimed Joe, 'that allus brings buyers – they think they're bound to be able to get summat for nowt.'

Frank handed over the rest of the mail. 'Mainly final demands and that sort of thing,' he remarked, 'there's even a postcard from a shipping company, confirming a booking for a voyage to Canada!'

'Here's your envelope, sir,' sniffed Miss Smith, quite haughtily.

'Ah, good – close the door behind you, please.'

'You were right, Frank, it's from a girl called Alice, addressed to . . .' Joe laughed aloud – 'my gentle loving Messiah! And yes – she says the doctor has confirmed her early fears and they must now make a voyage to another life together; she feels it will be God's wish that they start a family in a new and promised land, and to preach the gospel to unbelievers in such a wild, untamed, country must have been ordained.'

'Phew! That'll just about cook his goose,' said Frank, 'better seal it up again and hand it over to the police.'

Sale day arrived and Frank had to confess he wasn't looking forward to it. Joe had deliberately given his young assistant his head. Unknown to Frank, however, he'd made sure that Laurie Potter, a wholesale butcher of some repute, was going to be there. He was the sort of chap who could be relied on to keep other bidders on their toes – he steadfastly refused to join 'the ring' (local buyers who deliberately contrived not to bid against each other).

53

'Right, gentlemen,' Frank called out, 'it's time to start.'

Tant rang the handbell furiously hoping to gather up the pitifully small number of farmers who had made the effort to attend and brave the elements.

'Sorry about the rain.' Frank found he was addressing remarks to a mere handful of sodden onlookers huddled around the makeshift sale ring. 'As you are all aware, we are selling on instructions from the county sheriff – no reserve – everything to be sold. Each lot becomes your property at the fall of the hammer. Conditions of Sale are displayed on the wall of the old dairy, which we shall use as a temporary office.

'We require all lots to be removed as soon as possible. We shall be selling the sows first. As most of you are aware the owner has been detained at His Majesty's Pleasure, and they won't let him out!' Frank was hoping for some amused reaction – but all he could detect were a few sour glances from his very damp audience. 'We cannot guarantee the sows to be in pig and we've no dates – take every lot as you find it and there can be no back-reckonings.'

In the circumstances the sale went well. Laurie Potter proved to be a godsend – he bought over half the pigs and made sure nothing went cheap.

'Thanks for your help, Laurie,' Frank was able to remark as he hastily made his way towards the farmhouse. 'If you're interested in furniture, we've been instructed to sell the house contents. There's a pair of oil paintings early on that could turn out to be valuable. I could give you the "sharp tap" and knock 'em down cheap – what do you say if we then go halves on any resale value?'

'Right lad, you're on,' said Laurie. 'I've plenty to do getting these pigs away to the slaughterhouse; just knock 'em down to me and we'll hev a straightening-out do later.'

There were only a few desultory bids when the oil paintings came up for sale.

Bang! – down went the hammer – 'Sold, to Laurie Potter – ten pounds for the pair,' cried Frank.

A few days later Frank borrowed the pony and trap and, without telling anyone where he was going, rode out to Laurie Potter's 'ranch'. He had the two paintings aboard, safely concealed under hessian sacking.

He found Laurie busy skinning a bullock in his slaughterhouse. Two pigs and four sheep, already dressed, hung from hooks in the ceiling.

'I got those two paintings for you at the sale, Laurie – ten pounds for the pair; here's the bill and my fiver. You give me a cheque for the full purchase price and I'll receipt it to make everything legal and above board.' Frank was striving hard to control his revulsion at the smell of blood.

'I've had an art expert give 'em a quick "once-over". He's of the opinion they are both painted by the same artist and seems convinced they'll almost certainly be by this little-known Flemish painter name of Vincent Van Gogh – whose work has lately come into prominence. He's valuing 'em at around one hundred apiece.'

'One hundred what?'

'Pounds, of course,' said Frank.

'Where are they then?' demanded Laurie eagerly.

'Outside in the buggy, in a sack.'

'Let's have a peep.'

Laurie studied both pictures carefully. 'Nivver one hundred apiece, surely; five pund, perhaps; even that looks plenty if you h'ask me. So, what do we do now, then?'

'Well, in the first place we keep our traps shut. Secondly, we need to go to a professional and get 'em cleaned; then we offer 'em to an art dealer, and quietly spirit 'em away, down to London or somewhere.'

'And share the proceeds?' enthused Laurie.

'Yes, and share the proceeds. You'll have to trust me to organise things.'

'That'll do for me, boss!'

'Whatever happens,' urged Frank, 'I'd rather Joe Falshaw doesn't get to know what we're up to; you know how straight-laced he is.'

'I won't breathe a word and I'll leave it entirely to you – you haven't been here before?'

'No,' said Frank, 'But I can see why folks call it a "ranch".' They were standing in a large yard, flanked on one side by a range of traditional stone and slated buildings. On the other lay a series of fenced corrals, each containing an assortment of horses and ponies.

'Are all these horses here for slaughter?' Frank enquired.

'Aye, nearly all. Can't say it's a job I like. I'm a hoss-lover at heart but most of 'em are old and it's best end really. Somebody has it to do, besides it pays well. I allus gets 'em for little money, often nowt at all.'

'Don't know how you could,' said Frank.

Laurie shrugged his shoulders. 'It's me trade I suppose, and father's before me. I make up for it by breeding a lot, tha knows,' he said. 'I hev two herds of pony mares running wild on the fells up yonder, with Arab stallions. Been sending a consignment of foals to Topcliffe Fair for a few years. They make good kiddies' riding ponies, better than them New Forest things they've started bringing up from the south.'

'What are these two fine-looking animals?' Frank's eye had been caught by two identical, intelligent-looking horses' heads sticking out of adjoining loose boxes. 'They look like twins.'

Both horses were a rich chestnut colour, each with an identical long white snip running from forehead to nostril.

'Ah! Coincidence really though they are alike, I must admit. Both last crop of a little-known stallion called Tacitus – his sire was the world-renowned Hermit. One came in as a "knacker" – the other broke away from York racecourse – finished up in the city and smashed himself up. I was supposed to put him down.'

'I heard about that,' said Frank.

'Got the pair for under twenty quid,' gloated Laurie. 'This 'ere's won three hurdle races for me already, and the other fella, named Bar-None, can't miss on the flat at Pontefract next time out. I'll let you know when he's off.'

'Great,' said Frank. 'I'll hurry up and get these paintings sold, then we can have a real flutter.'

He managed to draw £200 for the pair, in crisp five-pound notes, and duly handed a half share over to a delighted Laurie Potter.

A few days later Frank was busy at his desk when Laurie Potter came ambling into the office.

'Bar-None runs at Pontefract on Saturday,' he announced. 'Bert Bradley what rides out for me reckons he'll win his race wi' his eyes closed.'

'Good – I'll pick you up and drive you over there if you like.'

'Suits me,' said Laurie. 'Eleven o'clock sharp at the Brown Cow here should be about right – oh! and think on you keep your trap shut; amazing how the odds can be cut if word gets out we're havin' a gamble.'

'Trust me,' said Frank, unaware that every word of their conversation had been overheard through the open window by Billy Binks, an evil little fellow who eked out a meagre living as an odd job man and boosted his income by acting as a bookie's runner. He was very adept at scurrying around the local pubs on race days, collecting small bets and delivering the money and betting slips to the bookmaker's office under the nose of the police.

'Bar-None runs in the second race,' puffed Laurie, as the two men hurried towards the secretary's office on the course the following

Saturday. 'I'll get him declared; then I want to get a good look at the runners in this first race. It's a seller – I've heard a whisper about a hoss down from Middleham who'll be a class above the rest – might try and claim him if he looks the part.'

Frank caught up with Laurie leaning on the rails of the unsaddling enclosure giving the third horse home a careful scrutiny.

'Well beaten into third place,' said Frank.

'All the better,' beamed Laurie, 'he won't have to be sold now, and I've put in a claiming bid; if nobody else wants him I get him for the value of the first prize money. They're only playing with him, see; waiting for a good-class race and then hope to romp in at a big price – a couple of hurdle races this back-end, provided he jumps, and then we'll have a crack at winning the Lincoln next spring.'

'Right, let's find out what odds we can git for Bar-None.'

On the way towards the bookmakers Frank was aware of a tall, distinguished-looking man hurrying towards them.

'I'd like a word, Laurie,' Frank heard him murmur.

'You go on Frank, I'll catch up with you later,' Laurie called out.

Frank walked down the line of bookmakers.

That's good, he thought, they've made Bar-None favourite, obviously frightened of him – better jump in before his price shortens further. He looked round for guidance from Laurie only to observe he was still in the midst of an animated discussion. Wonder if he's a steward or something, Frank thought, certainly looks officious with that big leather binoculars' case slung round his neck.

'I'd like to back Bar-None,' he said rather nervously to the nearest bookie, 'but there's no price on your board.'

'So would we all, sonny, so would we all. Shove off, there's a good lad.'

'Take six to four,' he heard a shout further down the line.

'Six to four Bar-None,' the same bookie called out.

In for a penny, in for a pound, Frank said to himself, plucking up courage as he approached him.

'One hundred pounds on Bar-None,' he said shakily as he handed over his bulky envelope.

'One hundred to win £150,' called out the startled bookie. A tick-tack man standing on an upturned box behind him urgently started waving white gloved hands about.

'Better count it, Fred,' said the bookie hoarsely as he hastily erased the odds against Bar-None and left the space blank. 'Ticket number ninety-four.'

Frank noticed Laurie Potter waddling towards him – he covered his mouth with his hand.

'We're not off,' he whispered.

'How do you mean?' asked Frank.

'We're not going to win,' hissed Laurie.

'I don't understand,' said Frank.

'Somebody's talked,' said Laurie, looking accusingly at Frank, 'the bookies are ready for us.'

'Well it wasn't me,' said Frank stoutly, 'besides I've backed him at six to four.'

'How much?' asked Laurie.

'My share from the paintings.'

'What! The whole hundred?' groaned Laurie.

'Yes, you said we couldn't be beat,' said Frank.

'Blast! – like a lamb to the slaughter,' sighed Laurie. 'I've arranged for my jockey to hold him back, then make his run too late to catch the leaders. That chap I've just been talking to – he trains the second favourite – you can get four or five to one on him. That's the horse I came to tell you to back – can't do anything about it now. The jockeys have had their orders and they're on their way to the start.'

In the circumstances Frank was very philosophical about the whole affair. He shrugged his shoulders and was heard to remark, 'Easy come, easy go,' as the second favourite romped in at four to one, with Bar-None a respectable fourth.

'All part of life's rich tapestry,' he remarked with a wan smile as Laurie came back from the bookies stuffing pound notes into every available pocket.

'Joe Falshaw remarked to me recently – it's no good sending lads on men's errands.'

8

Foot-and-mouth

It was the following spring, the 14th May and Charlotte's birthday – she was nineteen.

It had taken some time to get her to leave home and take up residence at Farrick House. Finally, three months earlier Frank had brought her down from the high dales to look after his mother. She had already shown herself to be a natural horsewoman and, urged on by Frank, had been taking instruction in the art of riding side-saddle. She had recently started playing tennis and somewhat reluctantly had agreed to take elocution lessons.

'Towards the end of this year you will be presented to the hunting fraternity and other society around here as a "gentlewoman",' he told her.

'But I am gentle,' said Charlotte.

'I know, but a gentlewoman gives off an air of being of good birth or breeding; and don't pout your lips and sulk,' said Frank as Charlotte tossed her beautiful head of curls and moved away from him.

'There's nowt wrong with my parents, I love them very much.'

'I know, my darling! But you remind me of a magnificent uncut diamond. I intend to take off all the rough edges and make you sparkle and glow, so that all can admire you.'

'Do you, Frank? And then can I be yours for ever. I love you so much, can we be married?'

'Yes, but not yet awhile. We're both too young at nineteen. And you don't say "there's nowt wrong" with something or other, you say "there's nothing wrong".'

'I'm sorry, Frank! Will you teach me everything I should know?'

'Of course.' Frank's heart went out to that beautiful, appealing face. 'Cat's eyes,' he whispered as he kissed her forehead. 'Now come into the yard and see what I've bought you as a present.'

Dick Boynton was waiting at the stable door as Frank led Charlotte outside; he came out leading a striking grey horse – 'Anglo-Arab; fifteen two; broken to side-saddle and he's all yours,' Frank said.

'How wonderful! Can I ride him now?' she said stroking the horse's neck. 'What a beautiful animal, feel how silky his mane is!'

'Yes, in a week or two I thought we might enter you in one or two small shows. I've bought a young horse to bring on for myself; second horse to Tuffan really.'

'Let's get changed and give 'em a spin around the park,' said Charlotte, 'I'll race you.' And with that she was running across the yard like a gazelle.

'I reckon you'd better see to breaking in that filly on your own, master,' said Dick, 'Too much of a handful for me, I reckon.'

Charlotte's bedroom was at the further end of the long passage which ran almost from end to end of the house; Frank realised his mother had engineered that as soon as she noticed her son's mounting excitement as the day drew near for him to bring this girl home.

Frank was ready first and as he left his room to approach the stairs he looked straight into Charlotte's bedroom; in her haste she had forgotten to close the door; she was about to wrap the special flared skirt she needed around her slim body and was almost naked from the waist down.

It was Frank's first glimpse of the most beautiful pair of legs he had ever seen or, as he maintained in later life, that he was ever to see. She turned. 'Frank Bowers!' she scolded him, clicking her tongue twice as she moved gracefully towards the door, then peeping her head around it, said, 'You do look silly standing there with your gob open,' and closed the door firmly in his face.

Frank failed to find sleep that night. He heard the grandfather clock strike midnight, and soon afterwards, a soft rustle as Charlotte came to his bed for the very first time.

'Thank you for my beautiful birthday present,' she whispered as Frank took her in his arms. Nervously she said, 'I couldn't sleep, then I heard those strange ghostly noises in the room below, and a girl sobbing. She made me want to cry, I felt so lonely, and I love you so much that it hurts, and...'

'Ssh! my darling, you're safe now.'

Frank kissed her full on the mouth; he felt the eager response, the vibrant young body relaxing against him, he found her firm breasts, the erect nipples.

'Tell me you love me,' she demanded.

'You're my first and my only love,' Frank said, 'there will never ever be anybody else.'

'Oh! Frank,' she moaned, 'you will be gentle won't you? Please make me into a woman.'

Frank rose early; Charlotte had left him before daybreak as silently as she came. He quietly opened her bedroom door on his way downstairs, but refrained from waking her. The look of fulfilment and the faint smile playing around her sensuous mouth filled him with a sense of power. To think that such a beautiful creature had wanted to lose her virginity to him. She stirred, stretched and became aware of his presence.

'Hello there, Cat's eyes,' he whispered as he kissed each eye in turn.

'You're not cross that I came to your room, are you?' she asked.

'Of course not,' said Frank.

'I couldn't help myself, I'm so glad I did. You won't ever leave me will you?'

'No, my darling. I'm going to leave you now though, first day's sale in the new cattle ring and Joe Falshaw specially asked me to get there as soon as possible. By the way, we've left evidence of your visit on the sheet; better not give mother the chance to find bloodstains in my bed. You know what she's like, she'd be packing you off back home immediately. I'll be back around teatime and we can take the horses out again this evening if you like.'

Although Frank was still unsuccessful in persuading the boss to invest in a car, he had managed to convince him that some mode of transport other than the horse would be of use and the firm had purchased a motorcycle.

'Don't suppose it'll be of much use in winter with all this mud about on the roads,' said Joe.

'Perhaps not, but it could save an awful lot of time getting about when conditions are right,' said Frank and, of course, here he was, heading for Walshford at full throttle, on a beautiful early morning in mid-May, the roads having dried out from the winter rain and snow; a young man, very much in love, on top of the world, exhilarated by the wind whistling past his ears. Flat cap on head, eyes protected by goggles, he leaned over to the left as his machine zoomed round a sharp bend about a mile from town.

Then suddenly, without warning, the whole road was full of cows; too late Frank realised that Ernie Towers, one of the largest milk retailers in the district, was bringing his herd of shorthorn cows in from pasture to be milked. He slammed on both brakes, there was a 'twang' as the cable operating the front brake broke under the sudden pressure, the rear brake locked on, and Frank continued on his way with no reduction of speed.

He hit the leading cow a glancing blow as it turned away to avoid him; one horn grazed Frank's forehead just below the hair line, the cow bellowed in anguish as the front wheel thudded into its ribs just behind the shoulder, then seemingly none the worse, it galloped away through the cloud of dust the skidding bike had left behind, bearing Frank's cap speared on one of its very sharp horns. Still wearing his goggles and enormous leather gloves, Frank finished up astride another beast; it kicked and bucked, striving to pitch Frank under the hooves of the remainder of the panicking herd. He heard Ernie Towers shout out, 'Daft young beggar, that's me best beast tha's hit, fifty pund, that's what it'll cost thee.'

'You've never owned a cow worth anywhere near fifty pound, Mr Towers,' gasped Frank as he was bucked off in the middle of the road.

'What's that! Best milk cow in Yorkshire, an she'll ne'er do any more good.'

Frank took off his goggles. 'Oh, I ken who yer are now, young auctioneer wi' Joe Falshaw, isn't it? Well, perhaps you're right, I'll let you know how she goes on.'

'If you could also let me have my cap back when you catch up with her!'

'Aye, I'll be coming to that sale today; good idea to tak' cattle off yon main square, I say. He's bin round, 'as Falshaw, asking for trade. I'll support him, so will lots more; nivver did like standin' all day in yon market square.'

Apart from a smashed lamp and a bent mudguard the machine was little the worse and Frank arrived in good time to organise their first ever livestock auction sale.

'I suppose we'll have to treat it very much like a farm sale, Frank,' said Joe. 'Here's a pot of glue and some lot numbers, give each beast a ticket as they arrive; newly-calved cows on their own; get the vendor's name and address and tell 'em they'll get paid in the office, less commission at tuppence in the pound, immediately after the last lot has been sell't. The order of sale to be newly-calved cows first, "lying off" cows second, store beasts last. We've advertised the sale as for "Cattle Only" so you shouldn't be bothered with any sheep.

'I'll ring the bell for the sale to commence at eleven. You can clerk for me at this first sale, but I shall look to you to do most of the selling in the future.

'I'm hoping Willie Pratt will be bringing some Scottish beasts down to the sale, he promised to do so. How are those Highland bullocks going on, I bought from him last back-end, are they fat yet?'

62

'They wintered well outside, as you know, but recently, since they've had a bit more grass to go at, Dick Boynton reports they're not going on as they should be. He's been worried about them for about a fortnight, thinks we ought to call in the vet.'

'I'll come over and have a look myself,' said Joe, 'don't believe in paying vet fees if I can help it. I was hoping we could put 'em in the next sale or two if we don't get many entries.'

'I think you're going to get plenty of support, Joe, lots of people I've talked to are wondering why nobody thought of this sooner.'

Indeed the sale was a resounding success; every farmer for miles around came just for curiosity, all seats around the sale area Joe had built were taken long before eleven. A great many people were also standing around the ring, blocking the way both in and out – much to the exasperation of the porters Joe had employed. Indeed, the only thing to shift them was a bunch of ten steers belonging to Willie Pratt, straight down from the Highlands of Scotland and almost completely wild – the crowd scattered in total disarray as they came into the ring.

Joe finally knocked them down to a Mr Cooper at twelve pound a head.

'Where's he from?' Frank asked.

'I've bought 'em myself,' whispered Joe, 'never had a bid; we'll send 'em out to the farm to join the others.'

Frank had kept quiet about the unusual lot due next; he wanted to see Joe's face when it came into the ring. The bleating of lambs heralded its approach.

'I thought I said this was a Cattle Only sale,' said Joe.

'It's my neighbour,' said Frank, 'Terry Foster.'

' So?'

'One shorthorn cow with six "cade" lambs.'

'How do you mean?'

'The cow's suckling 'em!' said Frank.

Into the ring came a very old shorthorn cow with its udders almost touching the floor; following in single file were six month-old lambs.

'Now, Terry,' said Joe as the owner approached the rostrum, 'what's this little lot?'

'The cow's correct, maister. Took to them lambs like a good un, milking 'em well, as you can see. Reckon you could soon "spane" 'em and give her a fresh lot.'

'There you are gentlemen; one cow, all correct in the bag, suckling six lambs. How much am I bid? Anybody start me at twenty pund?'

63

Shorthorn cow with family

'I'll arrange to send those cattle out to Farrick House with a drover this evening. Put 'em down by the river with the rest and I'll come out first thing in the morning,' Joe had said, and he was in the yard by seven-thirty next day. 'Right Frank, jump in, we'll go in the buggy; I want to be back at the office before nine. Is your foreman coming with us?'

'No, he's still out exercising my new horse.'

'What does he think is wrong with these cattle?'

'Well, he wonders if the abundant new grass by the river is too good for them.'

'You'd hardly think so; it's not as if they've recently been turned out, is it?'

By now both men had dismounted at the gate leading to the long pasture alongside the river Wharfe.

'Sight different river to yon at the top end of Wharfedale, Frank!'

'Yes, and a damned sight more dangerous, easily floods in a wet time.'

'That first bunch haven't half grown on,' said Joe, 'but you can tell they're not right. I think it's more serious than you think, Frank. See that beast slavering and them blisters around its mouth? Don't go any nearer, I reckon it's foot-and-mouth disease. Dick Boynton's right, we'll have to call the vet in. Look, some of them can hardly stir. Pity you put those other cattle with 'em.'

'Well, they didn't arrive till nearly dark. Bit like a rodeo getting 'em down here as it was; I told them to open the gate and let 'em gallop through, and then left 'em to it. I can probably ring for the vet from here,' said Frank.

'Yes, ring up Frank Hall from Tadcaster, I know he's just had the phone put in. Best man round here on cattle; not much of a horse vet, mind you, thinks they're a bit too lethal with all four feet! I'd better just disinfect my boots in Jeyes Fluid, if you have some, then you mon wait on for him coming. I'm going over to Leighton Priory; apparently the Abbot wants us to start doing an annual inventory and stock-taking, mostly in the wine cellar. It seems the monks are going through the stocks at twice the normal rate and he wants to know what he's got left! You join me when you've finished with the vet, you know the way?'

'Yes, it's that spot upriver with the large deer park,' said Frank, 'about five miles out of town.'

'That's it. Don't make too much noise with that damned machine of yours, the monks will never have seen one. By the way, Ernie Towers asked me to tell you he couldn't find your cap, but the cow you hit is going to be all right.'

Frank Hall arrived on horseback an hour later: 'Thought I'd better come at once since you think it may be foot-and-mouth.'

'I've never come across it,' Frank said. 'The cattle belong to Joe Falshaw, I'm just grazing them on for him. Joe remembers his father's herd having it when he was a youngster; tells me they suffered for a bit but they isolated them and they recovered.'

'You know how you come out in cold spots round your lips sometimes? Well, it's like a bad dose of that, really,' said the vet. 'Most animals get over it. Only attacks cloven-hoofed animals, and once they've recovered, they're sort of immune for life.'

'What about the horses?' asked Frank.

'No, they never catch it, but because it attacks the feet of cattle, sheep or even pigs, it does seem horses can spread it, if, say, they went into the same field. It's one of the five "f"'s that can stop hunting in a district.'

'What do you mean?' Frank said.

'Why – thought you were a hunting man,' said the vet.

'Well, yes; only just started though.'

'Well, it's "floods, fog, frost, foot-and-mouth and funerals".'

'Good job the hunting season's over, then,' said Frank.

65

'Aye. There's some talk of making it a notifiable disease, like anthrax, even compulsory slaughter to stop it spreading. Can't see that working though. I think it comes over from France, brought over by starlings.'

'Starlings!' said Frank.

'Aye, them blighters; mucky devils, you know.'

'That's the answer then!' said Frank.

'What is?' asked the vet.

'Well, these cattle have run out all winter down by the river. It's next door to Bickerton Big Wood, best covert around here, or rather was; always good for a "breed"*. This last winter it's been home every night for hundreds, maybe thousands of starlings; there's been so many they've covered the floor with about three solid inches of droppings; killed off all the ground cover. You can smell it a hundred and fifty yards away with the wind at your back; can't see a vixen wanting to rear cubs in there for years. I'll take your horse inside, we can walk down; gosh, he's a big chap,' remarked Frank.

'Bet you never clap eyes on another as tall as long as you live. He's a thoroughbred horse, eighteen hands high, in fact slightly over,' said the vet.

Frank leaned against his withers and put his left hand horizontally against his own nose, 'That's sixteen hands there,' he said, 'and it's a mile below the top of his withers.'

'I got him because, like a lot of big horses with rather too much front, he's gone in his wind. I've tubed him.'

Frank had been too polite to ask what the object was sticking out of the horse's windpipe.

'Bit of a nuisance, needs cleaning out twice a day, but it helps him breathe if you have to push him along sometimes. Because the thing's copper it starts to make a noise a bit like a trumpet. Anyhow, "time's money" and you're paying, so let's get on. Yep, that's foot-and-mouth all right; if you can isolate them down here so much the better.'

'We do have the river down one side and that wood across the bottom,' said Frank.

'Uh! Keep stock and people away from the other two sides, then you should be all right,' said Hall. 'There's nothing we can treat them with and they won't be easy cattle to handle anyway; if any get too weak to eat and move about they'll have to be slaughtered and buried here; do you have any quicklime?'

_____

*Breed – litter of young cubs.

'No, what do we need that for?'

'To cover the carcasses and destroy the infection. Better get a load delivered just in case; have it dropped at the top gate and tell the man you intend to lime the field. No need to panic anybody.'

'But we've just started the new cattle mart in Walshford,' said Frank.

'I'll suggest to Joe you stay away for a couple of weeks until this thing blows over. Best to say nowt to nobody unless somebody else gets it, then we'll have to see what's best.'

With that Frank Hall was striding back towards the farm.

'Where shall I send the bill when it's finally over?'

'Oh, to Joe Falshaw,' said Frank, 'not me.'

It was past mid-morning before Frank found Joe in the vast main cellar of the Priory. 'It seems one or two monks have been "hitting the bottle" and consuming much more of this wine than they're allowed; each of these smaller cellars is stuffed full, as you can see; comes over from one of their own monastery's vineyards in France. We've got to make an inventory for the Abbot. Seems to me they're living like "fighting cocks", and since they're nearly all at it, he wants an independent audit every year.'

'It'll take hours going through this lot,' said Frank.

'You're right, there's rather more to do than I expected,' said the older man, 'bit outside our scope really, but they run three large farms, there'll be livestock to sell if we can persuade 'em to use our new facilities at the market. That's why I volunteered your services for this job.'

It was almost dark when Frank finished his task; Joe had excused himself soon after lunch; a frugal meal taken in the main dining room in total silence.

'Gives me the creeps, this place,' said Frank.

'Never mind, you carry on. I've got to call at Bill Lonsdale's place this afternoon – talking of retiring at Martinmas. See you in the office in the morning; then I think you might as well nip up to Wilstrop Hall for a day or two. We're going to have to put their rents up considerably, and you'll have to go round to each tenant and break it to 'em gently. Oh! and one more thing; yon lass you're passing off as housekeeper, I suggest you leave her at home so's you get more work done.'

It was getting darker by the minute as Frank prudently decided to walk his motorbike quietly out of the Priory to the main road. He lit the wick of his new lamp. Doesn't show much up ahead, he thought; still I suppose it warns folk that I'm coming. He set off down the valley towards home.

There was a quick descent for the first five hundred yards and at the bottom a narrow packhorse bridge just wide enough for a horse and cart or pony and trap, but with a steep elevation from either side of the river.

'Used to be a very important crossing once o'er,' Joe had told him earlier. 'Five packhorse trails converged at that bridge. These monks built it a few centuries ago; they made a good living transporting wool into the West Riding. Legend has it way back that one of the royalist cavaliers held Cromwell's men at bay single-handed, long enough for King Charles to escape, presumably to be hidden in Wilstrop Hall; hence the special King Charles chair Lady Cecilia showed us roped off in the study. He was finally slain on the bridge; there's been many a tale of sightings of a strange ghostly figure wearing a long cloak and a plumed hat.

Frank was so busy thinking about Charlotte he failed to realise he was approaching the bridge far too fast and, of course, he had completely forgotten about the broken front brake; the machine took off as he sped over the hump, and there in the gloaming was a figure – a large man in a heavy brown cloak. Frank recalled seeing a bearded face under a strange hat, and closed his eyes as he hit him: but there was no impact. The bike wobbled and swerved badly as Frank fought for control. He turned back as a new moon, rising from behind the Priory, cast an early shadow on the river. A mallard drake quacked out a warning as he looked over the parapet; the sudden noise of ducks leaving the water startled him, the strange hiss and high-pitched, almost human scream, followed by the call of a barn owl in the branches of a nearby tree were enough to set Frank's teeth on edge. He restarted his machine and sped home. Later, as he recounted the happenings of the day to his mother and the anxious Charlotte, he made no mention of the strange apparition on the bridge; he had to admit to himself, however, that there must be something in this 'ghost business' after all.

9

Rent Review

In order to arrive at a satisfactory 'rent' for the various farms on the estate, Frank soon realised that a great deal of diplomacy was called for. The guile and native cunning of the tenants would have to be matched with something similar.

He decided to start with the Home Farm, let to a Mr Fred 'Kippers' Metcalfe, who got the nickname because before taking to farming he had been a travelling greengrocer in Upper Wharfedale; the sign on the front of his cart read 'Fresh Kippers for Sale, Daily'. Ably assisted by two strong, well-grown, sons he now ran the best farm on the estate; it had a superior house, useful buildings, a good quantity of level, sound pasture-land sloping gently to the river; and that's where Frank found Fred – literally in the river, in the sheepwash. He was up to his armpits in the middle of the river, and the two sons were catching and throwing him his sheep 'arse first'.

'They mun allus go in arse first,' one of the many onlookers was saying.

'Right, one of you lads,' Fred shouted when he saw Frank,'I've been in here about an hour, time to change ow'er.' He came out of the water wearing two pairs of trousers with a sack around his middle.

'We're just a bit early this year, tha knows, that river's a bit cowd like. I shall hev to change to dry clothes afore we can talk business,' he said to Frank.

'I thought most people had stopped washing sheep, Mr Metcalfe,' Frank remarked as they walked up to the farm.

'Aye lad, tha's reet, don't suppose them two lads of mine would bother if I weren't gaffer around here – tha gets a few pence extra for thy wool, it helps wi' th' rise and they're easier to clip. Besides these half-bred ewes need clipping early; moor sheep want doing next month by rights, middle of June's about best time. I remember when I was a lad living near Dent they'd wash three thousand in a day and be finished by three in the afternoon; then what a party – poacher's pie, whisky and as much mulled ale as they could sup. Th' entire dale would be theer, then wrestling and sports, what a going on.'

'Joe Falshaw's talking of setting up collective sheep sales this back end, one in Wharfedale, one near Hawes and another at Cow Hill.'

'Aye that's reet, top end of Deepdale. By, you're spreading your wings, arn't yer?'

'Well, he's made his mind up that folks would rather come to a central collecting point and have their stock sold for them, rather than walking miles to the nearest market town and having to stand all day selling 'em themselves.'

'Aye, well, I hope it works; now come yourself in, me daughter will hev a cup of tea ready and most likely something in t' tins she's baked, then we'll hev a talk in t'front parlour, once I get these wet clothes off.'

Fred Metcalfe readily agreed that the farm rent had been on the low side for some years now.

'Captain Pilkington tells me your rent has not been increased for almost ten years.'

'That's true,' said Fred, 'but we've had a terrible watter supply.'

'It's all right now though,' Frank intervened.

'Aye! Shame about old Simon, weren't it? They tell me his widow's livin' like a lady o'er near Lancaster somewhere.'

'Yes,' said Frank.

'Then nobody's done ony repairs, tha knows. We could nivver get owt done once the major stopped calling round, grand fella that, but you'd allus to lock up the womenfolk once 'is coach arrived in t'yard.'

'We thought we'd have to double it,' said Frank.

'Double what?' said Fred, an innocent look on his face.

'Double your rent,' Frank said.

'Hey, hold on,' said Fred. 'Things hevn't been going so well for me lately.'

'How's that?' asked Frank.

'Well, we had to hev th' vet early this morning, me best cow's down wi' milk fever; lost one last week wi' same job. "Grass staggers", I calls it.'

'I'm sorry to hear that,' said Frank.

'I've nivver had such a bad lambing time.'

'Those ewes and lambs we saw down by the river seemed well enough,' said Frank.

'Aye! but we lost ivver so many when they lambed.'

'Things are not going too well, then?'

'Lost me best dog, one I've won a few trials wi'; one of those new-fangled motor cars came through t'other day, she ran at it barking her head off like, silly fella ran reet over her, nivver offered to stop.'

'Well, perhaps we'll have to have second thoughts and see if we can't look for some slight reduction,' said Frank. 'What do you say to increasing your rent from sixty to one hundred pounds a year?'

'What else were it I were going to tell thee? Oh! Aye! nearly forgot, buried the missus last Thursday!'

Jim Hunter at Glebe Farm was just as hard and as crafty to deal with, prepared to talk about everything but the business in hand.

'Funny do about Simon Stott's twin brother, weren't it?' he said.

'What was that?' asked Frank.

'Well, when you buried him recently?'

'I remember,' said Frank, 'first coffin I've seen carried to the graveside on hay forks.'

'I bet those lads were pleased they hadn't to carry him much further,' said Jim. 'I think they were about sick of carting him about afore they were done.'

'Where does his twin brother come in? I didn't meet him afterwards.'

Jim laughed heartily. 'Funny do if tha had.'

'Why is that?' asked Frank.

'Well, that's what I've bin trying to tell thee,' said Jim, 'Yer know there was some delay, and a change of date due to some'at wrong wi' death certificate, him dying in strange circumstances like.'

'Yes.'

'Well, his brother came o'er from Bilsdale, where he lives, on that first date; boasting and crowing like, 'cos he said he allus told Simon he'd outlive him. He went home afore he were buried like – an' next morning he got dressed, went downstairs and afore he had breakfast sat in his armchair, lent down to tie his bootlaces, fell for'ard stone deead. They buried him day afore poor owd Simon. So I'm not sure who won like.'

'Now, as you know, I've come to talk about a rent increase,' said Frank. 'I see from the schedule your rent for one hundred and forty acres is forty pounds a year.'

'Aye, that's reet; mind you, most of it's rough pasture tha knows, an' we havn't had any repairs done 'as they promised.'

'Is there anything really urgent?' asked Frank.

'Stable roof's none too clever.'

'Right: let's have a look.' Frank was startled to find a horse with his head sticking through the roof slates. 'I see what you mean – when was he last mucked out?' Frank said peering over the stable door.

'Well, you see, he's running wi' a litter of pigs just now, there's nowhere else to keep 'em, they need plenty of bedding. We allus sledges plenty of bracken down off the fell at the back end; it soon builds up.'

Frank jumped back in alarm as a litter of ten well-grown pigs, in turn startled by the approach of a stranger, bounded out of the liberal covering of dried bracken, specially put down for Frank's visit; they all stampeded into a far corner.

'There's got to be two years or more bedding in here, Mr Hunter!' said Frank. 'That's why the horse has to put his head out through the roof.'

'Aye! maybe we did miss mucking it out last year, h'as you can see we need some new loose boxes or some'at.'

'Seems to me you can't look after what you've got,' said Frank; 'but if you want to erect 'em yourself you can have a certificate of compensation should you leave, but it'll be ten per cent depreciation.'

'What does that mean?' asked Jim Hunter.

'It means that you write off the cost over ten years; it then stays where it is and reverts to the estate owners; or the estate can perhaps build what you need and add eight per cent of the cost to your rent, in addition to the extra we try and agree today.'

'Seems to me you're trying to put me out of business,' complained Jim. 'I shall nivver be able to make ends meet, nivver again. How much are you going to want?'

'Double,' said Frank.

'Eighty pund a year,' wailed Jim.

'That's it,' said Frank, 'you've all had these farms too cheap for years, and that's been a mistake. You're all going to have to pull your socks up, make more money, farm more intensive like.'

'They tell't me yon Joe Falshaw was a hard man; it seems he's training thee well, young man. What if I don't agree to pay?'

'You can get another valuer in and we can negotiate with him; you'll have to pay his fee though.'

'That's settled then, I'll get Bill Tordoft over from Kendal way and we'll have an arbitration if needs be.'

He's not as daft as he pretends to be, thought Frank as he left Jim Hunter and made his way back to the Estate Office. That's the last thing we want, these tenants talking of arbitration.

He was surprised to meet a strange gypsy wagon pulling out of the rear yard to the Hall. A magnificent piebald horse caught Frank's eye; he was aware of the unusual semicircular canvas cover on the cart, but most of all his gaze centred on the driver; straight from a wild west show! thought Frank.

He was wearing a large, greasy stetson, a red polka dot necktie; a leather waistcoat over a coarse flannel shirt; corduroy trousers, tucked into brown leather knee-length brown boots; he had a plaited leather driving whip in one hand, the reins in the other and an enormously long clay pipe in his mouth.

'Whoa!' he bellowed at his horse, somehow managing to keep the pipe in place. The horse shied and reared on its hind legs. 'Shut that bloody thing down young man, afore this hoss takes off. Whoa lass, it waint hurt thee, whey, that's it, steady.'

'Can I help you?' said Frank dismounting from his bike.

'Nah! I were nobbut looking for th'old Captain; ah couldn't get no answer so I thout as how I'd hev to call agin.'

'Who should I say called?' asked Frank.

'Ned Spicer's me name, young man, general dealer; cash on the nail, that's me motto; nivver leaves a premises wi'out payin in pund notes.'

'I can't imagine Captain Pilkington wishing to have dealings with you, sir!'

'That's where tha's wrong, young fella, no need to tak' a high-fallutin' tone wi' me. Who might you be? If I may be so bold as to ask.'

'I'm the new agent in Captain Pilkington's place.'

'He hasn't snuffed it, has he?'

'No, but if he doesn't want to see you he'll just stay quiet indoors.'

'Oh, he'll want to see me alreet! Ah paid him twenty-five quid for that last lot of h'antique furniture, an' he said to come back in six months time for another load; beautiful stuff tha knows, real class. Hev you got it in hand now?'

Frank's next call was to see Bill Crossland, who ran the local flour mill. Most farmers in the district managed to grow a few acres of wheat and oats, and all they produced would eventually find its way to the mill to be ground into flour, then taken back for home consumption.

However, Bill was an enterprising hard-working fellow, who in middle age had started to build up a thriving business, buying grain from the Plain of York, processing it into flour and transporting the finished product westwards over the Pennines as far as the Lancashire coast for use in the manufacture of biscuits.

Frank had last met him on the market square of Ripon where open air transactions, a sort of unofficial corn exchange, had been carried on for centuries.

'Hello, Mr Crossland,' said Frank. 'I've called to see you to discuss a suitable rent increase on your premises.'

'Hev you lad, who thought that one up? Joe Falshaw, I'll be bound.'

'No not really, the trustees feel you tenants have been paying far too little rent for years.'

'Maybe so, maybe so, but they've done nowt for us tha knows, nowt at all. Motto round here's bin "if tha wants owt doing, do it for thi'sen!" and that's just what I'ave done, spent a fortune on't place wi' very little thanks. Ah reckon trustees should be payin' me for all t'improvements, not comin round askin' for more brass. You can go back smartish and tell 'em there's nowt doin'. Ah'll show thee round wi' pleasure, but not a penny more rent's comin' out of my pocket, not for a year or two onyway.'

Frank sensed here was a man who spoke his mind and meant it. Back-pedal here, he thought.

'I'd like to see that magnificent water wheel of yours in operation, Mr Crossland. Frank had shrewdly hit his man below the belt, he already knew many hours of loving care had been lavished on the wooden wheel to bring it back to its former glory.

'We'll need to be on t'first floor to see it in action. Here y'are, if you just pull t'lever, that'll set it in motion. Mind I hev to warn thee, once it starts it must signal food or some'at to them rats out theer.'

He pointed to the other side of the ford Frank had crossed on his way to the mill. 'They seem to gather up on yon far side and then they swim across, some as big as cats; they come at us sometimes like a swarm of bees.'

A short while afterwards Frank heard a shout.

'Sither, here they come!' He poked his head through one of the loading bay doors; the sight was alarming, literally hundreds of rats of all ages were swimming the stream and heading directly for the mill.

'By gum,' said Bill Crossland, 'they look as if they mean busines this time, we hevn't been grindin' for some weeks, they look to be fair famished to me.'

'Can't you stop them?' asked Frank.

'Naw, not even gunfire works when they're really clammed.'

'What do we do then?' quavered Frank, trying hard to keep his voice steady.

'Well; we climb up another floor, then pull t'ladder up after us'sens.'

74

'Then what?'

'Well, if it's all clear round t'back there's an outside staircase to go down, an' if not we're stuck here until they sense it's a false alarm and go off back ter fields on their own account. It's no use keepin' cats or dogs here tha knows, they'd just disappear wi'out trace if that lot got hold of 'em.'

'I'll have a word with Tweet Umpleby and see if he can tackle the problem; in the meantime I think we had better leave the rent as it is.'

'Aye! I thought you'd see it my way, young fella.'

10

The Grouse Moor

It was the evening of the 11th August, 1913 and Frank was booked in at the Whitwell Hotel for the night.

He'd been checking that all was well with the small grouse moor which went with the estate. It had been neglected for many years past but on Frank's insistence Joe Falshaw had agreed it made economic sense to employ Tweet Umpleby as full-time keeper and for the first time the grouse shooting had been let to a syndicate of West Riding industrialists.

Frank and his keeper had spent most of the day sorting out the best direction for the various drives; the rewards for Tweet's efforts were apparent in a good count of mature birds and an abundance of well-grown youngsters.

Two fell ponies with double panniers had been used to take the beer and other refreshments to the stone-built luncheon 'box' on the high moor. On the morrow the same transport would be used to carry the food and spare cartridges for the shooting party and would then be used for the return journey to carry the birds back to the game larder at the Hall.

Frank had employed 'Digger' Calvert as pannier man for the shooting season. A distinguished-looking man in his late thirties, he had been born in the local work house. His mother, former chambermaid at the Hall when Major Spencer was in his prime, had been 'paid off' before the birth of her boy child. She christened him Thomas after her late father; he acquired his nickname when he became the local gravedigger. He sported a magnificent blond moustache and with his military bearing and looks, no doubt was left in the minds of the older villagers as to the true identity of his father. He was a skilled drystone waller, capable of erecting six to eight yards a working day, and a prolific prizewinner at such local shows that held walling competitions.

As a young man he had made a considerable name for himself as a fell runner, and latterly was becoming equally famous as a skilled exponent of the art of Cumberland wrestling.

Frank admired his quick wit and cheerful disposition. He was a tireless and interesting companion, particularly for a long and arduous day on the moor; he was a great raconteur of local stories. His most recent grave-digging story had Frank and Tweet roaring with laughter as they made their way on foot down off the fell.

'There's allus a problem in that chapel graveyard,' Digger was telling his companions as they descended; 'if two folk want to be buried together, one coffin on top o t'other, like happened agin last week – some old girl from away near Leeds asked to be put in her hubby's grave –- we're short o' depth, tha knows.'

'So what do you do?' queried Frank.

'Well, if it's a fairly modern sort of coffin, made o' pitch pine, ah can allus reckon to flatten it wi' me shovel – then tha puts a green cloth o'er it and by the time they lower a new box into t'grave bereaved knows nowt about it.'

'So wheers th' problem, then?' asked Tweet.

'Well, in this h'instance, t'old lad had been down theer twenty-five year and they'd put him in an old h'oak coffin – shovel just bounced off – no chance of squashing that.'

'So what did you do?' they both asked simultaneously.

'We had to bury them head to head.'

'They both have the same headstone then?' suggested Frank.

'Aye, they're goin' to chisel her name on t'other side of his headstone – best I could do, I tell't undertaker. Got an extra pund note from t'head mourner; I reckon I might just spend that toneet.'

'No you don't,' said Frank, 'you'll be guests of the firm; supper first at the pub and then a few drinks; stay as long as you like, but don't forget we need a seven-thirty start tomorrow.'

Supper over and final tactics discussed, the three were just settling down to a glass of mulled ale around the blazing log fire when in walked 'Kippers' Metcalfe.

'Hello Fred,' said Frank, 'didn't know this was on your beat.'

'On my way home from a funeral,' said Fred, 'often get a game of dominoes here with a double nine set – better game altogether than sixes.'

'Never played it,' said Frank, 'Should we have a foursome?' The words were out before he caught sight of his two companions, behind Fred, vigorously shaking their heads.

'Aye,' said Fred, 'these lads know how – thirteen do's a piece – play out at four ends – sixpence a corner.'

Frank whistled. 'That sounds a bit expensive – threepence a corner sounds to be plenty.' His two companions showed obvious signs of relief; Fred reluctantly agreed and the game started.

Frank soon realised this game was all about memory – with all the dominoes in play it was imperative to remember who knocked, and at which of the four ends; it was also very clear that Fred Metcalfe was an expert who had spotted three suckers as soon as he walked in.

After Fred had gleefully raked in his winnings from five consecutive games, Frank was desperately thinking how he could terminate the proceedings when fate took a hand – into the bar walked an apparition dressed in a heavy tweed suit with plus fours; on his head a deerstalker complete with earmuffs fastened over the top; on his shoulder he carried an expensive leather gun case; like everything else, the heavy brogue shoes were obviously new.

'Good evening, miss,' the man boomed, 'I trust you're expecting me? Captain Owen. Here for a few days' shooting – I think I'll sample a half of your best bitter.'

'Good Lord,' groaned Frank. 'He's one of my clients.'

'Did you hear that?' Fred asked Tweet, 'You come down to this pub every night and sup four or five pints – this chap can walk in and he "samples" the ale – see – he doesn't even get charged for it. Hey up! He's coming o'er here.'

'Can I get you chaps a drink?' the voice boomed.

'Yes, Captain,' said Fred touching his forelock, 'four whiskies would be very welcome.'

'Four whiskies for these men if you please, young lady,' the Captain demanded – then turning to Tweet he asked, 'Do you shoot the grouse, my man?'

'No sir,' replied Tweet with a perfectly straight face; 'nivver can afford to, see; only sport I get is nobbling rabbits.'

'Never heard of it – nobbling rabbits – what sort of sport is that?'

'Well sir, you needs be as quick as lightning to get 'em, quicker than you with those expensive Purdy shotguns you're hanging onto.'

'You've noticed, have you; nothing but the best to get the best results you know! What type of shotgun do you use?'

'We can't afford shotguns, can us, lads?' he asked of his solemn companions. 'Thanks, Mary,' he said to the barmaid as she handed him his glass of whisky. 'Here's to your good health, sir, and a goodly bag of grouse tomorrow.'

'Cheers,' added Fred, smacking his lips.

'Now, all tha needs to catch rabbits is a stout ash stave – a few nets and a good ferret.'

'I don't follow you,' said the Captain.

'It's easy really,' replied Tweet, warming to his story, 'tha simply goes along to a rabbit warren with a ferret in a sack – then mak' sure they're all at home.'

'How do you do that?' asked the Captain, drawing up a stool.

'Show him, Tweet – show him how you mak' that squeal with your gob.'

'I'm just a little dry,' replied Tweet, 'perhaps another whisky would help.'

'Of course,' said the worthy Captain, 'silly of me – four more whiskies, is it?'

'He's very good at this, is Tweet,' said Fred, 'but he needs plenty of lubrication to get it right.'

'Make them doubles!' boomed the Captain in the direction of the bar.

'Well, tha makes this noise what sends 'em scurrying for safety down below,' explained Tweet, 'then tha stakes out t'nets o'er t'oles leaving yan free, then tha slips the ferret in.'

'Then what?' asked the Captain.

'Well, that's when t'nobblin stick comes in, tha needs to crouch down – thanks Mary, there's nowt I likes better than two whiskies in one glass – better colour somehow.'

Tweet downed the remainder of his first whisky at one gulp, smacked his lips, put them to the palm of his left hand and proceeded to make his famous rabbit squeal. 'There you are, Captain,' said Digger, 'frightens 'em to death.'

'I'm not surprised.'

'Now lads, move that domino board aside,' said Tweet. With that he climbed onto the table on his hands and knees, carefully placing his full whisky glass on the stool to his front. 'Pass me yon wading stick, boss.' Frank took down a heavily-weighted hazel thumb stick hung by its leather strap on the wall.

'H'as I said, tha crouches down, ear close to t'ole – tha can hear when rabbits scuttlin' towards thee, up tha goes wi' th' stick and – crash! – the glass oil-lamp suspended from the ceiling directly above the table broke into a myriad of pieces – the brass base fell fair and square on Tweet's head. The landlord returned to the bar just as he slumped to the floor, taking four empty pint glasses with him.

Both Fred and Frank had managed to snatch up their double whiskies and in some miraculous way Tweet had scooped up his full glass as he fell; he turned onto his back before hitting the flagged floor and, although only semi-conscious, held his glass in a rigid left hand and never spilt a drop.

Frank discreetly moved to the bar and agreed to pay for the damage; as he returned to the table Tweet was sitting up slowly shaking his head. 'I got nobbled mysen,' he was muttering to the Captain. 'I'd better drink this first, sir; and then I'll take up your kind offer of another.'

The following morning, if the worthy Captain was aware his companions of the night before had gently 'taken him to the cleaners' he failed to show it. There was instantaneous recognition as Frank, accompanied by Tweet and Digger arrived at the moor gate for the first drive, but no mention of the incident came from either side – scores were even and like all true country gentlemen, he adopted the old adage 'least said, soonest mended'.

Much to Frank's amazement the Captain showed himself to be a first-class shot; he bagged more grouse than any other member of the party, on what turned out to be a memorable first day's shooting.

It was the occasion of the first public sale of sheep at Cow Hill in Deepdale. Frank had arrived, soaked to the skin, grateful that Dick Boynton and two of the market porters had already made the long journey two days previously with the new sheep hurdles; these were already erected in a long line backing onto the limestone wall to the rear of the local public house.

The landlady, a buxom lass in her late twenties, persuaded Frank to retire to his room and divest himself of his wet clothes – she provided him with one of her husband's smocks and insisted he have a hot bath in a large tub in front of a roaring fire in the parlour. Frank found himself fascinated by her flaming red hair, glowing in the firelight as she proceeded to fill the tub from the side boiler of a spotlessly clean black kitchen range – nor could he fail to notice the low neckline of her bodice and the perfect outline of her breasts as she bent low over the tub, purposely allowing Frank a full view as she poured each pan full of boiling water very slowly into the tub.

He also noticed the scowl of displeasure on her husband's face as he returned from the cow byre – he noticed too the glint in his eye as he grunted and turned quickly on his heel. Frank was also aware that he was a much older man – probably more than twice his wife's age.

'Don't worry about old surly-chops,' the landlady chuckled merrily. 'Always like that if I make a fuss o'er a younger man.'

'You must be young Mr Bowers, then? I'm Ruth Merriman; is Mr Falshaw arriving this evening?'

'No,' said Frank, 'he will be through in the morning – I thought he wrote to let you know.'

'Aye, maybe he did. Well, I suppose that means there'll only be thee and me sleeping here tonight; although of course yon men will be outside in the buildings.'

'But, your husband?' queried Frank.

'Shouldn't think I'll see him till tomorrow, he'll be going down the valley to Deepdale soon; he's in charge of the Trotting Association in these parts and there's a race meeting there tonight. He allus gets drunk and nivver gets back here; sometimes he goes missing for two or three days.'

'Wouldn't mind going racing myself,' said Frank. 'I'll take my foreman with me if we can sort out some dry clothes – but I'll be back,' he added hastily as he noticed his hostess pouting her lips in mock disappointment. 'Now if you would excuse me, I'd like to get into this bathtub.'

This was only the second Trotting Meeting that Frank had attended; he lost quite a lot of money on the first occasion and was determined not to be caught 'napping' again.

'I reckon we need some sort of system, Dick, if we're going to make this job pay; any ideas?'

'Well, boss, you've got to be as sharp as they are, and that takes some doin', believe me.'

The two of them were sitting quietly in the corner of the public bar of the George and Dragon in the centre of the village. Seth Merriman had been persuaded to give them a lift in his dog cart and had purposely dropped them off at the front door suggesting this was the place to seek out information.

'Tell Joe Lister, who runs this place, you're friends of mine, he'll have spare race cards on the bar, and since he knows all the owners, he's the chap to mark your card. Buy him a couple of drinks and he's sure to oblige. I'd do it mysen only t'officials are banned.' By this time both men were leaning against a bar with a gleaming copper top.

'Evening gents, what's your pleasure?' Joe Lister, the landlord, was a giant of a man, almost as broad as he was tall; completely bald, he sported a handsome waxed moustache and a glorious black beard stretching halfway down his chest. Frank noticed the friendly twinkle and the heavy lines radiating from the corner of each piercing blue eye – I like a man who smiles with his eyes, Frank thought to himself.

81

'Seth Merriman told me to introduce myself; my name is Frank Bowers and this is my foreman Dick Boynton. We're staying at the Horse-breakers' Arms ready for a sheep sale tomorrow morning – we've decided to try and win a bob or two at the races. Seth tells me you're a likely chap to know of a winner or two. I'd like two large whiskies and a drink for yourself, of course.'

'Thanks kindly – a rum and pep for mysen – that'll be half a crown altogether if you please, and two race cards, three bob then.'

'I was hoping...' Frank's voice trailed off as he realised the landlord had left the bar as quickly as he had appeared. 'Let's sit down, Dick, and see if we can sort something out.'

'Plenty of runners, boss,' said Dick, 'but we know nowt about any of 'em.'

'I'll nip back to the bar and see if another drink will loosen his tongue a bit.'

Joe Lister appeared from the back parlour, even quicker than on the first occasion.

'Yes sir?'

'Two large whiskies as before, and you'll perhaps take a double rum?' queried Frank.

'If you insist sir; did you get any tips for tonight from Seth?'

'No, he said officials had to be very careful, but that you were some-what of an expert and a likely chap to mark this card of mine.'

'Indeed: indeed, sir, so I am. Nah then,' said Joe, drawing Frank to the corner of the bar, at the same time casting furtive glances over each shoulder. 'This mare'll win the final trot, or my name's not Joe Lister,' and with that he took a short stub of pencil from behind his ear, licked it, and taking Frank's card underlined No: 8, Lady Gertrude in the second heat.

'They'll run her second in her heat, but don't be fooled by that; first two from each heat go forward to the semi-finals; there's five or six runners in each heat, see – so eight of 'em for two semi-final races, and first two from them races for the final – he's a very clever lad in a sulky is her jockey – Alan Bane – smart enough to run her second in the semi-final so's they can get better odds for the final; if you've any sense I wouldn't put any brass on her till then.

'And there's another smart little hoss, very fast but tiny, well-handi-capped – Fair Alice – should win that first heat provided this chap Be Cautious doesn't catch her; she's got thirty yards' start. Here's the danger to them all – Hippodrome in the last heat, depends if his jockey is sober, been known to get so drunk before racing has Tom Brennand, known to all as "King Tom", that he doesn't allus get round – tumbled out of his seat on quite a few occasions through drink.'

'It's not going to be easy,' said Frank.

'No,' said Joe, nodding his head wisely.

Frank returned to his seat.

'Well?' queried Dick Boynton.

'Here's your whisky,' said Frank. 'He says Lady Gertrude will win the final, and not to mind if she runs second in her heats – and Fair Alice could win the first heat.'

'That's what I like to hear,' said Dick, 'If we can get hold of some bookies' money early on it can make all the difference.'

Racing was scheduled to take place on a large flat field immediately on the outskirts of the village, bounded on one side by the river, with high fells on either side. The scene made a lasting impression on Frank; he marvelled at the never-ending drystone walls rising high above isolated farmsteads, ever upwards onto the moors, over and beyond the skyline.

He paused to give thought to the men who spent a lifetime, in all weathers, with horse and sledge, collecting and then shaping and selecting with precision individual stones so that slowly and inexorably a timeless memorial to their dedication and skill emerged; giving shelter to the hardy horned sheep which form the life blood of these hardy farmers – the same sheep he would be selling on the morrow.

'Well?' said Joe Lister, a huge grin on his face as two rather crestfallen visitors managed to scramble their way to the bar. 'Did you back her? I had a right do, she went out to twelve to one just at the off.'

'Well no,' said Frank. 'I fancied Parlour Maid to win the final; I lost a packet on that Be Cautious the race before and then hadn't the sense to have a small bet as a saver, like Dick here, on your tip; still, I enjoyed it.'

'Two large whiskies, landlord,' said Dick rather smugly, 'perhaps you'll be after having a nip yourself?'

Frank awoke at daybreak not sure exactly where he was; his head felt as if it was on fire and there was a persistent throbbing ache behind his eyes. He staggered to his feet, slowly realising it was a strange drumming noise that had awakened him, and drew back the heavy curtains – 'Oh Lord!' he moaned, 'just what we didn't want.' Rainwater was cascading from the roof and seemed to be bouncing back off the courtyard.

Frank could hear the dull roar of the beck to the side of the pub – the fells, looking so beautiful the night before, had disappeared in low cloud and mist. 'A ruddy cloudburst,' he moaned, 'on a sheep sale morning of all days.' He lay back on the bed and tried to piece together the events following the racing.

He remembered quite clearly the earlier events of the evening, the hare stew that he devoured with such gusto on his return to the George and Dragon; the heated argument between committee members and the locals about allowing the horse Hippodrome to race in the final after he and his jockey had parted company; he had a vague recollection of Seth Merriman singing a bawdy song or two on a table top; the ever-present large jugs of frothing ale; of Seth's last wish before passing out under the table that Frank and Dick should take his pony and trap home – indeed where was the pony now? He remembered Dick and himself singing 'Nellie Dean' as the pony made his own way home along the winding valley road. I wonder if Dick stabled him? he mused, Don't remember getting here or indeed getting into bed. It was then he spotted the woollen shawl on the floor beside the bed, he picked it up and caught a whiff of cheap perfume. Oh no, he thought, what happened? I must have passed out; who undressed me? But try as he might his mind remained a blank.

Quickly he poured the jug of water into the bowl on the dressing table and dowsed his face and the back of his neck; it seemed to alleviate the pain across his forehead; but still his memory failed him.

The sale porters and Dick Boynton were already wading into large portions of ham and eggs, fussed over by the landlady, as Frank, failing to realise there was a step down into the kitchen, literally lurched into the room and almost fell on his knees.

'My, my, young sir,' quipped Ruth Merriman 'still a little unsteady, are we? Never mind, there's plenty of hot porridge over there by the fire, help thi'sen. Ham and eggs to follow, if that's all right?'

'Yes,' said Frank rather hesitantly, 'just one slice of ham and one egg please.'

'I'll fetch a strong cup of tea, Mr Bowers, to make thee feel better; tha'll need to get thee strength back after last night!' she said as a quiet aside.

The low seductive tone of her voice made Frank fear the worst and the remark did not go unnoticed by the foreman.

As Frank sat down, he saw Dick grinning at him; he watched him slowly move his head from side to side before jerking it quickly in the direction of Ruth Merriman as she disappeared next door. 'I trust you had a good night's sleep, sir?' he said, sarcastically.

'To be perfectly honest, Dick, I remember setting off with the pony and trap, I remember you insisting that I give you the reins and us both singing "On Ilkley Moor bar t'at" as we galloped past the local bobby at the entrance to the show field. I know you suggested we did a circuit of the racetrack before setting off up the valley, then me mind's a blank.'

'Thank you for seeing to the pony when you got back last night,' said Ruth Merriman as she returned with Frank's tea. He glanced up quickly to see she was directing her remarks at Dick.

'No trouble, ma'am,' Dick smirked.

'I thought at first that husband o' mine had decided to try and be different and come home, that's why I came down in me night attire, you understand.'

'Of course, ma'am,' said Dick, 'and very good of you to offer to look after my boss here; I didn't know what the devil to do with 'im.'

Frank decided he had better end this conversation.

'Right then,' he said with as much authority as he could muster, 'if we're all finished eating, time to get this sheep sale on the go. You'll need leggings on you, lads, and it might be a good idea the way it's raining, to fasten a hessian sack or two over your shoulders.'

The first draft of sheep off the high fell had already arrived – one hundred horned wether lambs from Bank House for Edgar Booth, and sixty mixed lambs, mainly half-bred gimmers, from Dalehead for Mr Mortimer.

'Where shall we put 'em?' a cheery voice called out as Frank arrived at the ringside.

'Pen them alongside that wall, my men'll give you a hand, then sort 'em out as best you can after.'

Frank found himself addressing a handsome young man in his early twenties, leaning on his long shepherd's crook, clicking his fingers at two collie dogs fussing around his feet.

'I'm Fred Mortimer,' he said as he shot out a large hand. Frank felt a vice-like grip from a hand almost twice the size of his own.

'These are me father's sheep, bin gathering up since before dawn. Mr Booth says he'll be down presently, he had to milk afore he could set off, so I brought 'em along for him. He's marked 'em wi' red ruddle into five lots of twenty.'

Just then Dick sidled up. 'There's ever so many lots coming down that valley road, boss; how can we separate 'em?'

'If you let them in one lot at a time off the road, find out how many pens they need; and if you get your lads to close off the alleyway at the top, then close it off behind 'em, it should all go like clockwork. What's more you'll soon have a few helpers.'

The heavy rain had stopped and most of the pens were full when Joe Falshaw arrived. He looked every inch an auctioneer, in his riding breeches, highly-polished brown leggings and boots, long check coat and brightly-coloured waistcoat. Frank, on the other hand, was very, very wet and looked somewhat dishevelled.

'You ought to wear a hat on mornings like this, you know,' Joe said as he strutted around the ring, slapping a willow cane against his leggings. 'And I think you'd look more the part if you got rid of that sodden sack you have tied round your neck. First impressions is allus best and these fellows around here have nivver seen thee before; tha looks like one of them porters, not the fella in charge.'

'If, sir! you had seen it rain early on.'

'I know how it can rain in these parts,' said Joe. 'Come through fairish mysen on the way over here, but I came prepared and you'll have to learn to do the same.'

Frank had never seen or heard Joe in this type of mood before; he stared hard at his boss, but apart from a slightly strained look around the eyes, a certain lack of colour in the face, he could detect little change.

'Yes, sir,' he said rather sarcastically. 'Has everything else been done to your satisfaction? How do you propose to sell these sheep?'

'On a first come, first sold basis. Where's pen no. 1?'

'Over here by the wall – one hundred wethers from Edgar Booth.'

'That's torn it,' said Joe, 'he'll play merry hell if he's first in the ring. I've nivver met a fella yet at any of our sales as likes going in first. Did you meet Mr Booth?'

'No,' said Frank. 'A young chap called Mortimer brought his sheep in for him.'

'Young Fred Mortimer? Best athlete in the North of England that lad – they can't beat him at wrestling or at fell running; he's a right dab hand at drystone walling an' all, dare say he could beat Tweet Umpleby every time.'

'Now that's Edgar Booth,' Joe pointed with his cane to a large man bending over his sheep; 'a big man in every way, he's by far the biggest sheep farmer around here. Owns a fair lump of land at the top end of this valley; this'll be the first time we've ever sold anything for him, he usually comes down our way buying. Nice to see you again, Mr Booth,' said Joe as they arrived at the sheep pens. 'You've some smart lambs there.'

'Aye, I thart I'd bring a hundred down to see how thee shapes.'

Evelyn at work in the hay field (page 4)

Tuffan as a 4 year old (page 18)

Wilstrop Hall (page 27)

Frank as a young man (page 40)

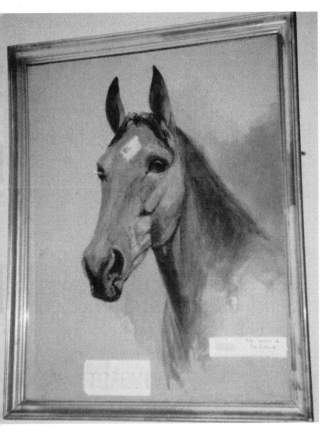

Tuffan (page 45)

Frank's first motorcycle, a 750cc Rex Acme (page 61)

Joe selling pigs (page 133)

Carved sheep horn (page 177)

Rescue teams - the search goes
on as they make their way
underground (page 172)

Passageway in Boroughbridge (page 227)

Tom Edwards (on left) as an officer cadet 1917 (page 207)

Tom Edwards marries Frank's sister - April 1919 Frank is on the left standing behind his formidable mother (page 221)

'Hambleton Springs' (show hunter). Royal Show Harrogate 1929. 1st Local Class (5 years), 2nd Open Novice (5 years) (page 217)

West of Yore original Hunt Kennels (page 257)

Car mascot (page 268)

Lady Webber raising her glass 'to the cowgown' (page 286)

'This is my young assistant, Frank Bowers,' Joe said casually, 'he'll be taking over from me shortly, I fear.'

'Not today I hope,' said Edgar Booth as he shook hands with Frank. 'I want thee to be selling when it comes to my turn, Falshaw.'

Edgar Booth – 'I want thee to be selling when it comes to be my turn, Falshaw'

I'm not going to like this man, thought Frank; he had to look up to meet his eyes – he took in a mean, coarse face with large bushy eyebrows and a large full mouth; on his head a high-crowned hat with an extra wide brim, a curious mixture of a top hat and a western style stetson, thought Frank – he must get 'em especially made.

Already Edgar was turning away and querying, 'Where do you start selling, Falshaw?'

'Pen no. 1 here,' said Joe, 'first come, first served, you'll soon be through.'

'I'll be damned if I will,' said Booth, 'You mon put Fred Mortimer through first; Fred's poorly in bed, that lad of his, young Fred, he won't mind.'

'Sorry, Edgar,' said Joe slapping his leggings with his cane, 'rules is rules and we start with Pen no. 1. Have you finished drawing them?'

'Aye, we're ready, but I'll mak' sure we don't get here as soon next time, might as well have laid in bed and taken 'em through t'Hawes market day to sell 'em mysen. Don't thee forget I've a few hundred more to sell, tha knows.'

'Yes, perhaps we can have a word about that before you go home tonight,' said Joe. 'Could easily come looking for a couple of hundred lambs myself to put in our sale down at the market, swell the numbers you know. I'm getting one or two of them West Riding wholesalers to come along to take biggish numbers of killing lambs.'

'Aye, well, you'll be welcome any time, just let me know.'

Clever stuff, thought Frank. That's pacified him.

The sale was a great success; the first two pens were unsold, Edgar Booth refusing to accept the price, but they were his best lambs and were sold privately later in the day. After that the sale took off. It was a very happy throng of buyers and sellers who gradually filled the bar of the Horsebreakers' Arms.

Joe Falshaw had started the sale off, but after about an hour Frank realised he was having difficulties getting his breath. A sudden fit of coughing halted the proceedings; as he drew his handkerchief away from his lips, Frank noticed it was stained with blood. With as little fuss as possible he took over the selling; as Joe got down from the makeshift rostrum Frank suggested he should take himself back to the office.

It was late afternoon before the last lot came into the ring. Frank then thanked the assembled company, suggesting that the sale might become an annual event. He pointed out that all vendors would be paid in cash in the small office in the pub yard; eventually, tired and thirsty, on the hour of six o'clock, he made his way into a very noisy bar.

There stood Joe Falshaw, flushed of face, jacket discarded, pewter pint pot in hand, rendering in a deep bass voice his favourite ditty – 'To Be a Farmer's Boy'.

'To plough and sow, to reap and mow,' his enraptured audience eagerly joined in each chorus.

11

The 'Bagman' That Got Away

Frank arrived home the next day to find his mother worrying about rumours of war.

'Don't worry, mother' he assured her. 'Not likely to happen, and even if it did, someone's got to run these farms of ours.'

She suddenly remembered, 'I've had a message from Lady Tanfield – something about arranging a Hunt meet at Ripon. She'd like you to call.'

'Blast,' said Frank, 'I've only just come back down Wensleydale, could have called at the Hall if I'd known. I'll nip up there on my motorbike after tea, and take Charlotte with me – by the way, where is she?'

'Out exercising the horses. I wasn't very well this morning, so she made me stay in bed; she looked after the housework.'

'What happened?'

'Oh well, when I got out of bed, I passed out or something; when I came round Charlotte was fussing over me, making me drink a tot of brandy. I'm all right now.'

Frank was in the yard when Charlotte returned; she was riding his new horse called The Painter and leading her own grey Arab. She dismounted and, holding the reins of the two horses in one hand, flung her other arm around his neck. 'Frank Bowers – have I missed you! Time just drags when you're away.'

Frank returned her embrace and even as he kissed her she murmured, 'You only have to kiss me once and I need you, promise to come to my room tonight,' then in the same breath, 'I do wish your mother would stop talking about war, couldn't bear to be parted from you for longer than two days.'

'I won't have to go to war, so don't worry that pretty little head – now bed these horses down. Has Tuffan been out?'

'Yes sir.' Charlotte curtsied in mock humiliation. 'I took him out first.'

'Right then, come along just as you are, on the pillion seat, we're going to Tanfield Hall to see her Ladyship. I've heard a rumour she wants to hold the opening meet in Ripon town square.'

Frank enjoyed the warmth and the closeness of this beautiful girl when she clung to him as the bike bounced around on the hard rutted surface.

'It rained nearly all day yesterday in Deepdale,' he shouted, 'pity it couldn't have dropped some here and softened this road up a bit.'

They were both covered with dust from head to foot and were hilariously knocking it off each other below the steps to the main entrance of Tanfield Hall when her Ladyship opened the door.

'Good heavens, Bowers, I wondered what all that noise was about. Don't think I'll ever get used to these infernal, what do they call them now? I know, combustible engines. I heard only the other day Lord Lonsdale of all people; he's changed over to these horseless carriages, has a fleet of twelve German cars, all painted yellow, Mercury-Bends or some such name. And all this talk of going to war with Germany, be a bugger if the Army want all our horses and we have to give up hunting, won't it?'

'It will, ma'am,' said Frank politely

'Now come along in; pray tell me, who is this beautiful young lady – have we met?'

'Well, yes, perhaps in the hunting field. She's been out with us once or twice, usually rides second horse for me. Mother's companion really – Charlotte Webster, meet Lady Tanfield.'

Charlotte curtsied gracefully.

'There child, no need for too much ceremony with me. You sly dog, Frank, hiding such a beautiful creature away, you must bring her here to the Hunt ball after the opening meet.'

'I will, my lady.'

'Good; she'll turn a few heads, I'll be bound. Now, let's have a drink.' Her Ladyship picked up a large hand bell, shook it vigorously. 'The butler is very old, and very deaf you know. Ah, there you are, Percy. Will you take a little whisky, my dear?'

'Well, I–' Charlotte hesitated and looked to Frank for guidance.

'Good, three large whiskies, Percy, and a jug of water; better bring the bottle on the tray at the same time.'

'Now, Frank, come over here and I'll tell what it's all about. You can have a look around with pleasure, Charlotte; next door in the drawing room is where most of the valuable furniture happens to be, feel free to look around, by all means.'

'Now, I'm trying to organise the opening meet in Ripon with a nice breakfast at the Unicorn Hotel. There's lots of room in the square and it's not too far after hunting for guests to come here for the ball. So! What do you think?'

'Well, I'm flattered you should ask me. It seems to be a very good idea, only I have heard there's an acute shortage of foxes around Ripon.'

'You're right, at least that's what Farrelly, the Huntsman, also tells me. He suggested I got in touch with you; he says you always make sure there's a breed or two on your farm, and that you keep them for the York and Ainsty.'

'That's true, my lady.'

'Here, have another whisky; he tells me there's usually a fox in your false earth and that it won't be too difficult for you to do something about it.'

'Ah, yes, I see. I might be able to send my man out the night before – he'll probably need a gold sovereign to keep his mouth shut.'

'Good, here you are, give him two; I'll leave the rest up to you. I know nothing about it of course.'

'Of course not, ma'am.'

'Shall we join Charlotte in the next room now?'

The next morning Frank arrived at the office early. The door to the street was already open so he guessed Joe Falshaw had arrived; the old beggar always seems to be here first in a morning, he thought to himself.

His eye was drawn to a spanking new car very badly parked on the road outside. It had Ford emblazoned in large letters across the bonnet – the people's car, made in America, saw the advertisement in the *Gazette* last week, Frank said to himself, wonder who owns this?

'Surprise, surprise,' he heard Joe boom as he turned to see him standing on the stone steps to the office.

'Is that yours, Joe?'

'No, me lad, it's ours, the firm's; thought I'd surprise thee, I shouldn't think as how I'll bother to learn to drive it; you'll hev to be chauffeur.'

'Great,' said Frank, 'I'll soon get the hang of it. I read in the paper where they've made over seventy-eight thousand of these over the last two years; this year they intend to double it, by the end of next year they're hoping for about three hundred thousand. I like this hamper box on the back, that'll be useful when we go to sales.'

The opening meet was scheduled for ten-thirty on Friday morning. Charlotte and Dick had worked hard on getting the hunters fit. Hardly a cub-hunting morning had been missed, and even though Frank had been forced to devote most of his time to the office, everything was set fair for the morrow.

Frank went round to see Dick at his cottage, proffered the two sovereigns, and suggested they both went down to the big wood to see if they could grab a fox.

Very quietly both men approached the false earth, and simultaneously blocked the two entrances.

'Good,' said Frank, 'now take care Dick, here's a thick pair of leather fencing gloves; when I lift up the boards on top here, you grab him.' Carefully Frank cleared the turfs off the top of the earth and slowly lifted part of the roof.

'Damn it!' he exclaimed, 'the cupboard's bare; Charlie's away from home! Now what do we do?'

'Well,' said Dick, 'if you must have a fox for tomorrow, the only fella I can think of at such short notice is old Billy Bamber over near Thirsk; he's sure to know where to go to get one. He's my great-uncle – in a roundabout sort of way, bit of a mix-up somewhere a couple of generations ago – they used to live way up in the Hambleton Hills and I've heard him say many a time it's a clever child in those parts that really knows his true father.'

'He lives a bit rough, he'll be turned eighty and fends for himself,' Dick had informed Frank as they chugged and lurched around on what was for Dick his first car ride.

Daylight was fading rapidly as they rounded the last bend on the rough track leading into a small untidy yard with low dilapidated buildings on three sides.

Their arrival startled a pony tethered in a trap to the front of the only building capable of occupation; it broke free, hurtled into the far corner of the yard, turned like a startled rabbit, then galloped past the car and was away down the track in a flash.

'That's buggered it,' exclaimed Dick. 'Who can be visiting Uncle Billy with a posh pony and trap at this time of night?'

'Why, it's Dr Mitchell,' Dick exclaimed as they both pushed their way into a dimly lit living room.

'What's that racket outside?' the doctor asked.

'Ah, you see, this here's my boss, Mr Frank Bowers, and I've brought him to see my Uncle Billy; we came in his motor car and your hoss wasn't too pleased like, he's bolted.'

'Well, you'll have to get him back,then,' exclaimed a tall, very angular man in his late forties, as he straightened up from the prone body lying on the kitchen table.

It was not so much the broad Scottish accent, as the authorative way the words were spoken that impressed Frank.

92

'What's happened to my Uncle Billy?' asked Dick, 'Is he dead?'

'Och no, man, but he is three parts drunk. It's taken more than a full bottle to get him like that – he's been plagued far too long with a large fatty cyst on his side; see here – and I'm about to remove it.'

They both peered curiously at the large pendulous growth on Uncle Billy's side.

'So, Mr Boynton, if you could go and fetch my horse back, I'd be much obliged.'

'Perhaps Mr Bowers, you could help me? I want you to hold his arms together, well back. There appears to be only the one oil lamp, but if you can keep both arms out of the way I shall be able to see. It's important you should keep his front end down on the table when I start to operate.'

As Frank bent over the patient, he heard him mutter, 'I'm nowhere near as drunk as he thinks I am,' then 'Do your worst, you Scottish bastard,' he roared out.

'He wouldn't consider any other form of anaesthetic,' the doctor explained as he started to make an incision. 'Now hang on – he's going to feel this.'

Frank felt his patient stiffen but apart from a muffled groan he gave off no other sound.

'Got it,' said the doctor triumphantly holding up the large offending tissue; he moved over to the kitchen range and dropped it in the fire.

Frank watched in disbelief as the lump of fatty flesh crackled and spat with a bright yellow flame, whilst rivulets of fat ran out through the bottom bars of the range onto the pile of cinders below.

'Best way to get rid of those,' said the doctor as he drew a red-hot gelding iron from the bottom of the fire.

'Now hang on even tighter, this'll seal it and prevent any infection.'

The combination of the sight of blood, and the smell of burnt flesh proved too much for Frank – down he went!

When he regained his senses, Billy Bamber was sitting on the table above him with the doctor applying a dressing to his wound.

'Rum do, young fella, you passing out like that, I'm th' only one who's supposed to be unconscious.'

'Sorry about that,' said Frank. 'It seems to be the sight and smell of blood that affects me. Can't seem to be able to do much about it, either.'

'Tha's not likely to be much use in the Army then, if this war comes!'

'No, I suppose not,' said Frank.

Just then Dick Boynton returned. 'That horse hadn't gone far, he's none the worse for his gallop.'

'Very good, gentlemen, I'll bid you goodnight; keep that wound clean and covered up for a day or two, Billy, and if you have problems let me know. Thanks for your hospitality.'

'I take it you must be Richard Bowers's lad?' said Billy, staggering slightly as he got down from the table; 'knew him well once o'er, before you were born. I found him his two best shire-horses that won everything before 'em, including the Royal; went all round Great Britain, they did, as six-year-olds; never beaten, then money talked and he sell't 'em to go overseas.'

'We have an oil painting,' replied Frank, 'over the fireplace at home, but my father never mentioned them. I remember once my mother pointing to them when they were having a bit of a row, saying the only worthwhile thing he ever did was to sell those horses and to use the money to help pay for me to go to a decent school. I wouldn't like to think he sold them just for my sake!'

'Don't think so,' said Billy, 'I think showing 'em became a full-time job and his farms were sufferin'; he got an offer he couldn't refuse even though it broke his heart. Nivver showed another hoss after they'd gone, I do know.'

'Now, Dick,' he said turning to his nephew, 'what do you young fellas want, coming round at this time of night?'

'It's like this, Uncle, Mr Bowers more or less promised to find a fox for the opening meet tomorrow in Ripon town square. He has a false earth see, on his farm, but when we opened it a couple of hours ago, it were empty. I tell't him you were the only fella I knew who could tell us where to go to find one.'

'That's easy, there's only one man I know who could oblige at such short notice, that's George Cook, gamekeeper for Lord Richmond; he catches 'em in box traps. He tell't me one day he had a good customer for pelts as long as they weren't damaged in any way.'

'Good, thanks Uncle. I know where he lives, middle of Pepper Arden Wood – we'd better get moving otherwise he'll be going to bed before we get there.'

'Thank you, Mr Bamber,' said Frank in his usual courteous way, 'pleased to meet you I'm sure, hope your side soon gets better. Dick – leave one of those guineas with your uncle for his help and assistance. Good day to you, sir.'

The keeper's cottage they were looking for was hard to find, the narrow track was difficult to negotiate in daylight; in the dark with the rather indifferent lights of the car, it was well-nigh impossible.

'We've got to find the entrance to Pepper Arden Hall; the cottage is in the middle of the wood behind it,' said Dick.

'I've heard 'em talk about this famous wood, one of the best coverts in North Yorkshire, I heard the Master telling one of his whips out hunting one day. Amazing to think we've come all this way and we're still in Bedale Country.'

'Here we are, sir, turn in here, half a mile down this track. Careful when you cross the Skell, it can be quite deep – no problem to a horse, of course.'

Frank braked with sudden alarm; the stream Dick had referred to gave every appearance in the flickering headlights of being not only deep, but also very swift-running.

'We could cross over the footbridge; the cottage is only round the corner.'

'Not likely,' said Frank, 'after we've come so far, just hang on.' The car sailed through the water splash without the slightest difficulty.

'That's just grand, boss,' enthused Dick. 'Here we are – this is George Cook's place, he'll wonder what the hell's going on.'

As Frank stepped down he could hear numerous terriers yapping indoors; the light went out and he was aware of a dim figure moving the curtain aside.

'It's all right, George,' he heard Dick call out. 'It's Dick Boynton and I've brought a gentleman to see you, we've come to ask a favour.'

The lights went on again, the bolts were drawn and George Cook stood in the doorway clutching a twelve-bore shotgun.

'Frightened me to death, coming here this time o' neet in one of them noisy contraptions. First time I've been near yan. Na then, what's your business?'

'It's like this, Mr Cook,' said Frank, 'I need a live fox for tomorrow morning, no questions asked. Dick has a guinea in his pocket for you if you can oblige us.'

'Now then: I only hev one o' me traps set up, we can nobbut keep us fingers crossed. If there's nowt in it then that'll be the end of it like.'

With a lantern in one hand, and a heavy sack slung over his shoulder, George set off into the wood. The pace he set had his two companions struggling in his wake. Suddenly he stopped and moved aside the under-growth. 'By gum,' he exclaimed, 'tha's in luck, young fella, I didn't catch your name.'

'We never gave it to you,' replied Frank.

'Aye, just so, just so. Lookyer – a girt big dog fox.'

'How do you know it's a dog fox, George?' queried Frank as he peered beyond the flickering lantern into the home-made trap.

'You see, it's like this. A dog fox will allus slink away from thee quietly and settle down wrapped around hisself as far away as possible – a vixen, she'd hev bin spitting and snarling an' coming for thee.'

'Na then Dick – you poke him quietly wi' this staff, I'll grab him bi scruff o' neck as soon as he grabs it.'

Frank held the neck of the sack open and in one quick movement George had grabbed the fox and dropped him in.

'Let me tie it wi' this band, allus mak' sure tha ties this round prop'ly else he'll be out like a flash and away.'

With 'Charlie' safely in the car, on the back seat, the two friends turned for home.

'Watch that water splash,' George called out as he pocketed his gold coin and safely bolted himself inside his comfortable cottage.

'The watter's way above the running board,' said Dick with some alarm, peering down in the darkness as the car started to slide in the middle of the ford.

More from self-preservation than skill, Frank turned the front wheels of the vehicle into the current and stamped his foot on the accelerator pedal; the car snaked one way then the other and with a lurch shot out at the other side, virtually out of control. It was then that Frank realised he had no brakes; the car missed a large oak tree by inches and finished up in a dense patch of gorse.

Gingerly Frank reversed back to the lane; almost prepared to agree with Dick.

' 'Twould have been quicker to have come on horseback, with a sack slung o'er t'saddle,' Dick kept repeating.

'No brakes you see, Dick, got wet through coming across that damned ford the first time, should have left the car this side as you said.'

Gradually, as they motored nearer home, the braking system started to improve, but it was a long way past midnight when Frank drove into the yard.

Charlotte dashed down the steps carrying a lantern. 'We've been worried sick what might have happened to you two – your mother's beside herself, sir, you going out at night in that machine for the first time.'

'Well, I promised to get a fox for tomorrow; here he is,' Frank said triumphantly as he lifted the bag off the back seat. Startled, Charlotte jumped back.

'But it's alive!'

'Of course,' said Frank. 'When we let him go tomorrow, if he takes the hounds back to where he came from there'll be a few empty saddles and some tired horses, I'll bet.'

'But you can't leave him in that sack all night.'

'No, we'll put him in the dog pen, and bag him up again in the morning. I want to leave about eight-thirty, Dick; but before we loose him off I just want to punch a small hole in his right ear.'

'Ugh!' shuddered Charlotte.

'It's all right,' said Frank, 'he'll hardly feel it; if we do make a kill, it's better to know if we've caught this chap. He's a very long way from home; if he should be left wandering around in a strange territory then we can soon arrange to have a go at him another day.'

Frank was running late the following morning. When he had finally pacified his mother the previous evening, he stealthily crept into Charlotte's bed. She was more passionate and demanding than ever before. As his arms crept around her smooth naked body she whimpered and clutched him fiercely. 'I can't wait any longer, my darling,' she whispered. He felt her nails ripping into his back. Minutes later and she was astride him. 'You fill me up entirely,' she moaned, 'hurt me, harder, harder, it's coming,' she panted – 'now! now! no-oow!' she screamed out, forgetting all else but the pinnacle of human pleasure which ran through her entire body. 'Whatever happens you must never stop doing this to me, promise?'

Frank stirred. 'Do you promise me?' she insisted.

'Of course, my darling,' he said.

'And we can be married and make babies?'

'Yes, my darling,' he said.

'I feel as if there's a fire inside me, this eternal longing; can we make a baby now please? Please?' she was moaning now to the rhythm of Frank's every movement. 'Now! now! no-oow!'

Charlotte collapsed alongside Frank, her whole body quivering and jerking violently. As Frank tried to soothe her she continued to twitch uncontrollably, and he was alarmed to find tears streaming down her cheeks.

'Charlotte,' he called out in alarm, 'are you all right?'

'Of course, silly,' she whispered. 'You can never leave me now, I think I would die if you did.'

Frank never made it to his own room that night. He lay awake for a long time beside Charlotte, unsure of himself; he was no longer the dominant partner. What had just happened was almost beyond belief; it was as if two souls had been lifted beyond everyday mundane earthly things, upwards to a different plateau.

Oh, how I love this beautiful girl, he thought, but marriage! Mother would never agree. It would break her heart if she had any idea what was going on. Her plans for her son do not include marrying a servant; she could never accept that. Oh, what the hell! he thought as Charlotte stirred in his arms, it'll sort itself out somehow' Little did he know how soon his thoughts would be turned into stark, horrible reality.

It had been arranged that Dick and Charlotte would hack to the meet, taking three horses, with Frank following later with his car. He had been invited to breakfast at the Unicorn Hotel by the Joint Masters at nine-thirty.

Frank was confident he could catch his fox single-handed and insisted he be left alone to bag him up. Having seen the horses off on their way towards Ripon, he approached the dog kennel with some trepidation. He had decided to try and pin the fox down with a hay fork, thus avoiding a powerful pair of jaws and very sharp teeth.

His plan failed miserably. Twenty minutes later, totally frustrated by the quick movements of what in daylight turned out to be a deep chestnut dog fox with a white tip to his magnificent brush, his mother appeared in the yard.

'What on earth are you trying to do, Frank?' she called out.

'Well, mother, it's a long story and I'm going to be very late, but I'm trying to catch this fox and put him in this bag, and take him to the opening meet in that car.'

'That shouldn't be too difficult,' his mother replied, soothingly.

'How so?' asked Frank.

'If you go to the larder you'll find a couple of rabbits hanging up; go and get one.'

Frank duly did as he was told.

'Now what, mother?' he asked.

'Tie a rope to its hind legs and throw it into the pen, he'll grab it from instinct. You'll find out that having sunk his teeth in he won't let go.'

Within minutes the fox was safely in the sack and Frank breathed a sigh of relief as he dropped him into the picnic box between the rear mud-guards.

'Bye mum, thanks, must dash. See you tonight.'

The horses were leaving Boroughbridge on the Ripon road before Frank finally caught up with them. He waved and sped on his way to Ripon.

The clock on the Town Hall said a quarter to ten as he pulled up outside the hotel. The brakes had been playing up all the way. Frank parked outside the front door and dashed inside, more worried about being late than the state of the brakes.

He quickly made his way upstairs, apologised to the Masters and sat down next to Lady Tanfield.

'I've got a spare flask with me, my lady,' he said quietly, 'and that young fella you suggested I bring along, well he's downstairs now in the boot of my car. Have you thought where we should drop him?'

'Yes, Frank, we've decided to move down towards the racecourse, then south towards Bobbie Dawson's at Malvern House. Just out of town there's an old sandpit, close to the river with a big patch of willows; Peter Farrelly has somebody –'

'Excuse me, my lady,' Frank heard a voice over his shoulder.

'Yes, my man?'

'Sorry to interrupt, my lady, but this gentleman's car has just run away, gone down the road towards the Cathedral.'

'Blast,' said Frank as he dashed downstairs, 'Joe Falshaw will skin me alive if I've smashed up his car.'

As Frank hurried around the side of the hotel, he was aware of a small but noisy crowd in the middle of the road; then he saw the car and breathed a sigh of relief. It had swung around the corner, fortunately on the same lock. Immediately adjacent to the rear of the hotel were wide steps leading to the Freemasons' Lodge. The car had bounced almost to the top; apparently without damage to anything or anybody.

Frank, however, quickly realised that the lid of the picnic box had flown open and the fox was gone. Slowly it dawned on him why the crowd was still gathering in the main road some fifty yards below him and gradually moving away towards the Cathedral.

As he ran towards them, he became aware of a moving sack containing the frantic fox, slowly rolling down the incline; a crowd mainly of children, were laughing and dancing around the moving object. Rather ominously the huge helmeted figure of Sergeant Proud of H.M. Constabulary slowly paced after them, still unsure of what was happening.

'It's all right, Sergeant,' Frank called out, 'that's my sack – brought a few chickens down for the hotel. My car ran away, as you see, and tipped 'em out.'

'H'm, most peculiar if you h'ask me,' the Sergeant was saying as they returned to the car. 'Strange smell comin' from that there sack.'

'Yes, I know,' said Frank as he quickly dropped it into the picnic box.

'You'd better take more care parkin' that machine in future.'

'Oh, indeed I will,' said Frank.

The square was filling up with horses and people as Frank slipped away towards the river. He found the 'earth stopper' waiting on the road near the racecourse.

Frank handed over the sack. 'Wait until hounds come into the covert before you loose him off, then keep yourself out of sight until we're all gone.'

'Very good, sir,' the man replied, 'Might I ask where this fella comes from?'

'You can ask if you like, but I don't know myself. I've just picked him up off the road near the Cathedral. All you have to do is make sure he gets a decent start, and that nobody knows anything about it.'

'Very good, sir.'

'If you can manage that, then I am to tell you there'll be an extra two quid in your wage packet next week.'

'Very good, sir. My lips are sealed, you can be sure of that.'

When Frank returned to the square the hounds and the hunt staff had arrived and a large field of mounted followers were being served glasses of hot punch outside by the hotel staff.

Having carefully parked the car this time – its arrival caused more of a stir with the assembled throng than any other event of the morning – Frank quickly found Charlotte.

'Where the devil is Dick?' he asked.

'He's taking Tuffan and The Painter for a quick walk. That point-to-point horse wouldn't settle once we arrived here, he's very much on his toes; they refused to stand still, nearly broke away on more than one occasion.'

'All right then, I'll ride Tuffan for a couple of hours, and Dick can keep in touch somehow as second horseman. I'll take over The Painter about midday.'

Finally mounted on Tuffan, Frank made sure he kept to the front as the colourful cavalcade moved out of the square, down past the Cathedral, then made its way quickly towards the first draw.

With mounting excitement he watched hounds, gently encouraged by the Huntsmen, enter the willow garth. He tightened his girth and shortened both stirrup leathers by two holes.

Suddenly there was 'his' fox streaking away along the river bank. So far no hound had made a sound, but one of the whips tucked in close to the covert had seen him go.

100

A 'holloa' rang out and there he was, standing in his stirrups, hat held high and forward, pointing in the direction of the fleeing fox, with still no sound from the hounds. Then one hound 'challenged' followed by two or three more.

'Yup, yup, yup,' he heard the Huntsman call.

'Get away onto him, my little beauties,' he shouted as he galloped around the covert towards the whip; then came a series of rapid blasts on his horn.

Tuffan, ears pricked, was prancing about. 'Whoa, fella!' Frank tried to soothe his anxious mount, 'Whoa lad, you know all about this job now.'

There was a crash of music from the main pack and then they were out of cover and running.

'Hold hard,' the Master was calling; 'he's either going to cross the bridge or run the river bank.'

As the mounted field moved steadily forward, Frank could see the fox heading for the road bridge, but there in the middle of it and moving right in his path, was a horse and cart. The fox hesitated briefly and then darted quickly away, down the riverside.

'He meant to be across the other side, sir' he heard the Huntsman call to the Master.

'Here we go Charlotte, stay close, straight down the racecourse; look at that marvellous sight!'

Hounds were streaming away hunting as a pack.

'Hurrah for the famous Bedale bitches,' Frank cried in exultation as Tuffan soared over the racecourse boundary fence; he looked back to see Charlotte jumping equally well.

Three miles further on it appeared the fox had been headed on the Bishop Monkton road. The River Ure takes a big sweep eastwards at this point. Hounds checked and then hit off the line, once again making for the river.

'Looks as if we're going straight to the ferry,' Frank shouted to the Huntsman.

Hounds were having to work much harder to hold the line by this time; eventually they feathered onto the landing stage, into the barge and then reluctantly, one by one, started the long swim across.

'Damn it, he's obviously gone across,' said the Master. 'It seems we pushed him too hard. Listen! I can hear lead hounds speaking in the Hall grounds; they must have got away and crossed before we got here.'

'Are there any bridges lower down here, Bowers?'

'No sir, it's either back to Ripon, or round left-handed about three miles to Boroughbridge. We're just halfway between them at this point.'

'I don't suppose Sir Robert will mind if we use his private ferry – Farrelly, send one whip that way and one the other, to try and pick up hounds should they swing left or right. Frank, you come with me, the barge should take about five horses at a time.'

'You will have to either go back or take turns to cross over here,' he shouted to the field.

Frank ordered Charlotte to go back, pick up Dick Boynton and then to hack home. The Masters gingerly led their horses aboard followed by the Huntsman.

'Come along Frank,' called out her Ladyship, 'you know the country over the other side better than most.' It was at that moment he realised he still had her Ladyship's flask in his pocket.

More horses were led aboard. 'Righto,' the Master called out, 'bring that big chestnut aboard; the rest of you'll have to be patient and wait till the boat returns.'

Frank watched anxiously as a very portly gentleman whom he'd never seen before tugged impatiently at the head of a big gangling young chestnut horse.

'Come up, yer brute,' he was calling as the horse pulled him backwards along the landing stage.

'Hurry man,' cried Lady Tanfield. 'Can someone crack the horse across the arse – these hounds will all get away if we don't get across soon.'

One crack of the whip was enough; the horse gave one huge bound forward, dragging his unfortunate owner off the stage to land in a heap in the bottom of the barge.

'I'm not aware who you are, sir, but I'd be obliged if you'd keep that nag under control,' John Mowbray, one of the Masters, bellowed.

'My name's Pearson, sir.'

'Help him for God's sake, someone. Right to cast off, boatman.'

It transpired that the gentleman in question was having his first and last day with the Bedale.

Frank learned later that he came from Lancashire; had made a lot of money collecting 'skins and offal' from slaughterhouses; ran a glue factory for a living and had earned himself the nickname 'Dripping'.

He was on holiday in the spa town of Harrogate, from whence he had hired his horse at the cheapest rate possible, in line with his frugal nature.

Halfway across the river, right in the deepest part, his horse panicked. It reared and plunged, driving the rest of the horses all to one end; the barge briefly rocked from side to side and, without warning, turned completely over.

When Frank surfaced he still had hold of Tuffan's bridle. He could feel the weight of water in his boots and sodden hunting coat gradually dragging him down. As the horse struck out powerfully for the far bank he had the presence of mind to transfer his grip to the saddle.

'Grab hold of your saddles,' he shouted. 'Let your horse do the work, then grab his tail.'

The Master, the Huntsman, the field Master Sir William Tassell and Frank all arrived safely at the far bank – Lady Tanfield, a Mrs Dunn and two other hunt members made it back to the landing stage; two more horses with their riders' heads bobbing alongside were swimming, with the current, in the centre of the river.

'What a bloody disaster,' the Master was saying; 'this has happened before you know, ever so many worthy men drowned that day. You get after the hounds, Peter, and bring them back to the meet; we can't go on now. Frank, come with me. If we ride down this bank maybe those horses will come over to us; just hope there's nobody missing, that's all. I reckon we all owe you a great debt of gratitude, Frank. That timely shout of yours saved my life; I was going under until I grabbed his tail.'

As the two men trotted down the bank, Frank recognised the big chestnut by the large white blaze on the face.

'Hang on,' he shouted, but suddenly as the horse turned for the bank, one bobbing head disappeared.

'The visitor's gone under, sir,' he yelled.

'Don't see we can do much about it from here,' replied the Master. 'He's the bloody idiot who caused all this commotion in the first place. That's Susan Robertson who's left – let's concentrate on getting her out.'

The body of Dripping Pearson was never recovered.

Her Ladyship was confined to bed that evening with a chill; she had hacked home, soaking wet, without the comfort of a flask.

Because of the tragedy the Hunt Ball was cancelled 'pro tem', much to most members' annoyance.

At an extraordinary general meeting of the Hunt a few weeks later, a special vote of thanks was offered and a presentation of a silver fox creeping over rocks, made of alabaster, handed to Frank, inscribed:

To F. Bowers, Esq
With Gratitude From the Bedale Masters And
Hunt Members
November 2nd 1913.

Lady Tanfield's first concern was that the origin of the fox which caused such a disaster should be kept quiet. In the main her wishes were observed. The secret was almost out, however, two days later.

Frank had joined Joe Falshaw and Edgar Booth in the small snug behind the bar in the Brown Cow, the favourite pub of Auction Mart clients.

Frank was doing most of the selling these days; feeling thirsty from his exertions, he emptied his pint pewter pot at one go when, through the glass bottom, who should he observe reeling towards him but George Cook, the keeper.

'Hello young man. I thought it were thee when tha come through yon door. They didn't catch him then?'

'Pardon?' said Frank.

'Yon fox, he was back home next day.'

'Yes – er, let's go through to the lounge bar; let me buy you a drink. You won't have heard.'

'Heard what?'

'That good fox swam the river in about the deepest spot possible, and trying to get across on the ferry we got turned over and a visitor got drowned. There's going to be an inquest, so we don't want it known we were chasing a "bagman". So here's a couple of pounds to make sure you keep your trap shut.'

'Count on me, boss, if yer wants him agin, yer knows where to come.'

'What was that all about?' asked Joe as Frank returned to the snug.

'Hunt business – just Hunt business.'

'Right, now if you could turn your hand to our business, a chap called Ted Boothman had a word with me earlier whilst you were selling, he and his sons farm in a big way – top end of Nidderdale – there's going to be a transfer of tenancy, to one of the sons, th'old boy's retiring. I told him we'd drive up there first thing Friday morning. There'll be a big flock of Swaledale ewes to value and from memory, there's a wild bunch of Galloway Cattle to bring down off the fell; plus his dairy shorthorn herd, all the implements as well as household effects. You'd best tell your womenfolk it'll likely be t'other side of midnight before you get home.'

It was a superb early morning for early November as they crossed the river bridge at Pateley, went past the showground and headed westwards towards the head of the valley. The beech and oak woodlands on either side of the valley were ablaze with colour; a slight overnight frost meant that a flurry of leaves was falling as a slight breeze stirred the tops of the trees. The ever-bumpy track crossed and re-crossed the river, each water splash getting progressively narrower, until finally the car could go no further. The final crossing of what was now nothing more than a bubbling stream was far too narrow to risk the automobile.

'Nothing more than a packhorse bridge,' Joe said. 'Used to be one of the main routes out of the valleys for lead and wool. We'll have to walk the rest of the way.'

As the two men walked beside the stream, Frank marvelled at the solitude; 'You can almost hear the silence,' he was saying to Joe when, with a strange croak, a heron took off from below the bank. They could hear shrill whistles ahead and as they came in sight of the 'sheep gather' coming down off the hill, it made a wonderful sight.

The two Boothman boys, with two sheep dogs apiece, were guiding literally hundreds of grey-faced ewes towards the compact homestead.

'You never told me what this valuation is all about, Joe, wrong time of the year isn't it?'

'Well it is a bit unusual, I suppose. From what I can gather, the old man has to go into hospital for a gall bladder operation, first time he's ever been away; lived here all his life, father before him. Naturally he's very worried and reckons he won't be coming out. He's a tenant of the Duchy; they think the world of him and have agreed to accept the youngest son as tenant, unfortunately the elder son wants his cut and that's what this valuation's all about. He's employing Tommy Wood, who's a shrewd old boy, to act on his behalf. We've had many a hard day's bargaining in the past; I feel I've come off worst just about every time. He gets a figure set in his head and no amount of bargaining can shake him off it. It will be a good education for you today, watching old Tommy working for his client. Wouldn't be surprised if he isn't here already, he'll have come in the other way on horseback.'

'Why doesn't the elder son just take his share and get out, presumably he could set himself up on another farm?' asked Frank.

'It's not as simple as that,' replied Joe. 'For one thing the normal changeover date in these parts is "grassday" – the twelfth of May – and for another this large flock of sheep are heathed to this farm – they keep within certain invisible boundaries and can always be gathered in. If you took part of the flock away and turned 'em out on another fell they'd roam away, probably finish up in maybe Lancashire or Westmorland. Ah! here's Mr Boothman waiting at the door.'

'Good morning, Ted, I believe you know my assistant, Frank Bowers.'

'Pleased to shake your hand, young fella, come along in both of you. Tommy Wood arrived about ten minutes ago.'

They were shown into a large pleasant kitchen. A small man dressed in leggings and a tough leather jerkin rose from a vast table. Frank noticed most of all the quick movements of his eyes, and a prominent hooked nose, a bit like Punch of Punch and Judy fame, he thought to himself.

Tommy Wood – a tough negotiator

'Hello, Joe,' said a rather squeaky voice, 'taken to walking these days?' The twinkle in his eyes was a dead give-away.

'I guess you already know we've bought a horseless carriage, all the way from America, they call 'em automobiles out there. This young assistant o' mine convinced me we'd be able to get about better, but as you can see we've had to leg it from yon packhorse bridge down the valley.'

'Pleased to meet you, Mr Wood,' said Frank shaking hands. 'Joe's been telling me quite a lot about you on the way here.'

'Has he told you how he allus insists on getting his own way when it comes to a valuation?'

'No, he said it was the other way round.'

'Don't you believe it, young fella,' he said, his blue eyes twinkling again.

'Now then you auctioneers,' said a large-framed, white-haired woman who had been hovering about the enormous kitchen range. 'Save your arge'ing for outside; sit yersens down, yer can't work properly on an empty belly. Here's a bowl of porridge apiece; there's some new-baked bread on the table, we've plenty of fresh butter. Now then, get on with it whilst I get bacon and eggs for you all.

'By the way, I'm Mrs Boothman,' she said directly to Frank. 'Me husband tell't me they'd a grand young fella training to be an auctioneer at that new Auction Mart. Now father, you just hand these plates to your guests – nobody's allowed to leave here wi'out good food inside 'em,' she said fussing over Frank; 'Just you get that plateful down, young fella.'

Frank was delighted to do as he was told.

'Now Mr Boothman, I understand you would like us to put a value on everything, including some of the house contents, is that right?' asked Joe.

'Aye, if you could start with the dairy herd – then that Galloway suckler herd – the sheep – and then there's two workhorses – two fell ponies – haymaking machinery, such as it is – then some small tools, "tinclement" as I calls it – four good collie dogs – oh, and the hay crop.'

'Do you think we can get through that lot afore dark, Tommy?' asked Joe.

'Of course, if you'll shape yersen and not be as stubborn as tha' usually is.'

'There'll be plenty of vittals for us all, won't there lass?' asked Ted.

'Hev you hivver gone short?' she snapped. 'No. Well – right then, get yoursens about your business, and send them two lads in; only two as doin' any wark around here as far as I can see!'

Watching and listening to the two experienced livestock valuers bartering and cajoling for the rest of the day was one of the most enlightening days in Frank's short career. He never forgot it. The clear message Joe was forever preaching 'always do your best for the man you are acting for' cropped up time and again during the long day.

Finally after a hearty supper, they were ready to take their leave.

'We've agreed a figure for everything, Ted,' said Joe. 'I'll send you a valuation book with totals for each class of stock; how you divide the job out is up to you.'

'What about your fees?' queried Ted.

'Yes, based on the total sum, we think a fair charge will be twenty guineas, and Tommy and I have agreed to accept half each – split it down the middle if you like.'

'Right; mother, fetch me yon cash box. You hev th' key.'

Mrs Boothman disappeared into the front room.

'She likes to be in charge of the money, tha knows. Lads and me nivver gets a look in, she has th' key to t'chest of drawers hidden away someweer.'

Mrs Boothman returned proudly clutching a battered tin box to her ample bosom.

Frank barely refrained from whistling as the lid opened displaying wads of five-pound notes.

'There's yours, Tommy, and that's for thee, Joe. I nivver lets onybody leave here without bein' paid if I owes 'em owt, allus best. "Pay and Be Paid", that's our motto, in't it mother?'

'You really ought to have all that money in a bank somewhere,' counselled Joe.

'Nivver bothered wi' 'em as yet,' said Ted. 'Tha nivver hears of onybody pinchin in this valley, besides nearest bank's too far away. Allus done cash, all me life, wouldn't know how to use one of them there cheque books.'

'Well, you know your own business best, I reckon,' said Joe, 'but if someone gets their hands on that tin box and makes off with it you'll hev lost your life's savings.'

'Naw I weern't,' said Ted. 'We hev another of 'em tucked away, don't we mother?'

All this time Frank had noticed how intently the eldest son Neil was watching his mother's every move. As she returned to the front parlour he made the excuse, 'Someone's goin' to hev to milk them cows,' and moved silently from behind his father and into the parlour.

'You get out of here, our Neil, in them workin' clothes,' he heard Mrs Boothman say, 'an' stop pryin' on me, if you hadn't decided to leave with your highfallutin' ideas none o' this "valiation" would hev taken place, fair makin' your father ill wi' your fancy ways.'

'All is not well with that eldest son,' Frank remarked to Joe as they walked down the stream side in the failing light towards the car.

'I heard his mother rebuke him for having "fancy ways" – surely there can't be much to lead him astray up here?'

'From what little I've heard I think it's only "woman trouble" and a bit of a drink problem; seems as if he prefers mature married women to girls his own age. Handsome young fella, isn't he, but he just won't conform to the set pattern of life in these parts. Strong Methodists most of 'em, and Ted there, he does a lot of preaching at local chapels, very highly thought of and a very devout man. But this lad roams about a lot at night, seems to make a play for landladies or barmaids. You know that pub at Cow Hill, where you stayed for the sheep sale?'

'Yes,' said Frank eagerly.

'I've heard tell he rides away over there once or twice a week, landing back at any old time; that redheaded landlady, could be "flighty" so they tell me.'

Frank realised Joe was watching him closely out of the corner of his eye, measuring his reaction.

'She seemed quiet enough to me,' he replied nonchalantly. 'Here's the car, I think we'd better light the lamps now and I think I'll put the hood up, the weather's been changing since lunchtime, wind's in the north east, Joe; is it too early for snow?'

'Funny you should ask that, ever since we left the farm I've had the feeling we might be in for some snow. I heard Ted Boothman tell his lads he didn't like the look of the weather just before tea, and not to let those ewes straight back on the fell, but to let 'em run on the "in bye" land for a day or two.'

'Nice flock of sheep,' suggested Frank. 'I thought you did well to keep the price for those two, three and four shear ewes down to twenty-two shillings apiece.'

'Aye, Tommy Wood were stuck on twenty-five bob a head for ages; his client wanting just as much as he could get. He was right of course.'

'You convinced me they weren't worth any more.'

'Good, that's what it's all about, but he'd had his own way with most of the cattle; fifteen pound a head on those suckler cows was on the high side. By God, weren't they a wild bunch! Whoever buys this year's calves is in for some trouble before he gets 'em to market.'

As the car drew closer to Pateley Bridge the road improved and Frank was able to increase speed.

'Whoa! Not so fast young man, there's a good pub round the next bend, and I'm thirsty.'

Oh Lord, Frank groaned inwardly, here we go again. Aloud he said, 'This is the pub, I think, where one of the Welburn brothers finished up the day after the show two years ago. I think I told you we lost him; he'd set off to walk home and took off in the wrong direction.'

'Yes, I remember,' said Joe, 'you came looking for him and got into another party lower down the valley.'

'Something like that happened. But we never landed here.'

'Good,' said Joe, 'there's two curios in here I want thee to see. Well you can see one, but you only see when the other works, if you see what I mean.'

Frank suspected Joe knew all along there was bound to be a good sort of crowd in the bar. It had apparently been the opening meet of the Nidd Vale Harriers that morning, and the place was crowded, mostly with foot followers eating their traditional supper of hare stew – at the same time downing an apparently never-ending supply of free ale. There was a great reception for the two of them as soon as they walked in.

'I was hoping Bill Booth would be here. Come, meet a lifelong friend of mine,' said Joe, 'we were at school together. He spends a lot of his time out in the Argentine.'

Frank was introduced to a large handsome man in his late fifties.

'Nice to see you, Bill, are you back home for long?'

'Three months this time, Joe.'

'Meet my young assistant, Frank Bowers; we've been on a big valuation at the top end of the dale since early morning.'

'You'll need a drink or two then, let's sit over in the corner.'

'Nancy,' he called out to the landlady, 'a jug of mulled ale for my friends – if you please.'

'I brought Frank in to take a peep at the statue you brought back from Peru a couple of years ago, you know the one with the "skirt", and to show him the so-called "haunted chair".'

Frank followed Joe's gaze and there in an alcove stood an old ladder-backed chair with a tatty leather seat; access was barred by an elaborate twisted rope, and hanging above was a storm lantern painted to give off an eerie red light.

'The landlord claims he never lets that light go out,' said Bill, 'night and day, year in year out, same as his peat fire next to it, it's never allowed to go out.'

'I reckon he's frightened of that chair, if you ask me,' said Joe.

'Well, it's uncanny how many people have said "baloney" and gone and sat in it and been dead within a few months.'

'I think it's just a gimmick,' said Joe, 'a clever way to drum up trade in summer, when there's more people about; they reckon folks come from far and wide to gawp at it.'

'And what's this statue you're on about?' asked Frank.

'That's a full-sized statue of an Inca warrior. This crackpot here picked it up in Peru and brought it back and set it up here.'

'I don't see it,' Frank said.

'No, well it's a bit of a joke really, it's down the passage, by the ladies' room; stood almost outside, carrying a spear; made of bronze with leather boots and a leather hat which covers his ears. He's wearing a metal skirt and it's obvious a piece at the front lifts up.'

'So?'

'There's a thin wire attached to the piece that lifts up – connected through to that bell above the bar.'

'I don't see.'

'Good Lord, Frank, are you half asleep?' asked Joe.

'I don't suppose any of the lasses here tonight will be caught out, but most often in summer when some of these high-falutin' ladies nip off to wash their hands as they say, if they let their curiosity get the better of 'em and decide to peep under his skirt to see if there's anything there–'

'It rings the bell!' said Frank joyously.

'And, since they have to come out this way, the locals know what she's been up to,' laughed Joe.

'There's many a lady blushed purple,' said Bill, 'when they tell her what the laughter's for.'

'So what have you got to do with that old chair, Bill?' asked Frank.

'Nothing whatsoever,' Bill said, 'no connection at all, apart from the fact that we also had the chair at the manor where it built up its evil reputation over the centuries; Albert the landlord thought it would also provide interest if set up in a public place.'

'What reputation?' asked Frank.

'The family believe anybody who sits in it and denounces witchcraft as a fake, is likely to be dead in a very short time. If he or she escapes then it seems somebody closely related meets with a similar fate; you won't catch me sitting in the damn thing, I've lost too many close relatives not to believe the blasted chair is evil,' said Bill.

Two hours later the party was still in full swing. Every known hunting song had been sung at least twice, when Bill suggested Joe should sing, 'To Be a Farmer's Boy'.

'Come on, Joe, give us a song,' the cry went round the bar.

'Come on, Joe,' the cry mingled with the banging of empty tankards and rose to a crescendo.

'Righto,' Joe's voice boomed out above the hubbub of noise. 'I want you all to join in the chorus, wait – I can't see you all,' and within a moment he was over the rope and stood on the forbidden chair.

'Who Killed Cock Robin,' he boomed out, 'and when you sing the chorus I want you all to flap your arms as if you were flying. For those who don't know the words, all you have to sing is – "All the birds of the air fell

111

a-sighin' and a-sobbin', when they heard of the death of poor cock robin, when they *heard* of the death of poor cock robin".'

After each verse the bar erupted. Grown men and women, thought Frank, acting like kids, as he sat quietly in his corner.

'What a man,' gasped Bill as he eventually flopped down on the bench beside Frank.

'He's not very well you know, Mr Booth, there's something wrong with his lungs; he won't go anywhere for treatment, he shouldn't be stood up there singing away in all that smoke.'

'Nonsense, that's exactly the Joe Falshaw I've always known; there's not many people blessed with a voice like that. They say auctioneers are born, not made; if you haven't the right sort of voice, then you're no good auctioneering for a living. Here we go, listen, he's on with the Farmer's Boy song now and they're loving it.'

Frank noticed Joe's face looked very pallid and drawn as he returned to the table.

'That's set 'em alight,' said Bill giving Joe a hearty slap between the shoulder blades. 'Just like old days.'

Joe collapsed on his seat with a fit of coughing. 'Can't hold me liquor as I used to in the old days,' he quipped, but his two companions both noticed blood stains on his large handkerchief as he withdrew it from his lips.

'You mon go and have that cough seen to by the quack; Frank was just telling me he was worried about your health, so am I now,' said Bill anxiously.

'We'll have to go, Bill,' said Joe, 'we've a longish drive and I see one or two latecomers have come in with snow on their cloaks.'

'Have that chest seen to, think on, get yourself well wrapped up now. I'm here till after Christmas. I heard tell you were intending having a special sale of fatstock and poultry at your new market, so I'll see you then. It looks as if it'll be the other side of midnight afore you get home.'

'Don't worry about that, Mr Booth, it's often that way,' Frank said.

'I know lad, he's been like that all the time I've known him, mind it doesn't rub off on you, tha knows.'

'I'm training him to try and be different,' quipped Joe, rather weakly.

A shock awaited them as they stepped outside; in place of the car was a mound of snow.

From the dim light of the lantern outside the bar door, Frank could see that almost a foot of level snow had fallen during the time they had been in the pub. It was still falling heavily.

'Will this thing go in so much snow?' queried Joe.

'Don't know, boss, we've never had chance to try it. At least it's down-hill all the way.'

'Never should have brought it; this would be no problem for a good horse.'

It proved no problem for the new car. Although visibility was bad, the heavy snow proved no obstacle and eventually, without a hitch, Frank drove down the main street of Walshford as the parish church clock struck midnight.

'Here we are, boss, bang on time; not as much snow down here.'

' No, and I hope it'll soon disappear. Never stays as long round here as it does up them dales.'

'Hope so,' said Frank. 'There's an excellent meet at Langton Hall on the twenty-first, not far from our old farm at Bolton-on-Swale; we've nothing special on for that day have we?'

'Not to my knowledge, young man, they allus say get as many days in as you can before Christmas. I aim to have a few special sales in December, as you know, but I can handle most things until then.'

Frank arrived home around twelve-thirty. As usual Charlotte fussed over him.

'Your mother got very worried when it started to snow, Frank, "and him out in this, with that infernal machine," she kept saying. I've prepared some hot broth; by the way a Mr Lancaster from Brompton called in, he said he was a horse-dealer. The message was that he's got a very nice cob for sale, five years old, grey colour and unbroken; he'd heard you were a dab hand "gentling" young horses. No reason why it shouldn't make a Master's horse in a year or two, was what he thought.'

'That's interesting,' Frank replied as he sat down at the table. 'Mr Mowbray is always on the lookout for a good cob.'

'He's staying at the Crown at Boroughbridge with a whole lot of "osses" as he called 'em, stabled there for the next two days.'

'Good, we'll go and have a look at them tomorrow if you like. The boss says he won't need me until into December, so if you like we can spend a lot of time together for the next week or two.'

'I like,' said Charlotte, softly draping her arms over his shoulders and lightly nibbling at his ear.

'There's no way I can eat this broth if you carry on doing that,' said Frank with mock severity. 'Away, woman, and let me have my supper in peace.'

12

A Hare Coursing Match

'His feet are in a bit of a mess, Mr Lancaster,' Frank said as he carefully walked around the grey horse in the Crown Hotel yard next day.

'Just as I bought 'im, sir. Came straight off a farm at North Cave, where he was bred like; not many of his stamp about, unbroken at five.'

'How much are you asking?'

'The least I can take is sixty-five pounds, sir.'

'Phew!' whistled Frank, 'I can buy made hunters for less.'

'Ah, but most of 'em'll hav some trick or vice, this yan knows nowt, so you can break 'im in prop'ly like.'

'I'll give you fifty pund for 'im,' said Frank, finding himself unintentionally copying the dealer's speech.

'No chance; here, give me thee hand.'

Frank felt his wrist held in a vice-like grip and his arm raised horizontally.

'There's nowt wrong wi' his hooves a blacksmith caint put reet, crabbin' a good 'oss like for him for no reason – here – sixty quid as he stands,' and down came the traditional slap across his open palm.

'No,' said Frank firmly.

'All right then, fifty-five,' and down came the slap again, harder this time.

'Right,' said Frank, 'he's mine. I'll send my foreman for him.'

'Charlotte, pay the man, and make sure you get some luck money out of him.'

'Charlotte smiled sweetly as she handed over eleven five-pound notes. 'Some luck money, please.'

'You strike a hard bargain, Mr Bowers,' Joe Lancaster called out; 'and then send pretty young things like this yan, beggin' for thee.'

'She won't settle for less than a sovereign, I can tell you,' replied Frank – and so the first of many transactions between the two men took place.

'He walked home like a lamb,' Dick Boynton reported to his boss later in the day. 'My, but his feet are in a bit of a mess. I've put 'im in the middle box.'

Frank followed his foreman into the box. 'We'll best have a look at those feet,' he was saying as he closed the door.

Bang! Dick had picked up a hind leg and was sent flying; the horse pulled back, smashing his leather head collar and, bucking and squealing, proceeded to career around his small box.

Thank goodness for kick boards, Frank thought as he tried to press himself out of range in a corner.

'Best if you'd left that door open, boss,' Dick yelled from the floor.

'That's why his hooves are bad,' Frank gasped, sitting down to avoid the flying hooves, 'he's never had 'em dressed.'

'A funny time to be finding out, if you ask me,' said Dick weakly, still recovering from a kick in the solar plexus. 'If he goes on like this someone's goin' to get killt.'

Fortunately, Charlotte heard the racket and dashed across the yard. 'Is everything all right?' she asked over the open top door.

'No, it bloody well isn't,' replied Frank calmly. 'Open up so this blasted animal can get out, and stand back as he comes out.'

'Now what do we do with him?' asked Dick when all had quietened down and the horse had been caught again.

'Tomorrow morning we'll yoke him up next to good quiet Bess, and see how he behaves when he's pulled a plough all day. A few days' hard labour is what this chap needs, and then when he's good and tired we'll see about tacklin' his feet; but outside, think on, Dick, then when you've bossed him we'll send for the blacksmith.'

'Oh, I see. It's when "I've" bossed him, is it, then "we" can send for the blacksmith.'

'We've every confidence in your ability to master this chap, haven't we, Charlotte? I think we'll call him Hasty Retreat 'cos he sure as hell had us back-pedalling. Let me know when you reckon he's ready to go hunting.'

'Yes, sir,' said Dick touching his cap in mock humility.

The morning of the twenty-first dawned overcast, but fair. It was cold, following overnight rain.

'Looks as if it could be a good scenting day, boss,' Dick remarked as the three of them hacked north, past the Bedale Hunt Inn towards the kennels, Frank on his beloved Tuffan, Charlotte on her grey and Dick on The Painter.

115

'You know what Jorrocks said – that famous hunting man of yesteryear, noted for making many a profound statement, don't you?'

'No, boss,' said Dick.

'Jorrocks said, "There's nowt so queer as scent, 'cept women!" ' Dick roared his approval; Charlotte made a pretence of raising her crop to him.

'Remember when we used to drive cattle between the two farms as youngsters, Dick? They're talking of making this green track into the Great North Road. Instead of it wandering about from back there at Borough-bridge through Dishforth and Topcliffe then by Busby Stoop to North-Allerton – just a straight road instead, from Boroughbridge to Catterick.'

'Makes sense, I suppose,' said Dick.

'That's the way the Romans used to go. Aldborough, just back there, was their administrative centre for the north, and they built a road almost dead straight as far as Corbridge as a start to bottling up the Brigante tribe.'

'Frank Bowers, you do come out with some strange facts.'

'No, it's true Charlotte, the Brigantes were never subdued by the Romans. Their headquarters used to be Aldborough; it was a little knoll of high ground once upon a time, surrounded by swamps but overlooking the confluence of the rivers Swale and Ure. After the Romans consolidated York, they could get there by boat if they wished; anyhow, they pushed the Brigantes north, then they built this road we're on now, to Corbridge. They did the same at the other side of the country from Chester to Carlisle and then they built Hadrian's Wall. That fastened in these warlike northern tribes in a way, and then they left 'em alone.'

'Very clever, if you ask me,' enthused Charlotte. She allowed her horse to draw close alongside Tuffan so that as the horse walked, her thigh was touching Frank's knee.

'Everything I know, you have taught me, my darling,' she said softly; 'how to ride, how to make—'

'Dick,' shouted Frank, 'there's a bunch of riders way up ahead, canter on, we might as well join them – and you behave yourself, young lady,' he said out of the corner of his mouth as their mounts, taking their cue from The Painter up ahead, gratefully broke into a canter.

Tuffan was indeed well; he was 'boring' with his head, demanding the freedom of more rein. 'Whoa, lad,' Frank was saying firmly, slightly unbalancing the horse by gently pulling first on one rein, then the other. The Arab was moving superbly, he was a 'high blower'* and with his

---

* 'High blower' – inclined to make a snorting noise when expelling air from the lungs through the nostrils.

beautiful head carriage almost erect, he and Charlotte made a spectacular sight.

'Could a man wish for more, could anything be more exhilarating?' he called across to his companion. Only when he observed the haughty toss of her beautiful head and the rigid fixed stare ahead did Frank realise he hadn't quite said the right thing.

As they cantered on he decided to quote a verse of poetry he had recently learned about the Arab horse:

> The jewel and pride of the stable
> The brightest and best of her race
> Reliable, willing and able
> Unequalled in fencing and pace
> Light footed, light mouthed and light hearted
> Of lineage as old as the flood
> The worth of those flyers departed
> Condensed in each drop of her blood.

'Did you make that up specially for me, my love?' asked Charlotte, breathless, as they slowed to the trot and then dropped in behind a cavalcade of other riders.

'No, my sweet, I'm not so clever, but I read it then memorised it because it reminded me of you and your horse. It was written by George Whyte Melville who used to stay quite often across the fields there at Bedale Hall.'

'Frank, you are so marvellous to me,' she said quietly. He could tell from the misty look coming over her eyes that he'd scored heavily.

'I'll drop back now,' she said dutifully, 'and keep Dick company. You go on and meet your friends. Where do you think he wants to be to change horses?'

'I'm told these Langton foxes have a bit of a habit of going round in circles, keeping to the estate coverts; there are so many of them they never get properly educated at cub-hunting time. If we should get one to leave, the usual run is south following the River Wiske. If Dick gets himself down the road to Thrintoft and Ainderby Steeple, we should be able to find each other.'

They were at Leeming Bar now, briefly joining the Great North Road before bearing north-eastwards to the kennels. The Master, J.J. Mowbray, and hunt staff were almost ready to leave, to hack the few miles to Langton Hall.

117

'Hello, Frank,' beamed the Master. 'You've hacked a long way.'

'Just from Boroughbridge, sir. I had my horses stabled there overnight. Now I have the use of my firm's car, it makes it much simpler getting around to distant meets.'

'Splendid, splendid, we need keen young fellas like you to keep fox-hunting alive.'

'By the way, sir, I'm hoping to run a horse in the members' race next March; there he is, the bright bay, he's second horse today. That's Boynton, my foreman.'

'As long as he's hunted fairly and squarely then he'll qualify. Wouldn't be surprised if this year's point isn't the last for some time, all this war talk. Rum do if all these good horses that you see around here are commandeered for the Army; you only get a set price they tell me, nowhere near the true value of an experienced hunter.'

'About fifty pounds is the average price,' said Frank. 'Wouldn't like to think Tuffan here had to go to war. Five hundred wouldn't compensate me if I lost this fella.'

'We'd best get on our way to Langton. I shall be looking for some new horses for next season, if there is one. A strong active cob suits me best, so if you come across anything suitable in your travels around the country-side, let me know.'

'I will sir, I will indeed.' Better not tell him I've already bought one with him in mind, Frank thought to himself.

After being well entertained by Major Fife and his staff in the glorious setting on the forecourt of Langton Hall, a busy morning ensued.

There were foxes a-plenty, but scenting conditions favoured the quarry. A big dog fox left the first covert almost immediately. Frank had been sent to the far side on point duty and had scarcely taken up position when the fox dashed out, 'almost under Tuffan's belly' he enthused later. A circular hunt by Streatlam Plantation and back to the Hall grounds clearly showed that hounds were having the utmost difficulty in holding the line. They lost him by the river.

A second fox found in Thrintoft Whin was hunted for a short while and then abandoned.

Streatlam Whin provided a lame fox; he was viewed away moving slowly on three legs. Hounds bowled him over very quickly.

'Glad we caught him,' Frank heard the Master telling Major Fife, 'dreadful septic wound on one hind leg, must have been in agony and probably unable to hunt for his food.'

Felgill Moor provided the next fox, it was early afternoon and in the usual strange inexplicable way, because it was coming in cooler, the scent improved. Hounds fairly screamed away and fortuitously not only headed almost due south, taking Frank more than halfway home, but also ran close to Ainderby Steeple where Dick was waiting with The Painter.

The pace was fast and furious; leaving Worlaby and North Otterington to the east the fox had borne right handed and crossed the Swale near Maunby Ferry. Here the Master met with an accident – his horse whipped round as soon as they were aboard and knocked him clean over the side. In the middle of the river it might have been dangerous; fortunately there was no strong current, and the water was not very deep just at that point. He was quickly hauled aboard – not without a certain amount of hilarity.

'Shades of "Newby Ferry", eh Frank? But nowhere near as deep this time,' said the Master. There was hardly time for him to empty his boots of water before they were across and the gallop continued.

This good fox had just touched the new whin at Pickhill and made his point as if to cross the Leeming Lane for Kirklington Big Wood. Apparently headed on the road, he swung left with Ainderby Quernow on his left through the Black Wood at Baldersby following the line of the River Swale through the gardens of Baldersby Park across the Dishforth to Thirsk road, close to Topcliffe Bridge, past Cundall and turned right handed, pointing for Kirby Hill.

'He must be well outside his territory by now,' the Master shouted to his Huntsman.

'Yes, sir, he's twisting about, they're sure to run into him soon.' As they approached Milby Whin, Frank counted only seven of the original mounted field in contention – the Master, superbly mounted on a blood horse called Don't Rush, the three hunt servants; and two others besides himself. A lot of hounds were dead beat and dropping back. Quite by chance Frank glanced over to his right and spotted the weary fox, only a field away, going back the way they had come.

'There he goes, sir!' he shouted.

'Well done, Frank! Let's give our horses a breather, I'll let these hounds bring the line back to us. I don't want to lift their heads by blowing at this late stage.'

The leading hounds came back on the line within five minutes. 'Forward on!' shouted the Huntsman, wearily and slowly three couples of hounds followed the line, past Umberton Farm as if for Brafferton, where the fox entered a stone culvert in the river bank short of the Helperby road bridge, where he was marked to ground.

'Well done everybody,' said John Mowbray. 'What a run! We're well out of our own country so Charlie can stay safe and unmolested where he is.'

'Thank you very much, sir,' said Frank, 'I think I'm nearer home than you are, so I'll say goodnight.'

'Yes, we must be easily twenty miles away from the kennels. I reckon we should be able to gather up lost hounds on the way. Are the stables at Baldersby Hall still in use? There's one of the hunt horses in a bad way; I think we'll have to arrange for some hot gruel and a stopover for him.'

Frank decided to plod home. The Painter seemed reasonably fresh. He had originally intended to stable his horse for the night at the Crown in Boroughbridge and drive home. He made the mistake of deciding to call in anyway and, having seen the horse bedded down with a nice warm feed, felt he was in need of some sort of refreshment himself.

Although it was only early evening, the main bar was crowded. 'What's going on?' he asked Betty the barmaid, when he finally squeezed through to the bar.

'I thought you would have known, sir, there's to be a hare coursing match just below Aldborough tomorrow. It's the Old Yorkshire Club against a similar lot from Ireland. A young fella down at the other end of the bar keeps making passes at me, and he was telling me. We go over there one year and they come over here the next. Most of them are staying here.'

'Would you be after looking here, lads,' Frank heard a strong Irish voice say. 'To be sure it's an "unting man", begorrah.'

'Tell me a man is a fox-'unter and I love him at once,' said another.

'I'll be damned,' replied Frank, 'Irishmen quoting Surtees.'

'We live for it, young sir,' said another. ''Untin' an' hare coursin' are part of our lives.'

By this time Frank was surrounded by a happy smiling throng of half-tipsy Irishmen.

'Betty,' the first voice commanded, 'give this young chap a large glass of hot toddy!'

This was Frank's first contact with a group of sporting Irishmen and he soon began to enjoy himself. Before the evening was over he had become firm friends with Seamus O'Brien, himself an auctioneer, also very fortuitously a leading exporter of Irish cattle.

Frank was never permitted to buy a drink, nor was his glass of whisky ever allowed to become empty.

Towards midnight, with his arm around Seamus, he heard himself saying, 'Never mind the distance, you get your cattle to Liverpool Docks, we can get drovers to bring 'em across here by road, an' I can sell 'em in our new Auction Mart, just down the "hay one".'

'What's the "hay one", Frank?' asked Seamus.

'You know; the "hay one", the Great North Road, runs past here you know. I go down it to Wetherby to get home.'

So it came to pass, a mutually profitable, lifelong friendship had struck up.

'We can sell good Hereford stores in the spring; most farmers round here are graziers. Come back end, butchers in places like Leeds and Bradford come out this way, looking for fat bullocks,' Frank was telling his new-found friend.

Joe Falshaw's going to be pleased with this one, he was thinking to himself.

'Your turn for a song, Seamus,' someone called out.

'All right, all right, I was just talking business with this young man. I think Frank, my new-found friend, should give us an English tune, we've heard nothin' but Irish songs so far.'

Secretly, Frank, not to be outshone forever by Joe Falshaw and his 'To Be a Farmer's Boy' had been learning off by heart and practising 'Do Ye Ken John Peel' – here was his chance. He surpassed himself; the appreciative audience made the bottles behind the bar rattle as they joined in with each chorus – 'with the fox an his hounds in the mornin'.'

At the height of the fourth chorus the door to the bar opened and in walked Sergeant Proud from Ripon and two constables. As a hush descended Frank glanced quickly at the clock behind the bar; 'That's torn it,' he groaned, 'Eleven-forty – well after time, and all three know me.'

The landlord appeared behind the bar as if from nowhere; nervously he asked, 'What can I do for you, Sergeant?'

'I am of the h'opinion, Mr Elliott, that not only are you selling h'intoxicatin' liquor after time, but are holding an unruly house as well.'

'Ah, Sergeant, you see, but all these fellows have come over the water from the Emerald Isle, they're stayin' here as residents like.'

'But there's young Mr Bowers, he seems to be ringleader with this rumpus; I know he's not a resident.'

'That, Sergeant, is where you're wrong. His hoss is out yonder in the yard; both arrived about six o'clock, dead beat. It would have been cruel to tak' that hoss any further, on its last legs it were – so Mr Bowers's got my best room for the night.'

Fortunately, the hotel recently installed a telephone. Frank decided to

121

phone home. He knew Charlotte would answer, but he failed to convince her of the need for him to stay at the hotel.

'You have the car, even if The Painter is dead beat,' she said.

Good God! said Frank to himself, the car parked at the front, forgot all about it – came in at the rear entrance.

'Couldn't get it started,' he lied.

'Frank Bowers,' she said, 'I don't believe you.'

'By the way, there's a hare coursing meeting close by here tomorrow, might as well stay for that.'

'Hello? Hello?' – but the phone had gone dead.

'Women!' Frank was muttering to himself as he returned to the party, only to find the three policemen, minus helmets, propping up the bar; each had a frothing pint tankard of ale in one hand and a large ham sandwich in the other.

'Perhaps if you could moderate the noise from the singin',' he heard Sergeant Proud saying to the landlord.

'Ah. Mr Bowers, I take it that'll be your firm's car outside?'

'Yes, Sergeant, won't start unfortunately.'

'Just so, just so. Thought there had to be some other h'explanation as to why you're stayin' 'ere overnight.'

'You must have 'ad a fair day's 'unting from the look of yer boots and breeches.'

'One of the best ever, Sergeant,' replied Frank.

'Right you two lads,' boomed Sergeant Proud, 'get yourselves round the rest of the town; make your presence felt, but don't upset our Irish friends if you can help it. I'll stay here and probably try another pint of your best bitter, Mr Elliott.'

'Now, Sergeant,' said Seamus with one arm drooped across his shoulders, 'Can you give us a song?'

'No, but I can recite you a poem about "Harriers" written by a Mr De La Poer Beresford who lived in the Bedale country nigh on eighty years ago.'

'Silence please – silence,' called out Seamus. 'The sergeant will now recite.

'Arriers,' boomed out the worthy policeman.

'Twas at nine in the morn, and the weather was fair
When we set out from Bedale, in search of a hare.
There was Charley the Huntsman, and young Mr Mark,*

---

* Mark Milbank who took the Bedale in 1832, at this date 14 years old.

Dick Pierse and John Monson, not forgetting George Clarke;
A large field of farmers all eager to ride,
Each swearing to each as they rode side by side,
How the other would dash over mountains and dales
Leaving numbers behind them "hung"* at hedges and rails.
That the thing of all others they most wished to see
Jump up 'mid the hounds an old Reynard would be.
That hunting the hare was but moderate fun,
And they very much wished for a capital run.
Their wish was soon granted, for e'er it was late,
The hounds went away at a terrible rate.
Such a time they kept at it, and such was the speed
They quickly discovered a fox, 'twas indeed:
Who gallantly leaving the woods of Thorp Perrow†
To Watlass he sped, with the speed of an arrow,
So close were the hounds that he could not delay,
But over Snape Park he directed his way.
Where finding the pack still hard at his brush
He leapt the park wall with a terrible "rush".
And crossing the road towards Masham proceeded;
But disliking the country, or perhaps he was headed.
Turning short to the left came to Aldborourgh Hall,
Thence through Binsoe and Peter Wood arrived at Hackfall.
Where either disdaining the earths that were open,
Or feeling his strength unimpaired and unbroken,
He still rattled on, 'til to Tanfield he came,
Tho' dirty and draggled, yet his pace was the same.

*   *   *

Here after a chase of two hours and more
The hounds they were stopped – what a terrible bore.

The applause was spontaneous and earsplitting.
'More! More!' they cried.
'Sergeant, sure it's a "Bard" you are,' said Frank. 'Do yer know any more rhymes?'

---

* What we now call 'hung up', i.e. 'pounded'.
† Hounds changed from a hare to a fox, somewhere between Firby and Thorp Perrow. No one knew exactly where.

'Well, yes. My old grandfather who was a 'unting man like yourself taught me one about a hill fox.'

'Now lads, will you be quiet, here's our worthy sergeant to tell you about the hill fox.'

' "The Hill Fox",' boomed out the sergeant once more.

What had brought him so far
From the glidder and scar
And the moss where the rivulets croon?
Did he cross on a raid?
Or, like man to a maid
For a vixen that cried to the moon?

There are foxes that swing
With the wind on its wing,
There are foxes in circles that tread;
But he chose his bold line
Where the hilltops ashine
Touched the shadows in which he was bred!

'Tis a short enough start,
But a hill-fox's heart
Never quails when the peaks are in view;
Down the valley he dips,
Through the grey river slips,
With his mask to the Moors so blue!

There's the crash of a rail
As the crowd leaves the vale
And sweeps out on the heath of the hill,
And it's slow they must creep
Up the edge of the steep;
But the bitches are galloping still!

Over hilltop and slope
Still we stumble and grope
Through the tussocks where sheep drains are blind;
And the men that have led
Are gone further ahead,
And the slow ones drop further behind.

And the little hill-fox
Threads his way through the rocks
Where the burn makes a lather of foam;
Does he laugh at us now
As he climbs the last brow
That leads straight to the haven of home?

Once again the place erupted.

'You ought to have been a fox-huntin' man yourself, Sergeant,' said
Frank. 'You'll have to teach me that one. I think Joe Falshaw will be asking for you to visit the market next month, we have a special sale of
"Christmas Fare" and with one or two light-fingered people intent on
attending these sort of sales, the presence of the law, we hope, will deter
them.'

'Right, Mr Bowers. I'll write it out and bring you a copy to the market.'

'Good, now I think I'll try that car again and see if it'll start this time.'

All Frank's new-found Irish friends trooped out with him; for many this
was the first car they had ever seen.

Frank had retained his faculties in a remarkable way considering the
amount of whisky he had consumed; he remembered to crank the engine
once or twice, with the ignition switched off, feigning a difficult start. He
had learned to set the 'mixture' lever at 'rich' for a back fire or two and a
couple in quick succession sent some of his Irish audience diving for
cover.

Then with a 'whoop – whoop' and cries of 'Forward on' from Seamus,
he was away as he sped down the Great North Road.

The house was in darkness as he drove as quietly as possible into the quadrangle behind; he let himself in and noiselessly crept upstairs to his room.

He lay awake for some time, expecting Charlotte to visit, but she never
came and then, exhausted, Frank fell into a deep slumber.

Next morning it was obvious that mother was getting used to Frank's
nocturnal wanderings.

'Did you have a nice day, darling?' she queried.

'One of the best I can ever remember, mother,' he said, ignoring the disapproving glare and the toss of Charlotte's beautiful head of hair; then as
Dick knocked and entered the kitchen – 'Dick, just the man. I'll run you
up to the Crown Hotel in the car and you can hack The Painter home. He
might be a little stiff at first. I hope Miss Charlotte will accompany us;
there's a hare coursing meet near Aldborough. Some Irish lads and their

greyhounds are over to compete with our lot from Thirsk. Can you be ready in half an hour? You can always stay and watch the coursing, then hack back. How's Tuffan?'

'He's all right, sir, he's had a crack above the knee on the near fore; a bit swollen this morning but I've had the hosepipe on it, should be all right within a few days.'

'Do you want to see this hare coursing, Charlotte?' Frank knew she would pretend she didn't, but he also knew her curiosity would get the upper hand eventually. His query was met with a glare and stony silence.

'All right, please yourself; we'll be leaving in half an hour if you want to come.'

When Frank walked out to the car thirty minutes later, Charlotte was dressed in her travelling coat with a bright printed scarf worn under a brimmed hat casually fastened under the chin.

She'll turn a few heads at this meeting, he thought to himself. 'All aboard,' he called out breezily. 'We'll check on The Painter when we get to Boroughbridge, then you come to the meet if you like, Dick, afore you go home.'

A motley gathering were already congregating near a line of book-makers down one side of the 'killing field' as Frank deliberately described it. Charlotte asked what he meant.

'They have a minimum of four drives, one from each side of this square field, it is so fenced that a hare can escape through the bottom rails after each "course", but the greyhounds are unable to get through so the hare escapes.'

'Unless they catch it first,' quipped Dick.

'Yes, thank you Dick. I'll explain what happens,' said Frank, as Charlotte stopped in her tracks.

'They nearly all escape, my sweet– take no notice of him! There are only two officials in the field, one chap known as "the slipper" lets off two greyhounds; the one wearing a red collar is ours and the one wearing the green is obviously Irish. There's a mounted judge who carries two flags; he has sole responsibility to award points, then announces the winner to the scorer by waving his coloured flags.'

'But how do they know a hare will come into the field?' asked Charlotte, slightly puzzled.

'You send beaters out, just like they do on a grouse moor, carrying big staves; they drive the hares in front of 'em, and there are flankers on either side with white flags who make sure they sort of funnel 'em through the fence into the arena. There's the slipper moving out now, look, with the first two dogs. He'll take up position halfway down that fence behind the screen with his back to the drive, and as soon as a hare comes through, a chap on the corner blows his whistle which halts the beaters; the slipper lets the hare get nicely into the field, makes sure both greyhounds have seen him, then he'll run forward and unleash 'em simultaneously. Here's the mounted judge, in full hunting attire – well, I'm blowed, it's Seamus, this chap I met last night.'

'Be Jesus, it's Frank,' beamed Seamus, 'How's your head this beautiful morning, young man – do you ken John Peel, eh! Some party we had! This must be your beautiful colleen – is this why you had to go home, you rascal? Here's the address I promised you, get your firm to write and we'll send some cattle over next spring about grass day.' With that he turned his horse and cantered away, positioning himself close by the two eager greyhounds.

'That's why I was delayed last night; business.'

Charlotte, with pursed lips was staring straight ahead and ignoring him. 'He's going to start sending Irish cattle over, as you heard; I've told him we can handle a few hundred at a time.'

Just then a subdued murmur from the crowd heralded the arrival of the first hare.

'There he is, Charlotte, look he's only moving slowly, into the centre of the field.'

The shrill whistle, halting the beaters, made him pause, and at that moment the straining greyhounds ran forward with their handler and were away.

They closed fast; the hare only became aware of danger when they were within two bounds of him. He scuttled sideways and the dogs overran him by many yards; three times this happened and three times the Irish dog turned sharper. Then suddenly the hare ran straight towards the crowd – realising his mistake at the last moment, he jerked left and ran straight down the line of spectators. This gave the home dog the advantage; then everything happened very quickly, and there was a quick blur of a brindled dog wearing a red collar, a quick snap of jaws, a hare flying into the air emitting a slight squeal. The crowd pressed back, the hare bounced twice and finished up quivering at Charlotte's feet, stone dead with a broken neck.

Amid whoops from the crowd, Seamus galloped up holding high his red flag. Charlotte shuddered, and turned to Frank. 'Ugh! Horrid!' she said and stalked off to the car.

Frank followed. 'I want to be taken home, away from this murdering lot,' she demanded.

'That was a very rare occurrence, sweetheart, there could be two or three more courses on this drive. Just you come back and see, they'll be sure to get away.'

In fact that was how it turned out. The next hare appeared on the far side of the field, went straight across as the next two greyhounds approached, was quickly into overdrive and out through the rails before the dogs could close.

'No contest, see,' said Frank gleefully as he turned towards Charlotte, pleased to see her smiling. 'Now get ready, there's one of those flankers with his flag held straight aloft, he's signalling there's another hare in front of him.'

The dog handler signalled he was ready; a whistle blew and forward moved the beaters.

'Here he comes,' hissed Dick, 'he's come through the fence almost behind the dogs.'

The two greyhounds were soon away and a clever hare repeatedly dodged them. The Irish dog was the quicker of the two, but young and far too impetuous. He ran wide at every turn, allowing the home dog to pick up points; with his strength failing fast and the Irish dog within one bound of his long hind legs, the hare scuttled through the fence at the far side of the field.

'There you are, Charlotte, another's got away, it's a draw – look, Seamus is holding up both flags. Surely you're beginning to enjoy it, are you not?'

'Only if the hare escapes,' said Charlotte, her flushed cheeks a sure sign that the excitement was getting to her.

'Come on, Dick. Let's have a drink whilst they set up the next drive.' Charlotte followed dutifully. Frank pushed his way through a noisy throng of Irish supporters in the beer tent.

'To be sure 'tis himself,' a loud Irish voice exclaimed. 'Lookee here fellows – 'tis John Peel without his huntin' attire.'

'Why do they keep calling you John Peel?' asked Charlotte when Frank returned with his three whiskies.

'Well, I was persuaded to give 'em a song last night whilst I rested up at the Crown.'

'Rested up indeed, we weren't allowed to rest up, were we Dick? Somebody had to get back to see to the horses and the other stock, pacify your mother and . . .'

'Whoa,' Frank said testily, 'careful what you're saying, that's what I pay you for.'

An embarrassed silence was broken by a hearty slap between Frank's shoulder blades. It was Arnold Cheesman from Burton Grange at nearby Helperby.

'Frank, you old fox, didn't know you followed this sport – I hear you finished up near our spot yesterday, marvellous hunt they tell me.'

'Hello, Arnold, yes, fantastic run. I was lucky to be able to change horses at Ainderby Steeple. I think maybe we changed foxes in the round whin covert south of Rainton; the pace quickened up from there and had it been the original fox he couldn't have dodged us as cleverly as he did at the end and got to ground.'

'But I'm forgetting, you haven't met Charlotte, my mother's companion, and this is Dick Boynton who's come to take The Painter home from Boroughbridge.'

Arnold Cheesman took Charlotte's hand. 'Quite charming,' he said. 'Which painter are you employing from Boroughbridge?'

'No, you fathead, that's my point-to-point horse, he was about cooked by the time the fox got in yesterday, so I left him in the stable yard of the Crown last night.'

'And then he appears to have rested up himself,' Charlotte said sarcastically, 'Entertained half the Irish crowd who are here today also.'

'He would! He would!' chuckled Arnold. 'We were at school together, you know. There's a lot I could tell you about this chap in his younger days.'

'Come and have a drink,' Frank said deliberately, drawing his former school chum away towards the bar.

'That girl's in love with you, Frank; I could tell from her eyes when she looks at you.'

'Never mind that,' said Frank, striving to change the subject. 'What about your "Pointers"; are you racing next season?'

'Sure am, I've bought that good horse, After Me, from George Robinson; won your Farmer's Race three years on the trot. He'll have to be entered in the Open this time; are they racing at Well like last year?'

'No, it's at Hutton Hang near Leyburn, twenty-first March, my birthday. I'm hoping to run The Painter in the members.' Frank drew his friend into a corner. 'I wouldn't mind getting hold of a farm to rent in the "Bedale Country" Arnold, if you can help me, it's better hunting than "The York" you know; I feel a bit cut off, away from the sport at Farrick House.'

'What about the business and Joe Falshaw?'

'Oh, he's all for expanding, we think we can start an Auction Mart in Ripon.'

129

'Well, Lord Downe owns a lot of farms around there; I know the agent quite well, he's a relative of mine. I'll let you know if I hear of anything suitable. By the way, I hear your pal Bobbie Dawson at Malvern House has started importing hunters from Ireland.'

'Indeed he has, he's persuaded me to buy a chestnut four-year-old from him for thirty-five pounds; hell of a sort but he's got four white socks, nearly up to his knee.'

'You know what they say about white-legged un's, don't you, Frank?'

'No.'

Four white socks, send him far away,
Three white socks, keep 'im but a day,
Two white socks, you can lend 'im to a friend,
One white sock, keep 'im to the end.

If you can find a hoss with one white sock behind, a white star on his fore-head, and good big lugs, then he's probably a good 'un; keep away from chestnut fillies they tell me, usually a bit warm, although I see you've got one of them with you today.' The twinkle in his eyes said everything.

'All right, all right,' said Frank.

'What are you calling this Irish horse then?'

'I couldn't get any luck money out of Bobbie, but he gave me a leg of lamb so I've called the hoss Mint Sauce.

'You'll be coming to the Boxing Day Meet at the Grantham Arms, I hope, Frank?'

'Yes, I've just started working a heavyweight grey cob called Hasty Retreat; Dick Boynton tells me he should be ready to hunt around Christmas time. We've had him yoked up ploughin' to try and knock some sense into him, but he still has a mind of his own.'

'Usually the best sort, once you've bossed 'em,' Arnold said. The next drive's just started, look; are you coming to watch some more coursing?'

Three hares came into the arena in quick succession, and each one quickly fell victim of the greyhounds.

'That's enough for me, sir!' Charlotte said acidly. 'I shall be in the car, when you wish to return.'

Hell, thought Frank some ten minutes later, this female's beginning to rule my life.

'I think we'll have to go, Dick, it's coming on to rain, Charlotte's sat in the car and she won't have a clue how to put the hood up – you come along in your own time.'

Little was said on the return journey.

'Francis, you haven't been home so early for ages,' his mother said.

'No? Well the weather turned nasty and Charlotte wasn't too keen on watching those hares bowled over.'

'Quite right my dear, a male sport, don't you think, if you can call it a sport. You've just missed your cousin Miles. You know he was training to be a land agent; well he's qualified and taken over the management of a big estate in the North Yorkshire moors, in the Esk Valley. There's a river full of salmon, a big grouse moor, also some very good hunting, Goathland hounds, I think he said. Anyway, he's left his address and he wants you to go and stay just into the New Year; he says if you take it steady you can hack up there in a couple of days, there's stabling for two horses and rooms at a very nice, old-fashioned pub almost next door to the agent's house.'

'If I take two horses I would have to take Charlotte as well; Dick can look after the farm, but what about you?'

'I can manage to look after myself for a few days.'

'Good. If Joe Falshaw says I can have time off, I'll write to Miles and arrange perhaps a week towards the end of January. That all right by you Charlotte?'

'I'd love to go,' she cooed softly.

13

Christmas Sales and Meet

There were fourteen days to go to Christmas; the response to the first 'Special Sale of Christmas Fare' was overwhelming. The whole of the premises around the Auction Mart was full of turkeys, some alive, some dressed; ducks; flocks of geese which had been walked in; guinea fowl; cock chickens; old hens; cheeses; butter; home-made Christmas cakes; vegetables – 'You name it,' said Frank to a new young assistant, Tom Edwards, 'if you can eat it as "festive fare" then we've got it here today. You keep booking this lot down as it comes in; I'll go over into the other yard. I'll get the boss to sell the pork pigs when they've finished judging; have you seen Mr Falshaw?'

'Yes, he was here when I arrived, talking to the pig judge; I saw him pin his judge's badge on his lapel, then since it was so cold Mr Falshaw said they might as well go over to the Brown Cow for a rum and coffee. I heard him say he knew the landlady and she'd let 'em in the back way.'

'Thanks, I'll deal with it,' said Frank. He groaned inwardly; everybody knew the widow Agnes had been after Joe for years, and once she'd got him in the pub, he invariably found it very difficult to get away.

Better check the pig section first, he thought. There were pigs galore, but no officials; he cursed to himself, should have been judged by now.

'We aim to sell these first,' he said to a group of farmers, 'has anybody seen the judge?'

'If it's Bill Crowther tha's wantin', well I seed him goin into t' Brown Cow about an hour sin'; your boss was leading th' way like! If them two has getten on th' rum bottle, then if you hask me, this sale'll be a rum do, no messin'.'

Joe and the judge were not alone when Frank managed to get through to them; they had been joined by a very jolly throng of hardy Auction Mart followers, amongst them the brothers Marshall and Henry Taylor, very influential farmers – mainly cattle and sheep men – there was portly Dick

132

Swales, Barney Boothman from Lancashire; a couple of big wholesale butchers from Leeds who Frank knew only by sight; Jim Coates, a new director at the Mart; Jack Bainbridge, known to all and sundry as 'Barabas'; a very shrewd cattle-dealer called Bob Geldard; and the villain of the piece, with his arms flung wide at the sight of Frank – Billy Booth from Nidderdale.

'I was wondering about judging the fat pigs,' Frank said quietly to Joe.

'Good Lord! Is it that time; come on Crowther, time to earn thy keep.'

Frank followed as the two men staggered down the kitchen passage and attempted to unlock the back door; 'see you later Billy,' Frank called out.

'Goodbye, Agnes, my love,' Joe was shouting.

Frank noticed his flushed face and glazed eyes with some alarm. There's only two of us to sell this lot today, he thought. If Joe's like this before we start, then heaven help us!

The judging of the pigs with the sale immediately afterwards was a complete fiasco. The system they had employed was for the auctioneer and his clerk to walk a catwalk above the pens, so that the pigs, awkward to move at any time, remained in the same place. Halfway through the sale Joe fell off into a pen containing eight porkers; he sat there, totally immobilised, roaring with laughter whilst the pigs ran over him, snorting and grunting in alarm. Many willing helpers, provided they were not rendered helpless from mirth, struggled to get Joe out.

The Auction Mart foreman arrived. 'For Christ's sake take the boss into the office,' Frank said. 'Clean him up, don't allow him to open any of those bottles under the desk – they're for entertaining the buyers afterwards. Then see if you can get plenty of black coffee into him. I'll finish selling this lot and then start on the live poultry. I know he can be difficult when he's had a skinful, but if you could guide him back to the poultry section after lunch, I'd be very much obliged. Right, I'll carry on, Joe, see you in a couple of hours – Good God man, what's wrong, you look as if you've seen a ghost.'

'Look at me cane, the one I've had since I was a lad.'

'Unbreakable, you told me,' Frank said as Joe, pathetically holding on to a nine-inch stub of his willow cane, hastily started pushing people aside looking for the remainder on the floor.

'If tha's lookin for thee cane Joe, it smashed when tha toppled into yon pen of porkers,' said one onlooker, 'sither they're feetin over what's left.'

'In all these years, I've never sold anything without knockin' it down with that cane,' Joe said, almost in tears.

'Never mind, I'll buy you a new one for Christmas,' Frank said. 'I was wondering what to get, now I know.'

'Won't never be the same, never be the same,' wailed Joe as the foreman gently ushered him towards the Auction Mart office.

'Right, gentlemen, let's get on. What have we here? One fat sow for Mr Sutcliffe, must weigh all of twelve stone. How much? Who'll start me at a tenner, eight pounds then, here's the owner, tells me she's been fed on the best of swill, with plenty of barley. Only had one litter, he says, nobbutt a young un, there y'are gents, give me six quid for her and let's away, six bid, six ten anywhere, six ten, seven pounds I'm bid,' then oblivious of time Frank was into his selling routine.

It was fully three hours before Joe reappeared. So many live geese had been entered that it had been decided to sell them in the main cattle ring. Each one had been given a number attached to the wing for ease of identification; suddenly Joe was amongst them swaying slightly and grinning rather foolishly at the audience; Frank knew instinctively from the bright red colour of his face that he'd been 'Christmassing' again.

'Hello, there's a turkey cock got amongst the geese!' some wag shouted out good-naturedly; 'Ten bob for him,' shouted out another.

Frank realised Joe was experiencing the utmost difficulty climbing the short flight of stairs into the rostrum.

'Go home, Joe,' Frank hissed into his face, so vehemently that the older man, who was striving to regain his balance on the next but last step, reeled backwards and was once more deposited on the seat of his breeches on the floor. His popularity was such that these fresh antics brought forth huge peals of laughter and prolonged applause from the audience; to shouts of 'Encore', Joe was escorted from the ring, waving and beaming as he went.

'Merry Christmas, everybody,' Joe shouted. Those were the last words Frank heard him utter.

At the end of the sale, when Frank had been selling non-stop for over five and a half hours, and the last item had been knocked down, he climbed down from his perch and went straight to the office. Instead of the usual cheery banter between office staff and customers, and the half-anticipated clink of glasses through in Joe's office, where Frank knew instructions had been given that a free Christmas drink was available for all buyers and vendors, there was nothing but a stunned silence.

'What's wrong?' he demanded.

Wendy, a perky little blonde office girl, looked up, with tears streaming down her face; 'We've just had the message that Mr Falshaw is dead!'

'That can't be, he looked so well, so full of beans,' exclaimed Frank.

'Afraid it's true, sir,' said the foreman, 'the doctor himself rang up and I answered it. Apparently he staggered home all right, went to bed and it seems whilst he was fast asleep he had a massive lung haemorrhage and it choked him, killed him.'

'It's almost as if he knew,' said Frank aloud 'he's been partying all day, the old blighter. I shouldn't have sent him home, I'll never forgive myself for that.'

'It's not your fault, sir,' said young Tom Edwards,'he really wasn't in a fit state...'

'How do you know when he was in a fit state, young fella?' Frank shouted angrily. 'He could sell snowballs to Eskimos could my boss – at the height of midsummer! If I'd let him get to the rostrum, he'd have rattled on at twice my speed and probably have been here right now.'

It was later that evening when Bill Booth revealed that he had been responsible for the second bout of festivities.

'My fault entirely, Frank,' he said. 'Joe was most concerned about leaving you doing all the selling, but I convinced him you would be all right; we more or less ganged up on him, you know, laced him with a few doubles, so it's my fault, not yours, that he wasn't fit to sell when he came back. "That Old Chair" claims another victim, eh?'

'Good Lord, yes,' Frank said, 'it's only a few weeks since we were up your way, that night in the pub when Joe stood on your chair to sing! Wants hanging up if you ask me, so no-one can use it.'

'I think it's about to be shifted, the landlord tells me he's moving to the Busby Stoop near Skipton Bridge this coming spring. I've said he can keep the blasted thing.'

'That means it's coming a lot closer,' said Frank, 'probably be quite safe in a new spot, provided nobody knows about it.'

'Who'll benefit from his will?' Billy asked.

'I don't really know,' said Frank. 'His wife died quite young, and there's no children; he had some sort of obscure relationship with his housekeeper, but never mentioned her much. I don't even know if he's made a will; he often said the firm would be mine if anything happened to him. I suppose his solicitor Mr Fitzgerald will be handling his affairs.'

Mr Fitzgerald was on the phone the following morning to the office soon after Frank arrived. 'Could you come here to my office in Boroughbridge before lunch, Mr Bowers? Mr Falshaw has left explicit instructions on what you and I have to do; he obviously knew he was a dying man. We can chat over lunch in the House of Lords across the street.'

'The House of what?' asked Frank.

'Oh, I'm sorry, I thought you would have known the nickname for my local pub. It happens to be the headquarters for the Boroughbridge Agricultural Debating Society, founded way back in 1825. I suppose it gets its name from having so many titled members; quite secretive and very select. Come to my office first, about midday if that's all right, we can run through his will. You come out of it very nicely, is all I can tell you at the moment.'

Frank arrived punctually at midday.

'Nice to see you again, Frank,' said the genial solicitor. 'Sit down and we'll open the deed box. My instructions are that you should be present when I broke the seal. Now, let's see, you are the main beneficiary, I do know; he altered his will only last year. Yes, here is his "Last Will and Testament" made out in 1908; there are also a couple of codicils which he added within the last twelve months, presumably when he knew he had a terminal illness.'

'I never knew that,' Frank said.

'No, only his doctor and myself knew – he had lung cancer.'

'I saw him coughing blood once or twice, but he never let on he was in any sort of pain.'

'Very brave, and a very tough man if you ask me,' said Fitzgerald. 'He's left very detailed instructions that you have to invite all his friends and customers to an all-day wake at the Brown Cow. You'll see on this second codicil that he's increased the legacy for his housekeeper, Miss Stephenson, to five thousand pounds, provided she is still in his employ at the time of his death. There is a separate sum for the widow Agnes Walker, or whosoever shall be landlord or landlady of the Brown Cow, of one hundred and fifty pounds, to be spent on ale, porter, grog, flip and such victuals for as long as the assembled company shall demand; the residue to go to the widow Agnes in lieu of all her "kindnesses" over the years.

'This first codicil is the important one for you, young sir, signed in my presence, whereby he leaves you the business, as it stands; you are the sole beneficiary. He also changed his mind about the house; you get that as well, in the hope that with the business expanding it will be used solely for office accommodation.

'There might be a little bit of a problem here; I know he intended his housekeeper to have his house at one time, in fact it's here in his original will, but part three of this first codicil quite clearly states you are to have the house to go with the Auction Mart premises; it's fully signed, sealed and witnessed so there's nothing Miss Stephenson can do about it. The increased legacy of five thousand pounds is supposed to compensate for his change of mind.

'When she vacates the premises is up to you, of course. I rather thought it might be best if you handle this rather delicate matter as gently as possible.

'There's a small legacy for a godson, two hundred pounds for the vicar and churchwardens of the parish church, a thousand pounds for his niece, Miss Evelyn Coverdale of Norton near Malton and such house contents as she would wish, with a proviso that Mr John F. Bowers personally delivers that amount in cash – that's a slightly unusual bequest, Frank?'

'Oh he's only being mischievous, the old monkey, bit of matchmaking. I think he's secretly been hoping we would hit it off together since my first day at the office when Evelyn almost knocked me off my feet in the corridor outside his room; nice girl, but plenty of her, not fat – just a big girl.'

'Then apart from one hundred pounds for myself for acting as trustee and executor, the rest is yours. Now, let's get across to the Three Horseshoes and have some lunch. Damn. I nearly forgot, here's a letter from Joe to you; it's marked Personal, only to be opened by John F. Bowers. I've an idea it's instructions about the wake and the funeral. I remember when he handed me the letter only weeks ago, he winked, nodded his head in that peculiar way of his when he was saying something funny, he said "I think they'll remember the day they buried me!".'

Later that day, when Frank returned to the office, he shut himself in Joe's room. Funny, he thought as he gazed around, everything in here is mine; I'm going to have to run the place on my own, my way. Even this paper knife is mine; and he deliberately slit open Joe's letter. He studied the paperknife hard and long, slowly turning it over and over between the forefingers and thumbs of both hands. How beautifully made from a sliver of brass, he thought. It's in the shape of a feather, held in the claws of a chicken's foot. The last fellow to use it is laid out in bed upstairs, dead; now it's mine. Suddenly the enormity of his loss hit Frank, he felt tears welling into his eyes, buried his face between his arms and sobbed uncontrollably; that was how Evelyn Coverdale found him as she quietly opened the door of the office.

'Forgive me,' said Frank jumping to his feet, 'mustn't be seen like this. I'm surprised to see you.'

'I hope I haven't embarrassed you, Frank,' she said, 'news travels fast, even in country districts. Our postman had heard; when he told me this morning I decided to come right over to see if I can do anything.'

'Well, you've saved me a journey. Uncle Joe left you a thousand pounds, and I have to see you get it, in cash. The Auction Mart, this house, and the business, he's left to me. Miss Stephenson, his housekeeper, gets five thousand pounds and the order of the boot, I haven't told her yet. You have the pick of the house contents. I'm instructed to retain the house for use as further office accommodation as and when the firm expands.'

'It will, I know it will. Everybody I meet seems to like you, Frank; you know I do,' she added coyly.

'I'm not looking forward to having it out with Maggie Stephenson; she has a very acid tongue and isn't going to take kindly to not getting this house. I think in a weak moment Joe promised her that she could have it, but he changed his mind; there's a codicil attached to the will to prove it. Perhaps you could tell her; after all you are family, and you've only got a thousand pounds against her five. I think you're the one who's come out of this worst.'

'I'll see what I can do. Where is she, upstairs?'

'I think so. Thanks, I'll ring mother. You'll have to come and stay with us until after the funeral. Have you any luggage?'

'Not really. I came on the train and brought just a small bag which I left in the outer office. I intended going home.'

'Nonsense,' Frank said. 'You sort out Miss Stephenson while I go round to see the vicar and the undertakers and find out how soon we can arrange the funeral. I was just about to read his last letter to me giving instructions when you came in. I'll ring mother first, then give me an hour and we'll drive out to the farm.'

Frank opened the letter; he laughed, 'The old monkey – here, read this–'

'How wonderful!' exclaimed Evelyn, 'He doesn't intend anybody to be unhappy. What have you got to do? Engage the Prize Band to play "oom-pah" music through the town?'

'Yes, and he says to dispense with the use of a hearse and carry the coffin on the car. Then at the graveside the band is to play his favourite tune "To Be a Farmer's Boy", he would like me to recite the poem by Eric Pentecost called "Anno Domini". He even gives the page number in a book of poems here in his desk; let's have a look.'

Frank read out the poem:

Anno Domini

Declining years in bird and beast
Means fighting for survival;
Man alone grows old in peace
Till Father Time's arrival.

Were you, when young, a little horror,
One of many spoilt young things?
A sapling sheltered from the morrow,
A nestling kept from spreading wings?
In manhood arrogant and ruthless,
Inherited from childhood's past,
And now you're getting old and toothless
Grumbling at life's winter blast?
A miser in the joy of giving
Though fearful that your race is run,
Complaining life is not worth living,
Abandoning work not yet done?

Would yours, as the decisive voice,
Though ailing name the wish to live?
Frankly, what would be your choice:
Old age or the alternative?

'That's my Uncle Joe,' said Evelyn, 'he's gone for the alternative, he wants us all to rejoice for him' ... with tears in her eyes she left the room. 'I'll go and try and pacify Miss Stephenson for you – coward!'

The vicar demurred at first: 'Perhaps I ought to ask the bishop, we've never had a brass band playing in the church before.'

'Only the same as the organ, vicar,' said Frank smoothly. 'My instructions are this has to be a happy funeral. Mr Falshaw had so many friends and customers you can expect a full house, standing room only I suspect. Can you manage it by Friday?'

'We might have a problem with the grave,' dithered the vicar, 'my normal digger is away this week. We have another funeral arranged for Saturday morning, and there was a spare plot right next to a Mrs Falshaw, Joe's wife I am sure. I never saw much of him, you know. Anyhow, that grave was dug out before he went away – the grave digger I mean. We could walk down and have a look if you like.

'Yes, here's the grave; that one next door is ready for Saturday. It's just a case of opening up this one and popping Mr Falshaw in.'

'I could send a couple of men from the Auction Mart if that would help.'

'Yes indeed,' said the vicar wringing his hands. 'If they came here Friday morning with the funeral at, say, midday; we could open up the old grave beforehand and we'll put a green cloth over the new one.'

'By the way, Mr Falshaw left you and your churchwardens a sum of two hundred pounds for the upkeep of the grave, or whatever,' said Frank.

'That's very kind of him, I'm sure,' said the vicar, still ringing his hands, 'and the collection?'

'If you can organise the collection, you keep it to swell the church funds,' Frank said.

The light was fading fast as Frank drove out of town and headed towards home.

'How did you go on with Miss Stephenson?' he asked his companion.

'Not very well at all,' replied Evelyn, 'in fact she was very upset at losing the house, and gave me a hard time of it; going to see a solicitor she said, but I told her you would sort it out with her as soon as possible.'

Charlotte failed to appear as Frank drove into the yard; usually when she heard the car she was down the steps like a greyhound. There was the soft glow of an oil lamp through the kitchen window as Frank led his guest towards the rear entrance; he glanced up towards Charlotte's bedroom and smiled to himself as he just discerned the slight movement of the lace curtains falling back into place.

'I thought you had electricity, Frank?' queried Evelyn.

'Yes, we do. It's mother, she still sticks to her old habits; when a neighbour asked her recently how she liked "the electric" she replied "Very useful, especially if you've been away and arrive home in the dark, you switch it on and then you can see to light the lamps."'

'Does she switch it off then?' chuckled Evelyn.

'She would if we let her, every time. She seems to prefer the warm glow and the smell of paraffin. Old habits die hard, particularly with older people.'

'How old is she, Frank?'

'Only sixty-one, and doesn't look a day over fifty, but very set in her ways. Here we are, come into the parlour.'

'Mother, I don't think you've met Evelyn Coverdale. As I told you on the phone, she's going to stay until after the funeral. I've fixed that for Friday morning. She's only brought an overnight bag, but she looks about your build so I reckon you can find her a black coat and hat.'

'Hello, Mrs Bowers, how nice to meet you. Thank you for putting me up, but there's no need really to find any mourning clothes. Uncle Joe has left strict instructions that everyone must enjoy themselves when, and I quote him, "we plant him". I can manage quite well with what I stand up in.'

'We can sort that out before Friday, my dear; men don't know about these things do they? I have a lot of things you can use. After all, you're about the only close relative, Frank tells me. Now I'll ring for my companion, she can take your bag upstairs and show you your room.'

Charlotte arrived within seconds; Frank's mother had hardly put the handbell down before she entered the room. Outside in the passage listening, the little beggar, Frank thought to himself.

When Frank and his mother were alone she turned to him excitedly. 'Frank, wonderful news! Your sister Eva is coming home. You know she was always sweet on Jacob Cheesman; they've been corresponding all this time she's been out in the Argentine. Apparently Jacob has proposed marriage, and she's coming home to arrange the wedding from here. They've fixed the day for Easter Monday.'

'Fantastic, I couldn't ask for a better brother-in-law. Bad news one day – good news the next. I suppose that's life, mother.'

'It's high time you were thinking of settling down, Frank. You're getting just like your father, inclined to get a bit on the wild side. Come to think of it, that guest upstairs is the first nice girl you've ever brought home.'

'Now mother! Don't you start. Joe was always suggesting Evelyn and I would match up a nice pair.'

'At least your sister has found herself a nice man.' Then she sighed as she mended the fire. 'If only your father was alive, he would have been proud to give her away. He's been gone many years now; you are so like him, you remind me of him every day. He was really a married man with bachelor habits, you know.'

The morning of the Friday dawned crisp and bright. 'Looks as if we're in for a nice sunny day; Joe would have wished that,' Frank remarked.

'You look rather stunning in the black dress, Evelyn,' he said, and gloated inwardly at the look on Charlotte's face. 'Now, I'm off early, but I'll be back for you about eleven o'clock. Don't forget you two, apart from close relatives, nobody is expected to wear mourning; if you can find a nice bright buttonhole in the conservatory for me, I'll wear that with my morning suit. Joe wants to be carried through the town in procession, mother, as if we were going to a wedding, so get that look of horror off your face. It's going to be all right; those were his last wishes, and I intend to carry them out.'

Frank satisfied himself that the food and entertainment at the Brown Cow were well organised. The Prize Band arrived at the church on time.

141

'Now, Mr Fawcett, how much will you be charging for this effort, I'll pay you now.'

'Nothing, Mr Bowers, Joe Falshaw was a friend of mine. I retired from farming some years ago, before he took you on as assistant. He only charged me half commission, as I'd been having a hard time of it, so I owe him one. So far as the band is concerned it's a practice day, gettin ready for Christmas like, so you get us today for nowt like.'

'Well, that's very kind, but no mournful music think on; Joe wants this day to be a celebration. There's drink and food for everyone at the Brown Cow whenever you fancy some. Tell me, who's that chap over there with the sacks tied round his legs and leaning on a shovel?'

'That's old Tom Bentley, gravedigger; didn't you meet him when you were getting the grave ready?'

'No, he was away, the vicar said, but back today.'

'Well he obviously wants a word, he's coming over.'

'Mr Bowers?'

'Yes.'

'I'm Tom Bentley. I've just bin lookin' at th' mess yon fellows 'as made takin' top o' that grave.'

'Oh yes,' said Frank.

'He wearn't fit in theer, tha knows.'

'I beg your pardon?'

'Joe Falshaw, he wearn't fit yon grave!'

'How do you mean?'

'I mean he were a good foot taller than 'is wife, an' I measured coffin an' dug grave for her.'

' So?'

'So 'is coffin, it'll be a foot longer, an' it wearn't fit in yon hole!'

'Well we shall be burying him in not much more than an hour, so we'll just have to chance it. Are you back on duty now?'

'Yes.'

'Do you think you could stand by when we carry him to the grave?'

'Looks as if I shall hev to.'

'Good; now if you'll excuse me I've many much more important things to sort out.'

When Frank arrived back at the office, with Evelyn, having dropped his mother and Charlotte off at the church, a large crowd of customers and friends were gathered around the band, being well entertained. Frank sent young Edwards, his assistant, to the Brown Cow to warn them the procession would leave in five minutes. As the bearers brought out the coffin

142

Frank took Evelyn's arm and lined up with her behind the makeshift hearse, ably driven by a local volunteer garage owner.

The band struck off playing, as Joe had wished, the march 'John Brown's Body'. The driver caused a few anxious moments, when unused to the clutch, he caused the vehicle to lurch forward. 'Kangaroo petrol,' Frank quipped, as he managed to catch the firm's holly wreath before it fell to the ground; then narrowly missing the rear rank of the band the temporary hearse was on its way.

Exactly as Joe had intended, having known full well that the town square would be full of market stalls and shoppers, the procession made its slow way towards the parish church. The people stood slightly bemused for a little while – then, quite spontaneously started clapping.

Frank fought hard to keep back the tears.

'He wants 'em all to remember this day, does your Uncle Joe, Evelyn, but I bet he never bargained for the townsfolk to clap and cheer him on his way like this.'

'I think it's just wonderful,' Evelyn said as she laughed aloud. The church, as Frank had predicted was full to overflowing; the band were superb, their music carried into the vast roof space, thence outside to the many who failed to gain entrance.

Then, almost joyously, the coffin was carried out and laid on the grave. As the six bearers stood back Frank gazed down in horror. A voice at his elbow said, 'I tell't thee it wouldner fit.'

Unfortunately, also at that very moment, the three bearers on the side of the newly dug grave, all drawn from the estate with Tweet Umpleby in charge, as one, stepped back too far; all three disappeared from sight taking the green baize cloth covering the open grave with them.

The vicar hardly disguised a guffaw; many of the crowd fell about roaring with laughter; the three other bearers, comprising the Auction Mart foreman and two porters were having to hold each other up. Frank tried hard to be serious, but when he looked at Evelyn and saw the huge grin on her face, he could contain himself no longer.

'The best of it was,' said Frank in the Brown Cow later that evening, 'we were left with a coffin we couldn't bury and three fellows in a six-foot grave, knee deep in water, unable to get out. The vicar went over to them and looking down, quietly asked if he should deliver the last rites.'

'What about poor old Joe?' asked Billy Booth, who Frank was to learn had taken a shine for the widow Agnes and had been in the pub all day.

'Oh, the vicar had to go through the motions; we all stooped and dropped a handful of soil on the top as it stood up there on the slats. When

143

nearly everyone had gone, we lifted Joe to one side and Tom Bentley, who'd warned me in the morning, had to set to and dig a couple of feet out of the grave at one end.'

'Joe would have approved,' said Billy dreamily as he tried unsuccessfully to find his lips with his tankard.

'I think you'd better come home with me tonight, Billy; we have one more spare room.'

'Wouldn't think of it dear boy! The landlady of this fine h'establishment has offered to look after me. "Where I eats I drinks, where I drinks I sleep" – allus bin my motto – written by William Shakespeare I think – you know that Prize Band?'

'Yes,' said Frank.

'Did you see their advert in the local rag last week?'

'No,' Frank said.

'Hilarious,' gurgled Billy. 'You know there's an "At Stud" column – either a bull, or a boar, stallion or something. Well, there must have been nowt forthcoming but they left the "At Stud" bit in and underneath...' at this point Billy sat down, almost speechless with laughter.

'Well?' said Frank.

'Well, it read "Rainton Prize Band are now free to take engagements anywhere in the area. Fees moderate – distance no object".'

'Penny for them,' whispered Charlotte as Frank, in the early hours of the next day, lay quietly by her side, searching for sleep.

'I don't know, my darling. I buried a good friend and benefactor today, almost as he would have wanted. I wish we hadn't had that fiasco at the graveside though – for everybody to be rollin' around laughing at what should have been the really serious moment, was a bit much.'

'But you told me he wanted everybody to remember his funeral.'

'True.'

'Then that's exactly what happened. I'm sure he would have approved of that extra giggle at the end.'

'Perhaps you're right,' said Frank as he turned and took her in his arms once more.

'And that attractive niece of his?'

'What about her?' Frank asked.

'How long is she stopping here?'

'She'll be going home on the train tomorrow.'

'Good,' said Charlotte, 'Now, kiss me properly.'

'I think I'll take Hasty Retreat to Boroughbridge to the Christmas meet,' Frank had said to his foreman. 'Do you reckon he'll behave himself?'

'Sure is a funny hoss,' Dick replied. 'It still needs two of us to get the saddle and bridle on some mornings; then other days butter wouldn't melt in his mouth. He's much steadier now at exercise, and as long as you keep a good hold of 'im, you should be all right. If Miss Charlotte goes with you, as he knows her, provided you can keep together I would think he'll behave.'

'Well then, I'll exercise him for the next couple of days to get the feel of him. Perhaps we can tack him up together in the morning and maybe if you were to shampoo him today, give him plenty of straw bedding, he'll manage to keep clean for Friday.'

The next morning seemed to be one Hasty Retreat's off days. He simply refused to relax his jaws and accept the bit. Frank watched helplessly for fully five minutes as Dick tried vainly to get the bridle on.

'Come out of it, Dick, for Pete's sake. Let me have a go, I'm taller than you; I'll make the beggar open his mouth!'

Frank, having made one mistake by raising his voice, quickly made another by snatching the bridle roughly from his servant, and then broke one of his own golden rules, by losing his temper and making a grab for the horse's head. He promptly reared up and brought one of his hooves crashing down on Frank's foot.

There was very little pain at first, just a dull sort of ache, but Frank knew from the faint grating noise from within his riding boot that bones had been broken.

'The bugger's bust my foot,' he wailed, 'and all these days of good hunting coming up over the festive season. I wish I'd never seen this damn animal. Thought I could make a killing by selling him to the Bedale Master. First he laid you out, Dick; now he's put me on the sidelines for some time – best to sell him as soon as possible.'

'James Ellis – he'll be the man,' said Dick, 'likes a good hoss with an "if" about it. He'll buy him off you, boss, and get him away from the district too, somewhere down into the "Shires" is where this fella wants to go.'

Next day Frank limped into the office in some pain. He'd bandaged his foot but could not bear to walk on it; he needed a stick for support and wore a carpet slipper in place of his boot.

'That looks painful, sir!' said Edwards, his assistant.

'Yes, Tom; I fear the foot's got broken up. Worst job was getting my riding boot off after it happened; I don't recall ever experiencing utter agony like that before.'

145

'Perhaps it would have been easier cutting the boot off?'

'Not likely, only just bought 'em, twenty-five pound they cost – specially made to measure an all. There's no way I could have taken a knife to 'em. Should last twenty years or more if properly looked after; work of art, those boots.

'Get me Jacob Cheesman at Burton Grange on the phone, I'll take the call in my office. Seems to me I'll have to teach you to drive the car, you'll have to chauffeur me around for a while on valuations and the like. Another thing, get yourself in front of a mirror and practice selling – get your voice used to the continuous patter we need. Get some sort of style; try and drop the tone of your voice; delivery is what's needed. Now we've lost the boss there's going to be plenty of selling practice for you.'

No sooner had Frank sat down and eased his tender foot into position under the desk than the phone rang

'Mr Cheesman for you, sir.'

'Jacob – Frank Bowers here, you're a secretive dog. Mother tells me we're going to get related. Congratulations! I was wondering who'd be unlucky enough to get hitched to that sister of mine. And the wedding is on Easter Monday?'

'No, not yet awhile, Frank. As you probably know Eva is coming home in March, but I think she has to go back for another tour of duty, unless this war everybody's talking about intervenes. Now, what can I do for you?'

'Nothing really,' said Frank, 'perhaps I can do something for you! I heard the other day both your hunters were lame and that Arnold had flatly refused to lend you one of his.'

'I don't know where you heard that, unless that brother of mine told you.'

'Right, we had a few drinks together in the Crown. I've been laid low, and I'm going to see the doctor this morning, got a belt on the foot gallopin' through a gateway yesterday, looks as if I might have a broken bone or two. There's a nice young grey horse at the farm, only seen hounds twice so needs an expert rider like you to bring 'im on. I wondered if you would like to borrow him for a week or two; we can deliver him to the Grantham Arms on Friday morning. I'm hoping to follow in the car provided the Master gives his permission.'

'That's fantastic, Frank, I was getting resigned to being grounded – what do you call him?'

'Hasty Retreat. He's rising six; I was hoping he'd make up into a Master's horse but he's slow to learn; sort that will go all day.'

'Grand; it's not often the Bedale come as far south as this, right on the edge of their territory, aren't they?'

'Yes, the river's the boundary. They'll bring the hounds down on Thursday and kennel them at the Crown overnight – probably draw the coverts on either side of Leeming Lane on Friday, heading back towards the kennels all the time. There's usually quite a party Thursday night, mostly farmers and hunt staff – you're sure to enjoy it if you care to come along.'

Later that morning Frank hobbled painfully down the main street to the doctor's surgery. He'd been kept waiting fully thirty minutes and had been reading some magazines. One article in a 1912 edition of *Punch* was to provide important guidelines for the rest of his life. It read:

A sportsman is one who has not merely braced his muscles and developed his endurance by the exercise of some great sport but has in the pursuit of his sport, learnt to control his anger, to be considerate to his fellow men, to resent as a dishonour any suspicions of trickery; to bear aloft a cheerful countenance under disappointment, and never to own himself defeated until the last breath is out of his body.

'That'll be ten and sixpence, Mr Bowers,' said the doctor, following his very painful prodding examination of Frank's foot. 'Nothing much I can do. "Cold hosepipe" which you huntin' folk use to such good effect on your hosses could work wonders here; it'll reduce the swelling and help to take the pain away. Support it as best you can with bandaging, keep your weight off it – you should be able to ride again within a month.'

Back at the office Frank was confronted by an irate Maggie Stephenson. 'Joe Falshaw tell't me this would be my own 'ouse one day. He tell't me that first time he – well, first time I slept with him like.'

'Perhaps, Maggie, but that was before he started the Auction Mart, and turned the ground floor here into offices. He's left you money instead; things have changed, you must see that. Besides there's a clause attached to his will; I've seen it, I was there when his solicitor broke the seal on his deed box and produced his will, plus amendments. I'm afraid you will have to accept it; as far as I'm concerned you can have the use of the upstairs for your own personal use for the next year or so rent free, provided you can keep an eye on the offices, clean them and help out if we need mucking out in any way.'

'It's never been explained like that, Mr Bowers. Someone should have told me this earlier. I've told my solicitor to take action and I think he's already started the ball rolling – I'll tell him different, eh?'

The party at 'headquarters', as Frank named the Crown Hotel, soon developed into the survival of the fittest. The hunting farmers around 'The Boro' had long been known as a wild bunch; they certainly lived up to their reputation this night.

Young Tom Edwards had reluctantly been co-opted as Frank's chauffeur, but he was found before midnight curled up fast asleep on one of the benches in the bar.

'No good sending lads on men's errands,' said Bill Boddy, a timber merchant in the town. 'You'll have to train him different, Frank!'

'He's supposed to drive me home; it's a bit of a problem changing gear with my foot like this,' said Frank.

'I can drive you when you're ready; put me up for the night and I'll come back here in the morning.'

'But surely you're hunting yourself?'

'Nope – my hoss made a mess of a gate on Monday, and hit himself hard on the shoulder. There's heat and swelling; he's not really lame, but I daren't risk him tomorrow. Look out! Who's this just dropped off his perch?'

'It's Jacob Cheesman,' Frank said, 'out cold, look. He's supposed to be riding a horse of mine tomorrow. Look, if you were to collect your riding gear on the way to Farrick – stay the night – then hack back here to the meet, you could have a good day's hunting in his place.'

'Anything I should know about this fella?' Bill asked Dick Boynton as he mounted Hasty Retreat in the yard next morning.

'Well, sir, he's a bit green, definitely has a mind of his own, you'll just have to show him who's boss.'

It was only after Bill and Charlotte had moved off that Frank realised he had no driver. How am I going to get to Boroughbridge? he thought. Of course, the motorbike, surely I can manage that with a bandaged foot.

'I know I promised not to take the bike out in winter, mother, but they are starting to improve the main roads; you'll be amazed where this machine can go. In fact, apart from the noise and smell, I can think of nothing better for following the hunt.

'By the way, you seem to have got this wedding date wrong. Eva's coming home for Easter, but according to Jacob there's no definite date fixed; I do hope you haven't been ringing round and telling everybody that the wedding takes place on Easter Monday. If you have then you had better get in touch with them all again and explain your mistake.'

148

When Frank arrived at the meet he could see Bill was having a hard time keeping Hasty Retreat quiet. Jacob Cheesman sidled up, looking sheepish.

'Sorry about last night, Frank; I had no idea where I was when I awoke, but they handed me your message. Glad to see you've been able to mount Bill for the day; I should think he's keen for them to move off, and praying for an early find, the way your cob's prancing around.'

The early find was not to be – but wasting no time the Huntsman swept through various coverts until there was a crash of music in the centre of Baldersby Whin. A strong fox was halloa'd away on the west side of this good covert, hounds ran at a furious pace to Norton Coyers where they were unable to get over the park wall. Fortunately, a brilliant cast hit off the line on the west side of the park; they ran the river bank between Nunwick and Hutton Conyers to Sharow; past Copt Hewick to Marton-le-Moor; from there past the old Harrier Kennels, back to Boroughbridge, literally past the meet, following the banks of the Yore for about a mile, where hounds killed their fox in the river. This hunt lasted for close on two hours, eleven and a half miles as hounds ran.

Frank was able to have a quick word with Bill Boddy on the road outside the Grantham Arms.

'Hell of a hunt, Frank, best I've ever had.'

'No need to rub it in, Bill. How's this chap performing?'

'Splendidly, bit fresh at first but he's jumped everything; I've been up at the front the whole time and as you can see, he's still full of running.'

'Forward on then, you'll find me at headquarters when you decide you've had enough.'

It was six o'clock when Bill Boddy walked into the bar of the Crown, carrying a saddle and bridle.

'I'd nearly given you up for lost,' said Frank, by this time in high spirits. 'Where's Charlotte?'

'I feel sure she went home We drew nearby Milby Whin and a ruddy brace flew out. Hounds fastened onto one that came back this way, then swung round by the Hall and headed due east, crossed the Swale near Myton Bridge, ran on at a hell of a pace past Tholthorpe as if for Alne Whin, past there to Linton-on-Ouse, where he crossed the river. It was nearly dark by this time; one couple of hounds swam the river and are still missing, otherwise they're all on. There were still ten of us and the hunt servants when the Master stopped hounds; we've hacked back, they're hoping to get a van at the station to save the long hack back to kennels.'

'And Hasty Retreat, I suppose he's bedded down in the stable yard?'

149

'No, Frank, when we got to Aldborough, most riders headed south towards Green Hammerton; your hoss took a few paces after th'ounds; then dug his toes in and refused to budge, either way.'

'So where is he now?' Frank asked.

'As far as I know he's still there.'

'You what!!–'

'I lost patience with the beggar; took his saddle and bridle off, then left 'im in the middle of the road.'

Frank didn't know whether to laugh or cry.

'He won't go far, Frank, we must have covered another ten or twelve miles at a fair old gallop on this second fox; I think I was the only one not to change hosses. He's got to be about exhausted, but if he is he never showed it.'

Frank gave two of the stable lads a half a crown each to set off with a head collar and try to find him. Later the head lad came into the bar looking very pleased. 'Fun him hexactly where Mr Boddy said, Mr Bowers, laid down by the roadside, shivering like; bit stiff when we got him up, but he's well rugged up and bedded down now. I fed him some hot gruel and he's eatin' his chaff like a good un.'

'Well done lads, here's another half a crown apiece,' said Bill Boddy, obviously feeling guilty.

'Well!' he said turning to Frank, 'you couldn't expect me to stay in Aldborough all night, could you?'

'I'm not sure, Bill,' replied Frank. 'I hope we remain friends; I'm feeling very kindly disposed towards you at the moment, that Gordon's Gin allus gets me that way, but I will tell you something for nowt, Bill Boddy – as much as I like you, tha'll never borrow another hoss o' mine.'

14

A Tragic Loss

By the third week of January, Frank's foot was much better. He'd fumed quietly at all the inactivity he'd had to endure, seething inwardly every time Charlotte or some friend gloated on having a particularly good day. The frost, which he was secretly hoping might put an end to hunting, as it often did just after Christmas, never arrived.

Business was very slack; there was little to sell at this time of the year anyway; the weekly sale at the Auction Mart was more or less a waste of time.

Frank decided to give Tom Edwards his head. 'I'm going into the North Yorkshire Moors for a week's hunting, leaving next Saturday. You're in charge, do what you can, if anything crops up you feel you can't handle tell them I'll be back in about ten days' time. I'll try and get to a phone each day, say around nine o'clock. The experience should stand you in good stead, so good luck.'

Frank wrote to his cousin at Egton Bridge explaining that he hoped to arrive about lunchtime on Sunday, with two horses and a girl groom, to stay a week. He then worked it out with Charlotte; on Saturday they would hack as far as Thirsk for lunch, then on to Helmsley for early evening. 'There's a good spot in Helmsley I'm told, The Mucky Duck.'

'Pardon?' said Charlotte.

'The Black Swan.'

'That sounds more romantic, Frank!'

'Then we can set off early Sunday morning, leaving the Bilsdale country behind, through the Sinnington, turn into the moors at Kirkby Moorside into Farndale territory, then drop down into Egton Bridge; we'll try and get a bite to eat at Rosedale. Here you are, it's shown on the map.'

'I don't understand those maps and things, my darling; as long as I'm with you I don't care where I am. I just can't wait to set off.'

Over lunch in the Three Tuns on the following Saturday, Frank, well

151

primed on the larger share of a bottle of vintage claret, was persuaded to talk of his early hunting days.

'I won a whip on a lead rein pony when only seven. We were living at Bolton Grange at the time, and father took me to a local show. I was on a little Welsh pony. First meet I ever went to was at Hornby Castle when I was ten; home of the Duke of Leeds. Soon afterwards I was blooded when we met at Catterick; I learned later they were after a poultry killer. The fox had been living on the outskirts of the village; he was found almost immediately, and after going round about twice, took refuge in a stick heap, bolted out of there, went through an open door into an outbuilding which led into a cottage; and the owner had the presence of mind to fasten him in. Fred Holland, the Huntsman, went in with two hounds and killed him. I remember the Duke gave this chap a five pound note to make up for any damage; everybody in Catterick who kept poultry rejoiced, apparently he'd been killing geese, ducks and hens mercilessly for months. Fred Holland then singled me out, and the Duke daubed my forehead and cheeks with the blood from the fox, quite an honour for me really. But that's enough, I'm looking forward to a nice warm room at the Black Swan for you and me; the sooner we set off the sooner we'll get there.'

Soon the horses were straining hard as they climbed Sutton Bank – both Frank and Charlotte were standing up in the stirrups, leaning forward as far as possible, grasping the mane for balance.

'Is that making your foot hurt, my darling?' asked Charlotte

'Not too bad. Glad I didn't bring the car – there's some doubt whether it would get up here in a wet time – here's the top at last; let's give 'em a breather.'

'What a wonderful view,' enthused Charlotte as she dismounted. 'Must be like looking down from one of those airships they're talking about.'

'Never mind the view, Charlotte, can you hear hounds?'

'Yes, they're down below by the lake, look, there's horses and a pink coat.'

'Thought so,' said Frank. 'A fox crossed the road a hundred yards below us, wet through, obviously done a lot of work. There he is, look – running down that track at the top of the escarpment. This'll be the Bilsdale hounds, one of the oldest packs in the country. Better not holloa whilst they're running in case they lift their heads. Wish I'd brought Tuffan now. I'll point with my cap in the hope they see us.'

'But what about your foot, Frank?'

'Oh, to hell with my foot. If those hounds bring the line up here I'm off;

152

besides if this fox swings left handed we might be in Helmsley a damned sight quicker than we intended.'

'Don't leave me, Frank,' pleaded Charlotte.

'Sweetheart, I love you very much but here come the hounds; the Huntsman has spotted me, listen he's blowing 'em on, and if you think I'm going to sit here whilst one of the most famous hill packs in the land goes charging past! And me not having had a day since this blasted horse trod on me! Helmsley is about six miles down that road; if you don't want to join in off you go, it's the Black Swan in the marketplace, there's a room booked for Mr and Mrs Bowers.'

'Frank Bowers, I think you are a pig.'

'Don't forget to keep your glove on! See you later,' Frank shouted as he turned and galloped after the hounds.

'Frank,' she shouted desperately, 'leave your saddle bags.'

'Thanks, love,' he said as he turned and galloped back. 'Forgot we were carrying luggage, see you in a little while.'

Frank had to fight hard to hold Hasty Retreat back to allow the Master and Hunt staff to catch him up. 'Hope you don't mind my joining in, sir,' he gasped as the Master drew alongside. 'This fox crossed my path and I was able to view him all along here. Frank Bowers from York North and Bedale Country.'

'Glad to have you aboard, Bowers. I thought the hounds were wrong until I saw you pointing above me, they've had to struggle to hold the line.'

'Looked like a small vixen to me,' said Frank.

'Thought so, funny how nature seems to protect a vixen at this time of year. There's never as much smell with 'em; something to do with it being close to the breeding season, I suppose.'

Hounds had checked by this time and Frank was striving to get his bearings; to the south and west stretched the Plain of York, immediately below the steep, tree-covered escarpment of the Hambleton Hills fell away.

'I believe there's a strange outline of a horse along here somewhere?' he asked one of the mounted field. 'You can see it on a good day from the Boroughbridge area.'

'Tha's stood on its eye,' one of the field remarked. 'Kilburn White Oss! That's what we call it. There's his lugs above thee an' the rest of it's on here like.'

Just then hounds hit off the line below.

'Here we go lads, looks as if he's pointing for them badger earths above Byland Abbey.'

153

Hounds ran on slowly to a failing scent, and leaving the quaint hamlet of Oldstead to the south the line gradually swung left handed as if for Wass. The trees opened out and there in a clearing was the magnificent ruin of Byland Abbey. Hunting past the former Cistercian monastery, hounds marked to ground a mile short of Ampleforth village. The Huntsman joined the field on the road. 'We're just out of our territory here, lads, a small vixen we think, she'd gone into some empty badger earths. Thank you for your assistance, sir,' he said addressing Frank. 'Which way are you heading?'

'I want to get to Helmsley for tonight.'

'No problem; we're heading back the other way but if you follow this road, and signs to Sproxton, Helmsley is a few miles further on.'

It was past teatime when Frank arrived at the hotel. Charlotte's Arab horse was comfortably stabled, his saddle bags had been thrown into a corner of a large and well-furnished bedroom, somebody had lit a glowing log fire, but of Charlotte there was no sign.

'I think your wife has gone for a walk, sir,' the diminutive landlady remarked when Frank returned downstairs; then with a twinkle in her eye she said, 'We had a few words before she went out; she was complaining bitterly about men in general. I understand you left her entirely alone at the top of Sutton Bank and went off hunting with the Bilsdale.'

'Did she seem very upset?'

'No more than one could expect, sir, but I got the impression you might be "getting your ears pinned back" if you'll forgive the expression, when she returns.'

'Well,' said Frank, 'I see we have a roaring fire in our room, perhaps if we could organise a candlelit dinner with some wine for about seven-thirty, upstairs, I might be able to get my stripes back.'

'That's no problem, sir. Have you anything special you wish to order?'

'Yes, her favourite dish in the evening is duckling.'

'We always have one or two young ducks of our own ready dressed in the larder.'

'Good, could we have a nice soup to start with?'

'Yes, I've already made some thick vegetable soup; for sweet there's homemade apple pie with local cheese.'

'Sounds delicious. Now I think I'll take the bottle of wine up with me and await her return.'

Charlotte returned at dusk, and the combination of warm firelight, wine, and Frank's enthusiasm for his chance meeting with the Bilsdale Hounds soon melted her resolve to show her displeasure.

By the time dinner arrived, Frank's charm was already halfway to dispelling any animosity.

'I do love you so!' Charlotte whispered much later in Frank's ear, 'especially when you spoil me like this. I think this is the happiest evening I ever remember.'

Much, much, later as the young couple slowly undressed each other in the firelight, Charlotte allowed her sinewy frame to melt against Frank's rock hard body; as he picked her up and carried her towards the large double bed, his victory was complete!

There was a light covering of snow next morning as Frank hurried across the stable yard to see to the horses.

'Looks as if we might be in for it, sir,' the stable manager remarked. 'Wind's got round to the east; nivver knowd a winter like this. Hardly any frost or snow so far, allus makes up for it tha knows. Local "weather predictor" was tellin' us in the tap room last neet, he thinks we're in for a right pastin'.'

'Hope it holds off until I get through to Egton Bridge.'

'Bye, but it can be rough o'er that Egton High Moor, only bin o'er theer yance mysen. Bit of a rough old track after Rosedale Abbey, but at best there's marker posts every so often, if it does come on bad like.'

After a cosy breakfast in the pub kitchen Frank and Charlotte were on their way. They made good time through falling snow to Kirkbymoorside.

'We'll have a warm drink here, sweetheart, rest the horses for half an hour, then try and get proper directions; my cousin wrote to tell me to turn north just past this place, then go straight over Spanton Moor for Rosedale Abbey. We might get a bite of lunch there. Then it's up over Egton High Moor where if there's any visibility you can look straight across to the North Sea from well over a thousand feet up.'

'Sounds wonderful,' murmured Charlotte.

Frank failed to make out whether she was being sarcastic or not. 'We've just got to pray it doesn't snow much more!'

But the higher they climbed, the harder the snow blew into their faces.

'This lot's coming out of the north and the sky looks full of it, the wind's getting round to the northeast,' Frank said.

'When the north wind doth blow, we shall have snow – and what will the robin do then poor thing,' Charlotte recited. 'Anyhow I don't care, I have you to keep me warm and look after me.'

'Maybe so,' said Frank, 'but don't forget my cousin manages this hotel where we're staying. Apparently it's next door to his house, so you, young lady, will have your own room and will have to stay in it; you're only my groom when we get there, and don't forget it.'

'I wish I knew why you have to be horrid to me so often,' said Charlotte biting her bottom lip to fight back tears. 'Last night was so perfect and then you have to go and spoil it.'

'Sorry, sweetheart, I didn't think; very thoughtless of me. It's only that he is family and we are bound to come under close scrutiny by the local hunting folk; so we've just got to act out the part.' Frank brought the two horses together. Here, give me your hand. Last night was perfect for me too, one I shall never forget as long as I live. Forgive me?' Charlotte nodded. 'Now, let's push on, then perhaps we'll make Rosedale in about an hour. Don't know about you but I'm famished already; must be the change of air.'

Snow flurries had ceased and bright sunshine brought the whole of Rosedale into sharp relief as the two lovers paused at the top of 'The Chimney', the local name for the slippery winding track which now had to be negotiated.

'My cousin wanted me to come by myself and to bring the car; only because of you I said no.'

'Hmm!' said Charlotte tossing her head in the jaunty fashion Frank had come to love so much.

'So you see,' Frank said, 'how I'm always thinking of you?'

'No you're not, Frank Bowers; but I do know one thing.'

'Yes?' enquired Frank.

'As long as there's a breath in your body, you'll never fail to think about yourself. I heard your mother the other day say you were a "walking self-preservation society". I think you'll live to a very ripe old age and never fail to please yourself or look after number one.' As it turned out, this was a totally correct assessment of Frank's life.

Three quarters of the way down to the valley floor Frank halted suddenly. 'Whoa,' he said as he held up his arm, 'Can you smell cooking, Charlotte?'

'Only faintly.'

'I reckon I can smell roast beef,' said Frank, 'it's coming from that farmhouse just below. Here we are, look – there's a sign, "The White Horse Inn". Great, this'll be on a drovers' route; just the spot we need. There's even rings set in the wall where they fasten their ponies. Hitch up the hosses my sweet, whilst I find out what's to eat.'

Later on, as the horses laboured on the steep incline out of the dale, Frank remarked, 'They certainly don't overcharge for food and drink in these parts, two roast beef lunches, two pints for me, and a gin for you, for less than five shillings.'

'I liked the friendly way they let us sit at that big kitchen table with everybody else,' Charlotte said.

'Yes, adversity draws the community together, you know. It's so remote and wild, they have to rely on each other if things go wrong – how they can make a living out of farming this sort of land is beyond me.'

They paused at the top and looked back – 'I can't see any signs of an abbey,' Charlotte remarked.

'Apparently there never was an abbey, just a small community of nuns. The other interesting thing I found out; this dale survives from iron ore mines further up the valley on this side. Look, there's a whopping big quarry and processing plant! When we stopped on the other side, do you remember remarking what a strange place to find a small railway line; well, it curls all the way round the head of the valley, then I suppose it heads off for the nearest railway station towards Teeside.'

'Amazing,' said Charlotte, determined to show interest at Frank's enthusiasm for the unusual.

'All right, my dear, we can take it easy now; only about another eight miles to go. We should make it nicely in time for tea.'

It was still snowing heavily and starting to drift on a gusty north wind as they dropped steeply down into the Esk Valley.

'It's like arriving in wonderland,' said Charlotte, 'look at all these beautiful trees. What a lovely valley, Frank.'

The very first house they came to was marked 'Estate Office'. 'That must be where cousin Miles lives, and here, look, is a stable block and right there by the river "The 3 Horseshoes Hotel".'

'How romantic,' breathed Charlotte. 'I don't think I've ever seen such a beautiful setting; all this snow makes it look even more romantic.'

'Right, let's see to the horses first, then I'll pop next door to see if Miles is in and you can organise our accommodation – this looks like someone from the hotel now. Good afternoon, my man.'

'Good afternoon, sir, you'll be Mr Bowers I expect? Mr Miles informed me you were to arrive this day. This young lady will be your groom, I suppose. The stables are just there. I'm afraid we've no loose boxes, just stalls. It used to be a farm until about forty years ago, before my time you understand; nice big stalls made to house workhorses, Cleveland bays mostly, although there not many of 'em left nowadays.'

'Good, they'll be fine in here,' said Frank, deliberately cutting his man off in full flow; 'and accommodation?'

157

'Plenty of room, you've got the whole place to yoursens; nobody else about at the moment. Good job if you ask me, way the weather's closing in. If it comes straight up the valley from the sea like this, we usually get snowed in. Should soon be plenty of fishermen though – salmon season opens in a fortneet and the river's full of 'em!'

'I didn't catch your name?'

'Dave Hancock, sir, at your service. My wife Rosie, she does the cooking.'

'Splendid, I shall look forward to meeting her. Perhaps you'll carry the saddle bags up to our rooms after you've shown Charlotte where to find hay and water; and do you have some chop?'

'Yes, sir, there's plenty for them to eat, Mr Miles made sure of that. He said you'd be stayin' about a week?'

'I'm aiming to head back next Saturday or Sunday.'

'By train, sir?'

'How do you mean, by train?'

'We have the main line here, sir, Whitby to Middlesbrough, there's a station just the other side of the river.'

'Well I'm blessed, do you hear that, Charlotte? If we get organised we can go home by train, and we'll only need hack back from York to get home. If only Miles had said, we could have arranged to come by train and had a box for the horses.' Frank could tell by the toss of Charlotte's head that he'd said the wrong thing again!

'I wouldn't have missed the trip and the stopover at Helmsley for all the world,' she said meaningfully.

'No; good, right, well, I'll go next door, have a natter! And see you for dinner – at what time, landlord?'

'About seven-thirty, sir. I think Mr Miles is bringing his fiancée.'

'Oh, he's engaged is he, first I've heard of it.'

'Yes, I think he's only just popped the question. Parson's daughter! Caused quite a stir around here when the news leaked out.'

'Righto, table for four about seven-thirty. You must put the cost on my account.'

Frank awoke next morning with a thick head; the room was cold and as he hesitated before throwing back the clothes he heard the shrill whistle of the wind, then with some alarm saw the window was three parts obliterated with swirling, drifting snow. Using the warmth of his finger he was able to clear sufficient frost from the inside to peer out. A blizzard! That's put paid to any hunting for a day or two.

'I don't suppose there'll be any way out of here for a while, only by horse or on foot,' remarked Rosie Hancock cheerfully as she served Frank and Charlotte with a steaming bowl of porridge. Would you both like bacon and eggs to follow?'

'Just toast for me,' said Charlotte.

'I'll try the lot,' said Frank, 'two eggs if possible.'

'Then, my darling,' said Frank quietly when they were alone, 'I suggest we go for a long walk, leave the horses where they are, get well wrapped up and have a look at that waterfall Miles was talking about last night.'

'How do we find that Mallyan Spout, landlord?' Frank asked as he waited for Charlotte. 'My cousin tells me it's quite a spectacular sight at this time of the year.'

'Never been near, sir. It's down in a gorge, in the valley of the Murk Esk, quite easy to find, though. It's about five miles south east of here, upstream from a quaint little spot called Beck Hole.'

Frank and Charlotte had quite a struggle at times getting through the drifts. It continued to snow heavily on an east wind, and relentlessly the going became more treacherous.

'I think we ought to turn back,' panted Charlotte.

'Nonsense, we're nearly there, this must be Beck Hole. Let's rest a while in the little pub.'

They staggered into the Birch Hall Inn and were rewarded immediately with the sight of a roaring log fire. Otherwise the tiny room was sparsely furnished; there was a wealth of brass on the hearth, brass candlesticks in abundance occupied every ledge, each black oak beam seemed to be completely festooned with gleaming horse brasses.

'Pull a stool up to the fire, sweetheart, whilst I try to find the landlord.'

'Hello!' Frank bellowed.: 'Anybody there?' As he turned round to go back outside, a wooden serving hatch he had failed to notice was flung open with a crash.

'No need to shout, young man,' said a heavily bearded middle-aged man. 'I knew as how tha'd come in; bit surprised like to find onyone daft enough to be walking about in a blizzard. What's your pleasure?'

'Two glasses of hot toddy would be very welcome, if you please, landlord,' said Frank easily. 'We're looking for the Mallyan Spout.'

'Hev you travelled far?' asked Seth Kirby, the landlord, as he re-opened the hatch and held out two steaming glasses of whisky with sugar and hot water.

'No, we're staying at the 3 Horseshoes at Egton Bridge, my cousin is agent for the estate, Miles Smeeton.'

159

'Aye, ah ken im – fast worker if you hask me. Only bin 'ere five minutes and they tell me he's got 'issen hitched to the parson's daughter.'

'I don't see how that can be of much interest to you,' said Frank somewhat icily.

'That's weer tha's wrong, young fella!' said Seth bluntly. 'That lass as been riding o'er heer regular like! "Havin it off" if you ask me, with me son. Led 'im up the garden path like; I allus tell't him he was out of his class. Far too sharp for him if you hask me, I've allus said so.

'She came o'er heer one neet last summer wi' her local quoits team – ah could see she'd taken a reet shine for 'im right away. He's a big strappin' young fella like. He wouldn't listen to me. Next thing we heered, she's got engaged; that lad o' mine took off then an w'aint seen owt of 'im since.

'I hev to say tha's very much like thy cussin; I were sure it were 'im when tha came o'er th' bridge, and that tha'd brought thy h'intended wi' thee. Ah reckon as how yon lad o mine's livin' rough in them owd mine workin's close by yon waterfall you're haskin about. If tha sees owt of 'im tell 'im his mother's wurrittin' hersen ill and taken to 'er bed.'

'Yes,' said Frank impatiently. 'I asked you the way earlier and you chose to ignore me.'

'Sorry, I thowt as how you were 'im like. Follow this beck outside till tha meets main river like, then follow that up t'valley till tha's theer. It'll be frozen like, nowt else but ice.' Frank was unable to help himself mouthing the word 'like' but it never came.

'Righto! If I see him I'll do my best to get him to return.'

Hand in hand they threaded their way alongside the stream.

'It's definitely sheltered down here,' Frank remarked, as turning a sharp bend in the river they were confronted with the magnificent sight of a solid wall of ice, stretching up some forty feet vertically above them.

'Let's have a look at it from the top – it's certainly everything that cousin Miles said it might be.'

Frank helped Charlotte to scramble up the track winding upwards through the heavily wooded slopes of the gorge.

'Here we are. Hold my arm; see all those rocks below, covered with ice, they look like giant hail stones. Don't look round, I spotted a young fella a little way back following us; I'll deal with him on the way back.'

Then everything happened at once. Frank had gripped Charlotte's arm as they both peered down the glistening ice face. Some sudden sixth sense made him glance quickly around – the shadowy figure he had noticed lurking in the trees was charging forward, arms outstretched, scarecrow fashion.

He had time to see the mad frenzied stare in young Tom Kirby's eyes before self-preservation forced him to duck and stretch out his left hand; he was dimly aware of the assailant bouncing off his back. He heard the thud as Tom Kirby hit the leaning figure of Charlotte fair and square from behind; he never forgot the scream she uttered as she was torn from his grasp. He remembered listening for what seemed an eternity before two thuds below tore at his very being.

He found himself clinging onto a birch sapling growing out of a crevice at the very brim of the falls; painfully he glanced below, and knew immediately from the grotesque twisted way she lay across a huge ice covered boulder that Charlotte was dead.

Frank heaved himself to safety and virtually fell through the trees in his haste to get to the base of the falls.

'Bloody fool!' he sobbed, 'Mistaken identity; I hope for his own sake he's dead otherwise it's a murder charge.'

Frank sat for a long time on the icy boulder. Oblivious to the falling snow he cradled Charlotte's body in his arms, and gently kissed away each snowflake as it fell on a face now totally drained of colour. He found himself willing her to live, hoping the heat of his own body would bring her back to him.

'Why, oh why?' he sobbed. He kissed her cold lips hoping for the usual response, the quick intake of breath – he remembered her breathing in his ear 'You only have to kiss me once to make me want you' – now there was nothing, no movement. In a sudden rage he had an overwhelming impulse to hurl Tom Kirby's broken body down to the pool below. Common sense prevailed; I'll need to get the police down here fast, he thought.

He made a forlorn figure as he stumbled into the Birch Hall and recounted his story to the stricken Seth Kirby.

'I'm certain from what you told me about him, your son meant to push us over the falls, and I'm afraid he's lying there with his neck broken. Like you he probably thought I was my cousin Miles.'

In spite of his grief Frank was faced with the problem of getting the local police on the scene before the bodies disappeared under the ever persistent snowfall. He then had to rely on sufficient volunteers being found to cope with the almost impossible task of retrieving them.

'We'll put the deceased in our small Wesleyan chapel overnight, sir, if that's all right,' said the policeman.

'No, Constable, that's not all right,' said Frank barely able to speak from his sustained efforts.

'That fella tried to kill us both; his parents can take him home. I'll not have him lying anywhere near my servant. How soon can she be taken out of here and how do I get her home for burial? How do we even get a coffin into this place?'

'Well, sir, it's possible to hire a hearse from Lealholm; costs five shillings, I believe, for anyone outside the parish. But the way the roads are filling in you'll probably need two horses to pull it. Biggest problem'll be getting it up Limber Hill, it's nearly straight up, it's t'other side of Egton Bridge and, what's even more tricky, that Begger's Bridge at the bottom, it's nobbutt a packhorse bridge. Why they made it so bloomin' narrow I'll never know, but it's the only way across the river. They've had th' hearse stuck on it afore now.'

'How do I get hold of this hearse?' asked Frank.

'Well, sir, it belongs to "The Society for the Prosecution of Felons". It'll mean ridin' o'er to see the secretary tomorrow, then you'll have to hire a couple of big strong horses to pull it. Tiny Calvert has a big black gelding he rents out; he lives in Glaisdale, but by the look of the roads you'll sure need another.'

By the time Frank returned to the hotel he was totally exhausted and drained of all emotion. How the devil can I tell Miles what's happened, he wondered, there'll have to be an inquest and a full scale enquiry, which is bound to compromise his fiancée. He changed into dry clothes, lay on his bed and mercifully found sleep almost immediately.

When he awoke, stiff, cold and in the darkness of the early morning, the truth suddenly came flooding back. He heard the wind still howling past his window; he thought of all the problems facing him. If the snow kept on drifting, even the trains would fail to get through; how then could he get Charlotte's body home? Would the police release her?' He still had to inform Miles! His first priority would be to organise the hearse and a coffin; it might even need a sledge to get her out of Beck Hole.

I must try and get through to the office at nine o'clock,' he mused, Young Edwards will have to let her parents know.

Frank found himself cursing a God he believed in; how could he allow such injustice? It only takes a second to change or end a life, why Charlotte? Why such a beautiful young vibrant female? Frank began to weep. He felt entirely alone; sleep had come as a relief, a momentary escape from the harshness of the days to follow. Until now each awakening had been like a rebirth. He found himself drawn to her room, involuntarily calling out her name as he stared at the empty bed. There is a special conceit that lovers share, that their happiness makes them superior to the rest of the world; so it had been with Frank and Charlotte. He had felt protected by their love, almost immune from disaster; and now he bitterly regretted he had kept it under cover, hidden away for the sake of appearance. He vowed never to be two-faced again. The thought of having to survive without his love was disturbing, but not frightening. As he tried to eat his breakfast, the loneliness of the situation and the difficulties posed by the howling blizzard outside overwhelmed him. Dave Hancock found him bent over the table, his hair covering his face.

'The young lady not coming down, sir?' he asked.

Frank looked up, his face tear-stained. 'No landlord, not ever! We were attacked by a young fella from Beck Hole, called Tom Kirby, yesterday afternoon. He meant to push us both over the top of the Mallyan Spout – he's dead, so is Charlotte. I escaped by the skin of my teeth. She's laid out in the Wesleyan chapel; my problem is how to get her out of there and then home.

I need to find the secretary of the society who hires out the hearse at Lealholm. I was told by the police to contact him, but forgot to ask his name.'

'That'll be Fred Harrison, farms just out of the village, on the moor road.'

Frank had to struggle to get through the snow to the estates office next door. He recounted everything that had happened.

'There seems little doubt this youth mistook me for you. There's going to have to be an inquest, followed by a murder enquiry. My information is that your fiancée has been seeing this young fellow since last summer; according to his father he took it bad when he heard of your engagement. It's not for me to say, but you're going to have to look at your liaison with her in a different light from now on; it'll all come out at the enquiry. Bound to make great reading for the local paper and, who knows, probably papers much further afield.'

'Heaven forbid!' said Miles. 'If this weather continues to keep people away, we may be able to keep it local.'

'Right,' said Frank. 'What do you know about this "Society"? I understand they hire out a hearse at five shillings a day; also that a chap called Tiny Calvert has a big strong black gelding we can borrow.'

'I can tell you a great deal about the Society,' said Miles. 'The squire owns most of Glaisdale village, as well as the dale, so we're closely connected with the goings-on. Fred Harrison came to see me recently, he's been secretary for about fifteen years; brought me all the minutes to read, they dated back to October 1827 when it was formed. He wants to put my name down as a likely secretary when he retires this year.

163

'Briefly, they were started from public donations with powers to prosecute felons, usually the occasional sheep-stealer; also to provide members for jury service as far away as York and Darlington. They also collected about sixty-five pounds from parishioners in the townships of Danby and Glaisdale in 1827 for the construction of two hearses and two hearse houses. If anybody within the parish dies they can borrow the hearse for two shillings and sixpence a day, including a cloth – five shillings a day, cloth extra, for anybody outside the parish.

The original hearse, with shafts for only one horse, cost just over ten pounds; that was replaced with a similar model in 1901. It was used eight times last year. There's four large wheels and a heavy oak body; I heard Tiny Calvert describe it in the pub one night as a "hoss killer, far away o'er-heavy" he said. 'I wouldn't think one horse could pull it up Limber Hill in this weather.'

'No, but my fellow is used to being lead horse in tandem, pulling a plough, so perhaps we could yoke him up and get Charlotte here that way.'

'We can but try,' said Miles. 'I'll hack over to Glaisdale with you; we can call at the joiner's yard on the way, see if they have a coffin to fit. I'll introduce you to Tiny Calvert; get him to pick up the hearse from Lealholm. Then I'll square it with the secretary whilst you two get the harness on and we can come back to Beck Hole and pick up the body.'

How matter of fact, thought Frank. Little does he know Charlotte and I were lovers. Perhaps I should tell him of the unforgettable times we spent together. But no, he thought, it's none of his business; only Charlotte and myself shall know of the glorious moments we shared. He thought of her cold white body wrapped in a sheet, laid out on a bench in the tiny chapel. No scandal must ever be attached to her memory, he thought, fighting back the tears. He recalled his mother's counselling over the years – least said, soonest mended – and the impulse to tell all receded.

Things went well until they slithered down the winding road from Glaisdale to the River Esk. The scene was breathtaking; heavy snow on the tree branches on both sides of the river formed an enchanting backdrop to the magnificent packhorse bridge, built in a single span, the arch springing from rock formations at both sides of a deep pool.

'Can we get this hearse over such a narrow bridge, Mr Calvert?' asked Frank.

'Aye lad, it's bin o'er a few times afore, there's about an inch to spare, either side like, and as long as your hoss takes it steady you can get o'er wi'out too much trouble. You lead yon grey hoss o'er quietly and my hoss'll follow like; he knows what he's about.'

164

But suddenly Hasty Retreat showed the quirk in his temperament which made him so unreliable. In the middle of the bridge at the highest point he started to lose his footing and panicked; he reared to his full height, taking Frank up with him, pirouetted and disappeared over the side. Frank fell back on the parapet, his fall cushioned by at least a foot of level snow. He was unable to prevent the black gelding being dragged over the edge also; had the hearse not been wedged so tightly, that would certainly have followed the two horses.

Tiny Calvert was left at the front of the hearse, with the reins disappearing over the edge, cursing and blaspheming with words few people can ever have heard. As Frank looked over the edge he saw his horse struggle free from his harness and drop into the river; he ran round to the tail of the pool, caught hold of part of the headpiece as he waded ashore and quickly led the dripping horse back to the bridge.

It was soon evident another disaster had struck; the black horse had stopped struggling and was merely spinning at the end of his specially made harness; by a stroke of ill fortune the reins had twisted around his neck, looped over the shafts and strangled him.

'Bugger me!' said Tiny Calvert, a man well known for not mincing his words, as he came down onto the river bank and gazed up at his slowly

Beggars Bridge – 'Blimey, I think we've hung 'im'

165

revolving horse. 'We've hung him!' and then, with his natural cunning coming to the fore, 'Best work hoss I ever owned, nobbut a seven-year-old and right in his prime.'

'Yes, Mr Calvert,' Frank heard his cousin saying, 'you'll be fully compensated, you can be sure of that.'

'H'irreplaceable that hoss, I've nivver owned a better, nivver bottomed 'im.'

'All right, Mr Calvert, we can see about that another day; the immediate problem is to get him down from there and to shift the hearse off the bridge.'

'As far as I see it,' said Calvert, 'we'll hev to leave 'im yonder until Fred Harrison gives his permission like, to cut 'im down. It's special harness is that. If it'd bin like mine, then he'd a broken away and dropped in th' river, like fust un. We maresn't cut that till Fred says so.'

'What if somebody wants to get over the bridge?' asked Frank.

'There's nobbutt silly buggers like us out; if anybody's daft enough to want to go across in this weather they'll hev to wade across higher up. Yer can nearly allus get across; that's weer folk went afore that lovestruck fella had this bridge built, just so he could go courtin' a lass at t'other side and because he couldn't allus get to her when it flooded like. He'll be in th' pub toneet will Fred Harrison, nivver misses, so I'll slip down and see 'im. Good excuse to git away from't missus anyroad – we'll soon sort this end out like.'

'Right, then when the weather clears you come along to the office and we'll talk money. In the meantime we'll put a rope around the empty coffin and drag it through to Egton Bridge – seems to me we'll then have to try and organise a sledge to get that lass away from Beck Hole.'

The next day proved equally exasperating. Although it had stopped snowing and the cold east wind had moderated, travelling conditions had become intolerable.

'If a horse can get through to Goathland,' said Miles briskly, 'I'm certain we can borrow a bracken sledge from Bert Atkinson; it'll be nice and light. Although it's a sharp drop into Beck Hole it'll have a useful braking system attached; these hill farmers use them for collecting bracken for bedding and Bert has a particularly strong active dales pony we should be able to use to help get us out of there. I had a word with Father O'Connell last night and he'll be quite happy to receive Charlotte's body into his church until we can organise a box on the train to take the coffin back home.'

166

'I'm eternally grateful, Miles,' said Frank, 'couldn't have managed without you.'

'Nonsense! Least I can do, especially since you might easily have been bringing me out of there feet first. I'd no idea that young lad was after my blood. Good job Sarah's away, I saw her off on the train for London with her mother on Monday morning. Heavens knows how she'll handle the scandal of this little lot when she returns.'

Father O'Connell was busy lighting candles around the bier when the exhausted cousins returned with Charlotte's body.

'I've organised four of my estate men to carry the coffin, Father, if you're ready to accept her?'

'Allow me to dress, my son, then the Lord will accept the dear departed into his keeping.'

Frank, who knew nothing of the Catholic faith, gazed in wonder as the Father reappeared from his vestry, splendid in his embroidered regalia, incense-burner swinging in his hand.

He watched the pathetic procession proceed down the aisle, too tired to move; but grateful that in spite of all the trauma of the last two days, prayers were now being offered for his loved one. Wearily he leaned forward, head between his arms, and sobbed quietly to himself.

'How do you come to have this magnificent church tucked away in a hamlet such as this?' Frank asked Miles as the two men relaxed in front of a fragrant peat fire in the bar of the 3 Horseshoes Inn later that evening.

'Quite a story, really,' said Miles. 'These Whitby Catholics have quite a history. Seems they were never suppressed at the time when Henry VIII and his successors were destroying the monasteries. They persecuted any Catholic who stuck to his faith but they really couldn't get at 'em here, except by sea; the moors proved an almost impossible barrier. One of their important martyrs – a Father Postgate – was hung, drawn and quartered in York in his eighties for baptising a child. He was betrayed and arrested in a barn at Littlebeck not far from here; he lived by the river bridge. They hold an outside mass on the site every other year.

'The Abbey at Whitby used to be one of the most important centres for the faith in Europe at one time; that's why there is such a strong following around here to this day.'

'Certainly is a magnificent church,' Frank said. 'This Father O'Connell, he obviously takes his job seriously.'

'Yes, he's very popular and quite a card. Very keen on hunting, likes a drink and takes a day at the races whenever he can. There's a marvellous rumour going round about him, well not a rumour exactly, because time

167

has come up with the true facts – he's got seven of the young ladies in his flock all pregnant at the same time!'

'Seven?' asked Frank, incredulously.

'Yes, seven! And all beginning to show. Local gossip had it that the Reverend Father would hang his umbrella on the outside door handle of the vestry when engaged in deep meditation or instructing his young ladies. His flock were made deeply aware that this was the signal that he was not to be disturbed.'

'You wouldn't think that sort of thing could happen in a quiet backwater like this.'

'Oh, you would be surprised at the goings-on. The local Huntsman couldn't help blurting out a lovely tale the other night about a friend of his who's been staying with him at the kennels, a hunting fellow from somewhere down the East Coast, he said.

'Apparently he's been having it off with the local butcher's wife; a smart lass who worked at the kennels, exercising the horses and that sort of thing. She'd taken him home one night expecting her husband to be away; he'd arrived home unexpectedly, and caught them in bed together. Then apparently the boyfriend, dressed only in his underpants and clutching the rest of his attire, had been chased across the fields back to the kennels.

' "First thing I knew," the Huntsman said, "was waking up from a deep sleep to find this chap in a semi-naked condition scrambling under my bed."

' "Don't tell him where I am," he'd pleaded – whereupon they'd heard the crash of an opening door, the thump of steps on the stairs and an irate husband had burst into the bedroom shouting, "Where is the bastard? I'll kill him".'

'So did he find him?' questioned Frank.

'Apparently not; after a struggle to find a match, the Huntsman, whose wife was in hospital following the difficult birth of her first child, lit a candle, to find the irate butcher standing by the bed brandishing a broom handle.

' "He's not here," said the Huntsman, hastily arranging the bedclothes to disguise his bed companion.

' "He's in theer, next to thee man," snarled the butcher, throwing back the clothes, only to be confronted with the nude figure of another of the stable girls.'

'What then?' asked Frank.

'Then I think the irony of the situation hit them, and they all fell about laughing.'

'Apart from his friend, of course.'

'Oh, yes, the friend,' said Miles. 'I believe the Huntsman took great delight in keeping him under the bed as long as possible; he deliberately suggested that the butcher wait around downstairs, until such time as "the friend" showed up. Then because his female companion had no knowledge of anyone under the bed, deliberately made love to her again.'

Frank had still failed to sort things out with the police by the following Saturday.

'We are continuing to make enquiries, Mr Bowers,' he had been told. 'The body must not be removed from the church just yet.'

'The Glaisdale Harriers are meeting on Saturday morning,' his cousin informed him. 'Meeting in Glaisdale village at ten-thirty, going on foot.'

I just know Charlotte wouldn't mind if I go over there, Frank told himself; no good moping around the pub, nothing else to do but drink – far better following hounds. Besides, the exercise will do me good. Thus convinced, Frank persuaded Miles to accompany him; they walked along the densely wooded slopes of the main river about four miles due west past Beggar's Bridge until they came to the long, straggling village of Glaisdale.

'They usually meet at the top pub for a drink or two before setting off. I'll introduce you to the Huntsman, a chap called Zakariah Brown; but don't offer to buy him too many drinks, Frank, because he'll stand there and sup it just as long as you keep buying. Mind you, he'll need priming today, it's going to be hard work in all this snow.'

As the Huntsman in his red coat moved off into the dale, carrying a stout ash stave and followed by a motley crew of eager followers, Frank turned to his cousin with some consternation. 'Where are the hounds?' he asked.

'Sorry, forgot to tell you, they're a "trencher-fed" lot. Most farmers keep one or two hounds, and you'll see in a minute the Huntsman will blow his horn, and they'll come running in from all directions.'

'Amazing,' said Frank as he stood next to the Huntsman, witnessing hounds gather around him, each one greeted by its name.

'Here comes one of our best hounds, sir, come on Villager, what a fella, got him from your Bedale lot, goes back to the Belvoir draft bought by the Duke of Leeds. And here's another good hound, she has Belvoir blood in her too, Clara out of Belvoir Carnival by Stormer; this is another good un here, Marksman, he's Bramham Moor, eleven years old, been used as a stallion hound, he's got a perfect foot and a lot of bone below the knee with well sprung ribs carried right back, vital for standing hard work.'

'Absolutely vital,' said Frank, airing his scanty knowledge.

'We're hoping to breed a few of our own hounds this year using Marksman here; he has everything, nose, drive, voice; once he speaks I know we're in business. He's not so keen chasing these rabbits round in circles but we're not without foxes, nearly sure to find a fox or two at Dalehead today; then you'll hear him, or at least I will, very deep powerful voice. The other thing he has is plenty of perseverance; I think that is specially hereditary, don't you?'

'I agree,' said Frank, realising he was being treated as an expert on hound breeding. He recalled a remark overheard at a puppy show – 'I like a hound with a real typical foxhound head and a good broad neck, shoulders not too lean.'

'That's exactly right, sir!'

'And they do say,' said Frank casually, 'there's more foxes killed in Kennel, than anybody's aware of.'

'I agree, sir, no good for work unless they're in tip-top condition. They won't persevere on a cold scent unless they're absolutely fit.'

'Ah, scent,' said Frank. 'That's one of the great imponderables; you know what Jorrocks, the noted hunting man, had to say about scent?'

'No,' said the Huntsman falling into the trap set by Frank.

'There's nowt so queer as scent, 'cept women.'

There was the usual hearty laughter from the entirely male audience; then suddenly Frank remembered the last time he had pulled that one out; on Leeming Lane, hacking to a meet with Charlotte by his side. He remembered the lovely toss of her head and the raised crop in mock anger; suddenly the truth hit home – he would never ride alongside her again, there was only the painful journey home, the complicated explanations. How would he be able to make her parents understand this cruel death?

'Right, lads,' said the Huntsman, 'two, four, six, eight couple, that'll be enough, let's make a start. I'll draw up one side of the dale, then down the other. If we should find a fox, we've been asked to hunt it. The head keeper says there's one been killing an awful lot of grouse on the moor above Bank House.'

Following a couple of merry little hunts after a hare or two without much success, the Huntsman was heard to say, 'Not a halfpenny worth of scent so far.' He then decided to move across the valley to the crags above Bank House.

'We might have a better do up here,' said the Huntsman. 'It's getting colder now the sun's dropped in.' He gave a couple of short blasts on his horn to encourage the hounds.

170

Suddenly a hound spoke – 'Get away on to 'im,' he called.

'What a fella! Get away on to Marksman, on, on, on.'

'There he goes, sir, there's Charlie on the skyline, look there's Marksman the dark hound well in front,' shouted Frank.

The Huntsman blew a series of staccato blasts on the horn, not only to encourage the hounds, but to let the foot followers know he'd seen a fox. Frank was floundering in the deep snow, desperately trying to keep up with a man more than twice his age.

'Seems to be making a bolt for the old jet workings in the woods above the river,' said the Huntsman. 'Just got to hope the snow can slow him down enough for 'em to catch 'im afore he gets in.'

When Frank finally caught up with the action he realised just how fit these hill men really were. Drawn down into the woods from off the moor by the sound of hounds marking to ground, he was surprised to find that nearly all the followers had made it before him., The Huntsman was blowing a succession of long blasts on the horn. 'Where the devil's Adam got to with his terriers?' he asked.

Hounds were marking at a hole almost at the top of a large rock pile.

'There's various ways in and out of this lot,' he was explaining to Frank. 'It's a deliberate rock fall; when mining came to an end about sixty years ago, they blasted this lot down to block the entrance into what was a drift mine. Hounds got in at the bottom a few years ago and it was nine days before the last un came out. There must be plenty of water 'cos he was none the worse for it.'

It was fully ten minutes before Adam Pickering arrived with his two Border Lakeland terriers, Rip and his son Nigger.

'Right lads,' said the Huntsman, 'pull those hounds back and give the fox plenty of start. Now Adam, put 'em both in at the top and stand back.'

An hour went by and nothing happened.

'Can you hear aught, lads?' shouted the Huntsman.

Adam, who had been listening out at the various exits, hoping to catch the sound of his beloved terriers yapping, shouted back, 'Not a squeak, they must 'av getten into yon mineshaft.'

Frank glanced at his watch. It was exactly three-thirty and already the light was fading. At four o'clock when the Huntsman reluctantly blew for home, it was snowing faster than ever. With a heavy heart Adam was persuaded to go home. Nothing more could be done; little did he know it would be six days before he got his terriers back.

Frank made his way to the rock pile next morning and already half a dozen volunteers were at work, heaving rocks out of the way with crowbars, attempting to smash others with heavy hammers.

'It's no good unless we saw down this elm tree,' somebody yelled.

'Aye, an we'll nivver shift half this lot unless we can get some dynamite.'

'Have you heard the terriers yet, Adam?' asked Frank.

'I heard 'em scrappin' last neet, about midnight.'

'Perhaps they were fighting with the fox,' Frank suggested.

'Naw, that crafty sod's bin long gone. I came back up the track carryin' a lantern an' I could see his yellow eyes watching me all the way. He weren't afeared, an' let me git within five or six feet. He was sat reet on top o' th'pile, clever like, h'as if he knew there were a couple of dogs fast in below as couldn't git out.'

'I have to try and get home tomorrow,' said Frank. 'My cousin Miles has my address; I do hope you'll write and let me know how you get on. I've told him of the plight of your terriers and he's promised to help if needed.'

'Thank you very much, sir; I'll certainly do that.'

The following extract from the local *Gazette* arrived on Frank's desk a fortnight later:

TRAPPED TERRIERS RESCUED

A farmer and dog-lover risked his life in the dramatic climax of a six day operation to free two fox terriers trapped near the bottom of a 30 feet deep crevice at The Coombs, near Beck Hole.

The terriers, Rip and Nigger, went down the crevice chasing a fox after a meet of the Glaisdale Harriers.

And for six days a team of up to thirty volunteers worked sometimes until midnight in atrocious conditions, to try and reach the dogs, spurred on by the barking of the helpless animals.

Working near the bottom of a 100 feet crag, the dedicated team were finally rewarded late last Thursday afternoon. The man who made the final hazardous descent into the darkness to reach the terriers, was Mr Fred Jackson, a farmer of Sawdon, near Scarborough, a member of the Middleton Hunt.

'We dug down 15 to 20 feet and Mr Jackson went down another 12 to get them,' said the delighted owner of the terriers, Mr Adam Pickering, of St Hedda's Terrace, Egton Bridge.

'I think we moved 100 to 150 tons of rock by hand without any mechanical digger or anything. They worked like slaves – everyone has.

'On Thursday I put a flash-light down to see where they were and I did not know how we were going to get them.

'Fred just said, "I am going down for them." I tried to stop him but he went down out of sight for the last 12 feet and brought them up alive and well, assisted by another two lads. He passed one up to another lad and then grabbed the other.

'If he had slipped he would have gone down another 12 feet and we would have been digging for him.'

Mr Pickering said the volunteers included members of the Glaisdale Harriers, the Saltersgate Hunt, the Middleton, Staintondale and Goathland Hunts and local gamekeepers.

The men worked non-stop through some of the worst weather conditions of the winter, with a blizzard and torrential rain.

'We lit fires to dry clothing and the lads brought up a generator for lighting so we could work at night.

'It seems a dream now but there was a lot of hard work,' said Mr Pickering. 'Everyone put their heart and soul into it.'

The covering letter expressed thanks for his concern, praised Miles for his help in providing lighting equipment and stated that the dogs were none the worse for their ordeal. They were recovered cold and wet, plastered in mud. The only injuries were a badly cut eye and nose to the older dog, entirely due to their own jealous nature and their eagerness to fight each other on the slightest provocation. The letter also went on to regret Frank's absence from the celebration in the local hostelry; this started soon after the dogs were recovered at four-thirty in the afternoon and lasted more than twelve hours.

15

A Helping Hand

'You are not to be allowed to take Charlotte home,' was the news that greeted Frank as he strode into the estate office the following morning.

He stared unbelieving at Miles.

'I've managed to get you a box for the horses on the ten-thirty train for Middlesbrough. However, the police and the coroner are not satisfied with the circumstances of Charlotte's death and as soon as possible they intend to move her to the mortuary in Whitby for a detailed inspection.'

'You mean a post mortem?' said Frank.

'I suppose so,' Miles said. 'It looks as if you'll be going home on your own. The chances are you'll have to come back to give evidence at the inquest; don't forget there are two bodies involved here.'

'Could be a lengthy process then.'

'No doubt,' said Miles. 'They have to be certain, for instance, that you didn't push 'em both over the falls.'

'What the devil do you mean?' said Frank angrily.

'I'm only quoting an example, Frank, I didn't mean that personally. But don't forget none of these people know anything about you, or indeed anything about the intrigue between Sarah and this other fella, or any of the circumstances leading up to the disaster. See what I mean?'

'I suppose so,' said Frank. 'You'll just have to keep me informed. Thanks for all you've done so far. I'll walk the horses to the station by myself.'

The journey home was uneventful. The ever-faithful Dick was waiting at the station and rode Charlotte's Arab home to Farrick House.

'The Painter's very well, sir, jumping superbly, but that round knee action definitely means he needs soft going.'

'Has he had an extended gallop yet?'

'Yep, gave him a slow canter in the snow one morning last week, followed by a mile and a half gallop. He was still on the bit and pulling my arms out. I think he'll stay three miles.'

'Good,' said Frank. 'Do we know the date of the Bedale Point?'

'Twenty-first of March at Hutton Hang.'

'Hmm!' said Frank. 'Not an easy course for him, he'll have to take his chance in the Members Race. Can't see him beating Captain Reynard's Tarboosh somehow.'

'Sorry to hear about Miss Charlotte,' said Dick.

'Tragic business. I don't really want to talk about it, Dick.'

'I understand, sir. Your mother was quite upset when she heard, I can tell you.'

Frank's visit to the pub high up in the dales a few days later was a harrowing one. Charlotte's mother was quite unconsolable when she heard the full facts of her death; her father said very little, but his attitude made Frank feel guilty.

'Seems to me she should nivver hev been out in them conditions in t' first place. Police enquiries and an inquest, you say. Nivver thought that beautiful lass o' mine would end up dying say far from home wi' her 'ead smashed in.'

'She's lying in state in a beautiful church,' said Frank, 'she was at peace and being well looked after when I came away.

He decided he'd spare them the thought of Charlotte being carted off, presumably on the train, to the mortuary.

'Thanks for coming specially to tell us, Mr Bowers,' the older man said formally. 'Now if we could be left alone.'

'I could arrange to get the body home for you,' said Frank, 'or she could be buried in the valley close to the church.'

'We'll think about it,' said her distraught mother.

Frank realised he was not to be included in the family grief. Why should I be, he thought to himself. These people are unaware of our marvellous relationship; best that things remain as they are.

He thought he would call and see Billy Booth on the way back. He found Billy by a roaring fire sharing a bottle of whisky with, of all people, Edgar Booth of Deepdale.

'I believe you've met my cousin Edgar,' said Billy.

'Sheep sale at Cow Hill,' said Frank. 'But I had no idea you two were related!'

'Right,' said Edgar as he heaved himself out of his chair. 'Sorry news about Joe Falshaw; dead and buried before I heard about it. Billy tells me it was quite a do, his funeral.'

'It was indeed! A most memorable day, exactly as Joe wanted.'

175

'Last time as I see'd him, he said he could do with a supply of fat lambs for his market.'

'Yes, Mr Booth,' said Frank.

'Well, I've been running about one hundred lambs on turnips and they're as fat as butter.'

'I could come over one day next week and if they're suitable we'll buy some off you.'

'Good, next Tuesday would suit me.'

'And me,' said Frank.

'I'm glad you called,' said Billy, 'perhaps you can help us. Edgar here has just been to see Ted Boothman at Nab End, apparently his eldest son has vanished, taking two cash boxes full of money with 'im.'

'Gone off wi' that red-headed landlady from the pub at Cow Hill,' said Edgar. 'There's hell on.'

Frank whistled. 'I'm not surprised about the money, but I never thought Ruth was the sort to take off like that.'

'Oh, so you remember her name, do you?' said Edgar.

'Yes, she looked after me very well when I stayed.'

'I'll bet,' said Edgar sarcastically. 'Falshaw told me tha wouldn't tak' much training.'

'The fact is that Ted Boothman owes Edgar a fair lump of brass,' said Billy, 'and it was only when he went for his cash box to pay, that he fun out all his money had gone. Edgar called to see me to get some idea of what I thought; perhaps you might have some ideas?'

'I was very impressed with the whole family, having spent all day with 'em, apart from that eldest son. I decided then you wouldn't be able to trust him too far,' said Frank. 'You can tell old Ted if he comes to see me, it's almost certain the Auction Mart Company will lend him sufficient to get himself out of trouble.'

'Good lad,' said Edgar, 'I'll send him down and then he'll be able to pay me out.'

You're a grasping, greedy sort of a fellow, Edgar Booth, Frank thought.

Frank decided to take Tom Edwards with him the following Tuesday morning. 'Bring a couple of blue marker sticks with you, Tom, we're going buying sheep.'

Heavy rain over the weekend had more or less melted what snow remained as Frank drove up the long, winding, bumpy road which eventually brought the two young auctioneers into the yard at Hall Bank House on the lower slopes of the mountain.

'Good morning, gentlemen,' said Edgar Booth breezily as he came across the yard wearing his large stetson and carrying a huge hazel staff with its curved horn handle.

'Good morning, Mr Booth, this is my assistant Tom Edwards.'

Edgar Booth nodded curtly in Tom's direction.

'I like the look of your staff,' said Frank, following Joe Falshaw's guidance. 'Never get straight down to business if you're buying owt from these hill farmers,' Joe had advised. 'Talk about the weather, the crops, the family, the journey there, aught but the immediate business in hand. They'll think you're too keen if you come straight to the point. Keep 'em waiting and don't show too much interest in whatever they're tryin to sell; a bit of flattery about something or other often helps to get 'em thinking your way.'

'Make 'em mysen,' said Edgar beaming; 'tup horn off a dalesbred, I find best for the top like.'

'How do you carve such an intricate design?' asked Frank.

'Hours of patient scrattin' wi' a sharp knife; helps pass long winter neets, tha knows,' said Edgar.

'You don't seem to have had much snow up here,' said Frank. 'I was fast up in a blizzard for days near Whitby a short while back.'

'Aye, I heard about that. Called to see old man Webster t'other day, he says his daughter was with you. He's tellin' every yan she's been murdered.'

'It's not quite like that, believe me,' said Frank. 'A wild young fella mistook us for someone else and tried to push us over some falls. I managed to get hold of a branch, but Charlotte and this other fella went over and were both killed.'

'He says the police still haven't allowed her to be buried.'

'That's because of a delayed inquest,' said Frank. 'Nobody could hardly stir. I've never seen snow like it; came howling straight off the North Sea and brought any sort of travel to a standstill. Anyhow, where are these sheep?' he asked, hastily changing the subject.

'We've got 'em penned up round the back of yon buildings; sorted out the best fifty like you asked.'

Frank went through the hoggetts thoroughly, touching their backs and paying particular attention to the root of the tail. As Edgar had said they were indeed fat and ready for slaughter.

'Perhaps a bit short of condition for our buyers,' he remarked.

'Never!' said Edgar Booth.

'We'll maybe need to keep 'em a week or two longer on stubble when we get 'em home.'

177

'Balls!' said Edgar.

'How much a head then?' asked Frank.

'Thirty-two and a tanner,' said Edgar.

Frank raised his arm and slapped Edgar's palm. 'Twenty-eight bob.'

'Nivver.'

'Thirty bob then, and you pay the drover.'

'Done,' said Edgar. 'I'll not do you too hard, 'cos we've plenty more deals to come.'

'I'll pay you now in cash,' said Frank.

'Come inside then, we'll have a drink on it. Are you comin' in as well, young fella?' he said turning to Tom Edwards.

'No,' said Frank, 'he's going to put a blue mark on 'em, so we can ken 'em when we get 'em home. He'll be in directly.'

When Frank was alone with Tom he said, 'I don't trust this chap entirely, Tom, mark 'em back of the head like this, then give 'em all a blue stripe under the belly here, just back of the forelegs. I'll be interested to see how many are marked underneath when we eventually get 'em home.'

Frank entered a huge kitchen. 'There you are Edgar, seventy-five pounds. I take it there's sure to be some good luck money, seeing as how this is our first deal together.'

'I should be able to find you a couple of half crowns,' said Edgar producing his leather money pouch from a front pocket of his corduroy trousers.

'Nay, a couple of quid,' said Frank.

'Nivver,' said Edgar in mock amazement, slowly rewinding the cord around the neck of his money bag; 'you've got 'em at your own price, expect me to pay the drover, then hev the nerve to ask for pund notes to make 'em lucky.'

He reached into his back pocket and produced a huge wad of pound notes.

'Here's yan and let that be the end of it.'

'One pound's no good. Come on, Mr Booth, there's two of us, we're certain to need to buy plenty of vittals before we get back to the office tonight.'

'I can see that ruddy Joe Falshaw in you, more and more,' said Edgar Booth grudgingly. 'All right, two pund it is,' licking his fingers and peeling another note away from the wad. 'You've caught me at a weak moment, but don't expect your own way every time.'

'I haven't heard anything from Ted Boothman,' said Frank.

'Probably too proud; besides, it's not easy for him to travel all the way down the valley.'

'Well, we've got to call at Wilstrop Hall estate office, we might just slip up and see him afterwards. I remember Joe warning him something like this could happen if he didn't get his money into a bank.'

'I'm told there's a fair old sum missing; rumour has it as much as three thousand pounds.'

'Wouldn't surprise me,' said Frank. 'I saw a tin box full of five pound notes and he boasted there was another boxful hidden away.'

'We'll have to leave the car at this bridge, Tom, and walk the rest of the way.'

'I never knew Nidderdale went so far westward into these hills,' said Tom. 'It's amazing to me that anyone can farm this sort of land and make sufficient to live, never mind saving up as much as three thousand pounds.'

'They couldn't if it wasn't for these hardy Swaledale sheep; a lamb a year and a good fleece means all these hill farmers around here can make a reasonable living. I think this chap we're going to see is just about "daddy" of them all.'

The barking of the sheep dogs brought Ted Boothman to the door as Frank and his assistant walked across the yard. A much thinner and a much older Ted than I remember, thought Frank, and it's only four months since I was here.

'Good day, Mr Boothman,' said Frank, meeting the old man's suspicious gaze with a friendly smile. 'Frank Bowers, remember? I was here last November with Joe Falshaw – you were just about to go into hospital for an operation.'

'Aye lad! I ken thee, Edgar Booth said some'at about thee wantin' to see me; h'as yer can see, I haven't bin too well like. Come in, both of you.'

'This is my new assistant, Tom Edwards.'

'Glad to meet you,' said the old man courteously.

'He's going to be taking over the management of the Hall estate, and our business around these parts; I suppose you know Joe Falshaw passed away just before Christmas?'

'Aye lad, sorry business; he'll be missed around here for monny a long year. I heerd as how he went out in style?'

'He did indeed,' said Frank.

'Grand chap, straight as a dye, allus prepared to help anyone in trouble.'

'That's right,' said Frank, 'and that's why we're here, really.'

179

'I suppose Edgar's bin tellin' thee about yon older lad o' mine!'

'Yep; he has indeed. I want you to let the Auction Mart help you out.'

'How so?'

'Well, I'm prepared to buy all next back end crop of lambs and your draft ewes.'

'But there's no lambs born yet.'

'That doesn't matter, Ted, they will be; what ewes we passed on the way here looked to be in tip-top order. I can give you a cheque now, for a thousand pounds say; it'll be like an interest free loan, all you have to do is send your stock down to the Market when they're ready and anything they make will be credited to your account, until the loan's paid off.'

Mrs Boothman, who'd come into the kitchen as Frank was speaking, sobbed quietly as she said, 'There you are, father, I told you last Sunday in chapel, if we prayed hard enough.'

Ted Boothman clasped Frank's arm. 'God bless you, young fella. I was worried sick about owing yon Edgar Booth money; he has bin known to tak' fellas to court when they've hardly owed him owt. He's the sort o' chap as lends a fella half a crown and taks five bob back given half a chance.'

'Yes, I've heard stories about him; that's why I'm here. I heard your eldest son had gone off with all your savings.'

'Terrible thing to 'appen,' said Mrs Boothman, wringing her hands. 'That I should ivver give birth to a son who'd do sike a thing; then mak' off wi' someone else's wife; an' his father a lay preacher. We'll nivver be able to hold our heads up ivver agin.'

'Yes, you will, Mrs Boothman, no shame attaches to you, he's the villain. It wouldn't do if all folks were the same.'

'This 'ere cheque you're talkin about, Mr Bowers?'

'Yes?' said Frank.

'A thousand pund would be grand, mare than I need, I suppose.'

'Good, I can give it you here and now.'

'But what am I supposed to do with it like?'

'Tomorrow morning you go down to the bank.'

'Yes?'

'Take Mrs Boothman with you, ask to see the manager; he'll open an account for you. It can be in joint names if you like, you can even include your youngest boy; he'll then give you a cheque book and all you do is sign as many cheques as you like until you've spent the thousand pounds. Also, when you sell something, you take the cash or cheques and pay them into your account; that way nobody can pinch it.'

*'Now Ted – tomorrow morning take this cheque to the bank, and take
Mrs Boothman with you'*

Mrs Boothman started sobbing again. 'We'll nivver be able to thank you enough, Mr Bowers,' she wailed as they made their farewell.

'Amazing to find such simple god-fearing folk in this day and age, with no idea how to use a cheque book,' said Tom, as the two men strode down the valley towards their vehicle.

'We'll try and go straight home tonight, Tom. My mother hates being alone in that haunted house after dark. She's missing Charlotte – and so am I, more than I care to admit.'

'That was interesting, what the old chap had to say about our Mr Edgar Booth, eh? Can't understand how he came to be owing him money in the first place.'

'Oh, that's easy,' said Frank. 'Old Booth yonder has some good connections in Scotland. He gets a lot of really good hardy cattle sent down, mostly Galloways or Highlands which suit this sort of terrain. Ted Boothman can be a bit of a soft touch, so Edgar Booth sends him anything he might have left on his hands after they've stood a market or two like

Hawes or Pately Bridge here. It's a system that works both ways like, it saves these rather isolated farmers having to stand around all day in a distant market town, hoping to pick up something they fancy, then having to drive them home.'

'It cuts out all the preliminaries, but they probably pay extra to the cattle-dealer in the long run?' said Tom.

'You've got it,' said Frank. 'We'd better drive straight past this pub. I was with Joe last time we came along here; finished up driving home in a foot of snow, wrong side of midnight.'

Carved Oak
panelling
from
Wilstrop Hall
(page 31)

Bedale Churchyard (page 49)

The Sheepwash (page 69)

Newby Hall Ferry and Landing Stage (page 101)

The Mallyan 'Spout'. The author is certain he was alone in this wild and desolate place when the snapshot was taken. The camera lens appears to prove otherwise (page 159)

Birch Hall Inn, Beckhole (page 159)

Beggar's Bridge as it remains to the present time (page 162)

Memorial to the 'Waggoners Reserve' at
Sledmere Hall (page 209)

16

First Point-to-Point

It was late the following Saturday morning before the sheep arrived. Frank had been waiting impatiently all morning; he was hoping to get away to Scotch Corner to the Old Raby Hunt Club point-to-point, and he needed to size up the opposition.

'Thought you were never going to get here,' he said gruffly to the drover when they were all safely penned.

'So did I, sir,' said a lean, weather-beaten, scruffy sort of fellow holding out his hand.

'Oh yes,' said Frank, 'here's two shilling for you. Do we have fifty?'

'We do, sir.'

'Are these the same fifty that you set off with?'

'They are sir, all marked blue back o' th' head.'

'That'll do then; there's a good spot for a bowl of soup or bread and cheese next door to the Auction Mart office. Tell the lady I sent you, tell her she's to give you a square meal and book it down to me.'

'That's very kind sir, very kind indeed.'

Frank just had time to get a message to the farm asking Tom Edwards, who was there sorting out fat cattle for the sale on Monday morning, to check the hoggetts for his hidden markings before he scuttled off, as fast as he dare, northwards along the Great North Road. As he drove, he pondered at some length over the contents of a letter from cousin Miles received that morning.

'The good news, Frank,' Miles had written, 'is that the coroner accepted your written statement to the police and he was quite happy to listen to what I had to say, acting as your agent – you are not to be asked to attend personally any further enquiry there might be. However, you may be surprised to learn that Charlotte's father came to verify the facts of his daughter's death. I think he was beside himself with grief, perhaps not thinking straight, I certainly found him to be a very strange fellow.

However, he had a look at the graveyard and insisted his daughter be buried immediately in an unmarked grave close by the church. We complied with his wishes; he doesn't want me to arrange for a headstone or whatever, so it may be up to you at a later visit to organise some sort of memorial.'

Frank's eyes filled with tears as he drove along, the thought of that beautiful girl simply being placed in the ground so far from home with only one parent present, filled him with remorse.

'I should never have taken her with me,' he shouted. 'It's not fair, Lord, to punish her like that; I'm the one you should punish! I was the one seeking self-gratification.' Suddenly he realised he was driving far too fast. Race traffic, almost entirely horse-drawn, was building up on the road, and he had already passed several carriages, unthinking. He looked back– 'Oh Lord! I've put a couple of 'em in the ditch, and if I'm not mistaken that's Lady Tanfield's coachman waving his whip in anger.'

Once on the field, he parked his car discreetly alongside the wagonette placed opposite the finishing post, to be used by the judges and stewards as a vantage point. He glanced at his watch: perfect timing, eleven-thirty. First race would be off at midday. The horses were parading as he entered the secretary's tent.

'Hello, Bowers!' It was J.J. Mowbray, the Bedale Hunt Master.

'Hello, sir, nice day for it,' said Frank.

'Sizing up the opposition before next month, eh?'

'Sort of, come to watch Captain Reynard's Tarboosh; he runs in the Adjacent Hunt's Race. I think he picks up a three pound penalty if he wins today, but he's an experienced campaigner and he'll take a lot of beating.'

'A wily old fox, his jockey. Well named if you ask me, old Reynard; watch yourself whenever you ride against him.'

'I will, sir, already had a warning or two. I've been told he'll be first past the post if it's humanly possible.'

'Just so! My party will be having supper and a few drinks in the Junction Hotel after racing; be delighted to see you – oh, and keep out of Lady Tanfield's way, she's just been telling me your car flew past her carriage a mile from the course and put her in the ditch.'

'Did she seem annoyed?'

'No, she's told her coachman to make sure his horses get used to these "horseless carriages" as she called them.'

Frank retired to his car to study the racecard.

In the second race he was most impressed with the ten lengths' victory of Lord St Germain's big strapping bay horse Galoot. I'll have a few bob

184

on that chap if he runs in the Bedale Open, he told himself. Then to the business in hand – Captain Reynard's Tarboosh running in the third race. Frank awaited his entry into the collecting ring with keen anticipation. He knew Tarboosh well and had watched his performance in the hunting field with increasing admiration. He looked superb; ears pricked as he walked haughtily around the parade ring. Cool as a cucumber, taking everything in, and not a bead of sweat on him; a racing certainty, Frank muttered to himself as he scurried off to look at the betting.

Sawdust IV was favourite; 'Take six to four Sawdust,' one bookie called out as Frank walked down the line.

That's the horse that won the Bedale Open last year at Well, he thought. 'Five to one Tarboosh,' another bookie called out. Frank checked the boards; they were all offering five to one.

Right Frank, he said to himself, dive in.

'Five pounds Tarboosh,' he said to the nearest bookmaker, taking a five-pound note from his wallet.

'Five pund to win twenty-five, ticket number one hundred and ninety,' the bookie called out, hastily rubbing out the odds against Tarboosh with a duster and replacing the odds at four to one with a piece of chalk.

Frank's bold move seemed to actuate a lot of hesitant punters keen to find a horse at reasonable odds likely to beat the favourite. He watched in amazement as one after the other the bookies, besieged by keen backers, took more and more money for Tarboosh and continued to slash the odds; soon it was down to seven to two and then, on one or two boards, joint favourite with Sawdust at six to four.

Frank heard one bookie towards the end of the row call out, 'Tarboosh four to one without this favourite.' Quickly he moved towards him, dragging another five-pound note from his inside pocket.

'Five pound to win twenty, win or be second, ticket number one hundred,' Frank heard Honest Bert call out.

As he turned away he bumped straight into his friend Bobbie Dawson.

'Now Frank, you rascal, what's going on?'

'I've gone daft backing Tarboosh,' said Frank, already regretting his impetuosity. 'A fiver at five to one and now another at four to one and I really only came to watch the horse perform.'

'Phew!' whistled Bobbie, 'then you stand to win forty-five pounds with your money back.'

'I suppose that's about right,' said Frank.

'Well then,' said Bobbie, ever keen to do business, 'there's one of the best horses ever to be sent over from Ireland standing in my yard. A four-year-old, bright bay with black points; one white sock behind, backed and broken, just needs a fellow like you, Frank, to bring him on.'

'How much?' asked Frank.

'Exactly the amount you are about to collect if that horse you've backed stands up and wins the race. I've been told he's a dodgy jumper at racing pace, however useful he may be in the hunting field.'

'Thanks for telling me now,' groaned Frank.

'Mind you,' said Bobbie, 'although I don't know the Captain very well, apart from his reputation on the racetrack, I hear he's not averse to putting you through the rails if he thinks you might beat him on the run in to the finishing post.'

'I've had a warning or two; been told to watch out when I run against him next month,' said Frank.

'As I was saying,' said Bobbie Dawson, 'his head groom's sort of courtin' my housekeeper; they've been going out together now for twelve years so Mildred tell't me. Saving up for a little cottage somewhere afore they finally get hitched. He tells me they've had a "rough rider" putting this hoss through his paces this winter like; the cruel beggars have him jumping out of his skin, improved him no end, got him to stand back and really ping his fences.'

'How've they managed that?' asked Frank.

'With a sack and a draining rod,' answered Bobbie, a curious gleam in his eye.

'Don't understand,' said Frank.

'Well, what they've been doin' is lunging him around a fold yard with the sack over his head, blindfold so to speak, bringing him back to a halt, clicking him on with the tongue and at the same time giving him a belt across his ribs with the draining rod. It appears that his jockey only has to give the same signal just before take off, and he leaps anything afore him, gaining as much as a length or two every time.'

'Cruel but effective, eh?' said Frank; 'certainly if he wins this race I'll come and have a look at your Irish horse, maybe give you a lift home into the bargain.'

'Never been in a "Tin Lizzie" afore,' said Bobbie as the two of them wove their way past the homeward bound racegoers.

'You've got to be careful how you use this horn,' said Frank as he squeezed the bulbous rubber end; 'doesn't half make 'em scatter!' He was in high spirits, his pockets bulging with bookmaker's money. 'We'll stop off for another drink or two at the Bedale Hunt Inn on Leeming Lane;

there's a new landlord just moved in, brought two beltin' daughters with him, both good-lookers.'

'Captain Reynard won that race as he pleased,' said Bobbie.

'Yep,' said Frank, 'I ran down to that last open ditch on the final circuit, you could hear him click his horse on a couple of strides out. I'll swear he was a length behind the two leaders at the time, finished up well in front when he touched down. Then he simply went further away with every stride.'

'You've got your work cut out when you race against him,' Bobbie remarked.

'I'm well aware of that,' said Frank gloomily. 'Here's the pub, let's see if we can take these two lasses out for a spin. Surprising what they'll do for a ride in an automobile.' Frank winked meaningfully at his companion.

It was approaching midnight before the two of them finally arrived at Malvern House.

'Time you had electric in these loose boxes,' said Frank. 'Damned if I can make much out by lantern light; seems quiet enough though,' as he bent down and ran his hand down the nearside cannon bone. 'Surprises me how many of these Irish horses come over here with lumps and bumps all over them!'

'Clean as a whistle, this chap,' said Bobbie, 'nine-inch good flat bone, not a mark or a strain on 'im,' he hiccuped.

Frank made sure his companion had supped more than his fair share of liquor during the evening.

'Seems all right,' said Frank. 'How much then?'

'Sixty pund to most people, as a speshial favour to you, old pal, fifty-five quid.' I've plied him with drink all night, thought Frank, and he hasn't dropped his price by so much as a penny.

'What the hell!' said Frank, placing both hands on his friend's shoulders and staring him full in the face. 'I bring you home, provide you with supper, find you a willing girlfriend on the way – she was willing washn't she?' I must stop lisping! Frank told himself.

'Fantastic,' said Bobbie lurching sideways into his horse. 'Look there, Frank, told you! You can't upset him!'

'– And you're still asking fifty-five quid for him; here, give me your hand. Frank stepped back and brought his own hand smartly down. 'Fifty quid, not a penny more.'

'Can't be done,' said Bobbie, 'No way.' He stepped back, tripped over a

187

bucket and kept on staggering backwards until he hit the rear wall. Frank picked him up as he slid down the wall.

'You're drunk, Dawson. Stand up a minute. Fifty-two pund ten and that's it.'

'Righto, he's yours. What's tha going to call him?'

'I think I'll call him Tin Lizzie seein' as how you were so derog...' Frank had three goes before he finally got the word derogatory out; 'when you got into my car.'

'Sounds more like a filly's name,' said Bobbie, as he collapsed once more into the straw.

Frank picked him up in a fireman's lift, carried him into the farm kitchen, depositing him into a large oak lambing chair, and turned to leave.

'I'll send my foreman for th' hoss tomorrow!' said Frank, but there was no response, only a hearty snore.

Saturday the 21st March dawned fine and clear. Frank only had his mother to wish him a happy birthday. Mary Bowers at this time was sixty-two years old, quite sprightly for her age and had been widowed almost ten years.

'We've come a long way since your father died, Frank,' she said over breakfast. 'I do hope you'll be careful in this race today. With the business and the farms to look after you really shouldn't be taking any more risks than necessary.'

'I'll be all right, mother. It's a very safe cross-country course near Leyburn; Dick hacked the horse over there quietly yesterday, and he'll have given him a spin this morning – the going should be near perfect and everything's set fair.'

'But it's the first race for both you and The Painter; I never interfere, as well you know, but I'm told you should never put two novices together first time out; I do hope you'll be all right.'

'Don't fuss, mother, nothing can go wrong, I promise you.'

'I just hope you're right, son! I just hope you're right!'

Frank arrived at the course at two o'clock, just as the first race got under way, too late to have a bet on, he thought. He checked his racecard. Good, Lord St Germain's horse runs in the Open at two-thirty-five; must back him after his performance at the old Raby meeting.

He found Dick making final preparations. 'He looks well, Dick.' The Painter heard his voice, pricked his ears and snickered.

'He's taking it all in his stride, boss. Managed a canter around the outside of most of the course very early this morning, nearly pulled me arms out.'

'Off at ten past three; we've got a minimum weight of twelve stone to carry. I was twelve three at home this morning so we won't have to worry about any weight cloths. With age allowance and penalties the main danger, Tarboosh, according to my reckoning, has to give us ten pounds.'

'We'll give him a race, sir,' said Dick, always at his most formal away from home.

'I have until twenty-five past two to declare,' said Frank, 'see you in the parade ring before the race. I'll leave the number cloths for you to pick up.'

Once the formalities were over in the secretary's tent Frank ambled over to cast his eye over the runners in the Open race.

His Lordship's Galoot was plodding round head down, looking half asleep. He won't attract much attention, thought Frank, doesn't even look like a racehorse at the moment. He studied the recent form of the rest of the field; can't see any of that lot beating him, time to have a good bet.

As he walked down the line of bookmakers he was surprised to find they had Galoot third favourite at eight to one. He caught sight of three of his closest friends; Arnold Cheesman, soon to cover himself with glory in the Northamptonshire Yeomanry; his brother Jacob, and Bobbie Dawson. Little did they know that the First World War was no more than four months away, and that they would not all survive.

'Hi, Frank!' said Arnold. 'Bobbie tells me you're both in this third race hoping to beat Captain Reynard.'

'Well, his horse is giving quite a bit of weight away. What worries me, he's such a clever jockey.'

'What's your fancy for this race, Frank?' asked Bobbie. 'Bought a crackin' good horse from me with his winnings a couple of weeks ago,' he informed the brothers.

'Can't see anything getting close to Lord St Germain's Galoot, he's eight to one and I think you can put your shirt on him,' said Frank. 'I'm going to risk a tenner.'

'With information like that I think I'll put fifty pounds on him,' said Arnold. 'Woe betide you, Frank, if he gets beaten.'

Galoot cantered down to the start in a sedate sort of way.

'I've seen better movers on Scarborough sands,' said Jacob.

'Wait till you see him really gallop,' said Frank, 'and watch him out-jump the rest at every fence.'

Galoot was leading two out when he seemed to put in a short stride and hit the top of the fence hard.

'He's made a real duck's backside of that,' said Arnold, 'who's this

189

passing him? It's Colin Silvertop's Bluebird – won this race last year. That's torn it!'

'We've no chance now, Frank,' said Arnold despondently.

Frank watched the leader closely as he measured up to jump the last. 'If he clears this we've had it,' he remarked. He noticed a sudden lurch to the left on take-off; the horse cleared the obstacle but then careered left handed, almost into the crowd.

'He's broken down, near fore, they'll have to pull up, he's on three legs,' shouted Frank.

'Come on, Galoot!' shouted the four friends in unison, as their fancy swept past the post and won the race pulling up, by a clear six lengths.

'Close shave, Frank,' said Arnold slightly hoarse, 'that's four hundred smackers for me; pay for a hell of a party in the Bolton Arms tonight. If either you or Bobbie can win this next race, we'll make it last the weekend.'

Frank was feeling more nervous than he cared to admit as Dick gave him a leg up onto The Painter.

'Up to you now, sir,' he said. 'I've done my best. I reckon he's dead ready, just needs steering!'

Dick had even produced a flask of neat whisky earlier when they'd saddled up. 'Take a good swig, boss,' he said quietly, 'Lepping powder, calm your nerves; th' hoss a'll know if you're nervous when you set off, it'll make him edgy straight off.'

Frank remembered little of his first race. He could recall trying to restrain The Painter before the first fence; his horse took a good look at it, wove quickly right and then left, before finally realising he had to go over it. He recalled the noise and the clatter as those in front went through the top of the brushwood; 'frightened my fellow,' he remarked later. He remembered how they galloped on, The Painter taking a strong hold and getting better at each obstacle. He found himself reciting a poem he had learnt recently:

So sure not to turn from a rasper
So sure not to fail at a pinch
At timber you've only to clasp him
He'll measure his stride to an inch.

At water, goes into his bridle
Yet never gets out of control
For under a tree he will sidle
Or creep like a mouse thro' a hole.

190

When rivals are floundering and blowing
In a plight that is simply absurd
So easy and smooth he is going
You'd think he'd the wings of a bird.

And whether in scurry or scuffle
And whether he can or he can't
With a temper that nothing can ruffle
And a courage that nothing can daunt.

So attend to my moral and sequel
Such treasures fall seldom to man
You never will ride on his equal
Make sure of him now while you can.

Thereafter, until Frank woke up in the Northallerton Cottage Hospital, he remembered nothing.

Frank regained consciousness slowly; he had a blinding headache and was alarmed to find he only had the use of one eye. The whole of his right side felt numb. He realised he was propped up in a strange bed; his mother was there clasping his right hand, but there was no feeling. He tried to lift his hand to his head but couldn't move it; he tried moving his feet, but only the left side moved. He brought his left hand up and realised his head and left side of his face were heavily bandaged. There was bright sunlight coming through the window opposite, dazzling his good eye. He tried to sit up, but gentle restraining hands held him down.

'What the devil's happened?' he heard his own faint voice call out.

'You came off your horse, dear,' he heard his mother say. She sounded faint and far away. 'I'm afraid your head's had rather a nasty bang.'

'Not half!' he clearly remembered saying out aloud.

'I'll come and see you again tomorrow, Frank.'

Her words seemed to be so distant. 'What about my horse?' he asked.

'Dick says he's going to be all right. He's got bruised ribs and a cut over the eye, he said to tell you.'

'I can't remember what happened,' Frank said as he lapsed into a deep sleep.

'What day is it?' Frank asked the nurse as she fussed around his bed the next morning.

'Tuesday.'

191

'Tuesday?' said Frank incredulously.

'Yes, you were unconscious two whole days after they brought you in on Saturday afternoon.'

'I can't move my right arm or leg,' said Frank.

'You've had a bad knock on your head, Mr Bowers, sometimes it can cause partial paralysis, quite often on the opposite side to the blow.'

'Is that bad?' asked Frank

'No, it usually means only partial impairment or loss of sensory function of the nerves where one side is affected.'

'Sounds complicated to me,' Frank said. 'What's all this bandaging doing, halfway across my face?'

'We think you've damaged both your ear and your eye, but the doctor will be able to tell you more about that! He'll be round to see you soon.'

'Lord Nelson only had one eye and one arm, but from all accounts he was one hell of a fella,' said Frank, clasping the nurse's arm with his good hand.

She blushed and half-heartedly tried to pull away.

'You're a mighty pretty young thing to know so much about these things,' said Frank. 'Can't be a day over eighteen?'

'Twenty next week.'

'And never been kissed?' said Frank pulling her towards him.

'Good morning, Mr Bowers,' said a man's voice. 'Thank you, nurse, I'll deal with the patient; he seems to be recovering remarkably well.'

'Hello, doctor,' said Frank meekly, 'you crept up on me on my blind side.'

'I hope it won't be as bad as that, young man. You've had a really nasty bang on the side of the head, as you may have realised. We won't finally know until the dressings come off what sight remains in that eye. You may also be deaf on this side for the rest of your life. A Mr Dawson brought you in, drove you down here in your own car, with you unconscious in the back; told me your horse had been forced out of the wing at the final fence. Both your eye and your ear were bleeding badly. I'm afraid you have a perforated eardrum, but we hope you'll have partial sight eventually.'

'What about this paralysis down my right side?'

'I've come to check on that; can you feel that?' he asked, jabbing Frank's right hand with a pin.

'Ouch!' said Frank, 'but I can't move either limb.'

'And that?' the doctor asked jabbing Frank's foot even harder.

'Lay off, Doc,' shouted Frank, 'that really hurt.'

'Good, that means you've got only partial ...'

192

'Loss or impairment of sensory function of the nervous system of the right hand side.'

'Right,' said the doctor, 'you a medical student or something?'

'No, I just listened to the lecture that pretty little nurse handed out before you arrived.

Bobbie Dawson and Arnold Cheesman came to see Frank during visiting hours that afternoon.

'Brought you some grapes, Frank,' said Arnold, 'and have you a cupboard? . . . bottle of Gordons Gin to slip into the water for when you're thirsty.'

'You lucky dog,' said Bobbie. 'Is this the lass looking after thee?'

'Meet Sandra,' said Frank as his nurse moved gracefully towards them.

'I must ask you to be very quiet, gentlemen, Mr Bowers is not to become excited or disturbed in any way.'

'You're the only one who's going to do that to him, young lady. Frank can't resist auburn hair and, yes, they are green eyes,' Bobbie said, turning to Frank. 'Shades of Charlotte, eh?' he said quietly and winked.

It was then that Frank suddenly realised how much like Charlotte she was; same height, same colouring, same willowy figure, more genteel perhaps, certainly more refined. I wonder, he thought to himself, I just wonder.

'Well, how are you, Frank?' said Arnold.

'I've got a damaged eye, a punctured eardrum, partial paralysis down my right side, otherwise not bad; oh, and I can't for the life of me remember what happened!'

'Captain Reynard's horse put you through the wing at the last and went on to win; I came second,' said Bobbie.

'I had one hell of a bet on the Captain,' said Arnold.

'Thank you for your confidence in us both!' said Bobbie dryly.

'If Frank hadn't made a mistake, The Painter would have won that race.'

'What mistake?' asked Frank.

'Well, I take it you can't remember anything?'

'No.'

'All right, well, you came from behind like a train between the last two, passed me as if I was stood still, tried to take on the worthy Captain over the last on the inside; his horse was tiring and had jumped badly to the left over the previous two obstacles. All you had to do, Frank, was take your time, come through on his outside and the race was yours. I shouted a warning but you can't have heard, all I could do was watch; his horse jumped across the fence left handed and you had nowhere to go but out through the wings.'

'I was warned that old Reynard would win at any cost, he must have done it deliberately.'

'No, Frank, sorry old mate, you did it to yourself, there's nobody else to blame.'

Neither The Painter nor Frank ever raced again. The horse was commandeered at the outbreak of war by the Army to go as a charger with the British Expeditionary Force. He was killed by shellfire on the banks of the Maan Canal in Belgium. (It was here that the British Army finally managed to halt the flood of grey-coated German soldiers prior to the start of trench warfare.)

Frank recovered the use of his limbs only slowly. He was permanently quite deaf in his left ear, only partially sighted in his left eye. It meant, to his chagrin, that he failed his medical for the armed forces at the outbreak of war.

He managed to entice Sandra, his nurse, out for dinner on a couple of occasions as he recuperated. He tried hard to engage her as companion for his mother, but she was too dedicated to her career to allow herself to be captivated by Frank's charm.

'I'm hoping to qualify as a doctor eventually,' she told him, 'then perhaps work overseas, maybe in Africa or some other poor country. I have no intentions of becoming involved with you, or any other man for that matter.'

They were to meet again a few months later, in a strange country and under very different circumstances.

17

Fat Betty

At the first opportunity Frank was back in the office. 'Thanks for holding the fort so well, Tom, is there anything I should attend to?'

'Well if you feel you can drive all right, we've had a letter from a Mr Bill Izzitt at Grangehead asking for someone to call as soon as possible; he states his intention is to emigrate and wants us to hold his farm sale as soon as we can advertise.'

'Old Cuckoo Izzitt, going abroad eh? Finally given up the unequal struggle.'

'Where's he get his nickname from?' asked Tom. 'Is he a bit simple or something?'

'Far from it, he gained his nickname as a much younger man. All over the place in them days, folks never knew whose bed he would sleep in next. He used to farm in quite a big way close to Ripon on Lord Downe's estate. Committed one of the seven deadly sins by failing to pay his rent on time and finished up on a scrattin' sort of sheep farm, miles from any-where. Write and tell him we'll call round in a couple of days time to take particulars. You can drive, my right leg's still a bit stiff.'

The following Wednesday afternoon, as the car rounded a sharp bend on the narrow road leading towards the head of the dale, the way forward was hampered by the broad back of a very fat lady; she was carrying a wooden yoke over her enormous shoulders, a wicker pannier basket dangled down on either side of her huge frame.

Tom sounded his horn with no effect.

'This'll be Fat Betty,' said Frank, 'we've never met. Stone deaf I'm told, married to a little chap called Billie Sunter who farms next door to Cuckoo. It's market day so those baskets will be full of provisions. She must have carried them four miles already, she's still two to go. Give her another honk.'

Tom was in danger of catching Betty up her ample rump before she heard him, but finally she turned round and glared. Frank dismounted, removed his trilby and shouted.

'Hello, Mrs Sunter, I'm Frank Bowers, auctioneer. Can I give you a lift?'

'You're going wheer, young man?'

'I'm going past your farm gate, can I give you a lift?'

'Don't you ask me to shift!'

'No,' shouted Frank, 'can I give you a lift,' gesticulating towards the car with his arms.

'Don't mind if I do, nivver been in yan o' these contraptions afore.'

'Renowned throughout the dales is this lass,' Frank said quietly to Tom; weighed in at over twenty stone when she was only fourteen, needed a double desk at school, quite free with her favours so I'm told in those days.'

'We'll drop you off in your yard,' shouted Frank having squeezed his passenger and her baskets into the back.

'Yes, they are a bit hard,' said Betty, punching the seat, 'nivver mind eh?' She made Tom wince as she poked him in the back; 'get on young fella, let's see how fast it'll go then.

'Reet grand that,' said Betty as she tried to prize herself out of the back seat.

'Stop gawping young fella and give us a shove from t'other side'

196

The two young men found it impossible to avert their gaze from the sight of the two huge thighs spilling out over knee length home-made woollen stockings with a large expanse of human flesh above that, slowly backing out, well covered with a voluminous pair of bright green drawers.

'He's only a little snip of a fella, is her husband,' said Frank trying to keep his face straight.

'The mind boggles,' said Tom, forced to turn away to hide his mirth.

''Ere, young man,' shouted Betty, 'get thissen round this other side, nivver mind gawpin at me backside, gi'us a shove t'other way.'

Eventually Betty Sunter and her baskets were safely delivered to the door of the farmhouse.

'Is Billy at home?' asked Frank.

'Naw, he's away on t'fell for that dozy beggar next door, tryin' to sort out his moor sheep; he's forced to sell up tha knows, goin' abroad; wrong sort for yon farm, tha needs to be bred on these sort of spots to mak' a go o'things.'

'We'll have to be away,' said Frank.

'Nonsense, you mon come in an' hev a cup o' tay.'

Frank had never seen such a spotless house. Brasses gleamed everywhere, the kitchen range had been polished until it was mirror bright; a peat fire still glowed in the hearth sending its warm fragrant glow into each dark corner. The sandstone flags were obviously scrubbed each and every day.

'Sit yersens down,' said Betty as she waddled into the pantry. 'There's a new baked apple pie and some home-made cheese to hev wi' your drink.'

'Then, Mrs Sunter, we really must be on our way,' shouted Frank.

'No it's made from curds, not whey,' said Betty, unable to understand why her guests were falling about laughing.

Frank found himself shouting at Tom, 'I feel better for that,' as the two of them drove further up the dale.

'There's Grange Head in front of us,' pointed Frank; 'halfway up the hillside. See if you can get us all the way, don't fancy walking far on this gammy leg as yet.'

'I asked him to meet us at three-thirty,' said Tom.

'Good, dead on time. Never could stand being late,' said Frank.

'I want you to sell everything, Mr Bowers, lock, stock and barrel,' said Bill Izzitt; 'decided to emigrate.'

'Have you fixed a changeover date with the new tenant?' asked Frank.

197

'Yes, twelfth of May, he's already taken over the land so he can get his muck* out.'

'Are you going to claim for seeds and cultivations and residual manures?'

'Naw, there's nowt to valee over to him, only sheep. He's promised to be a good customer at the sale, there's quite a bit of good hay left, some's hoss hay two years old, he's maybe wantin' to tak' that o'er if you can fix a valee.'

'So, let's take particulars of what we have to sell,' said Frank.

'Household furniture, tinclement, hay-making machinery, anything else?'

'There's a good muck cart, specially made last year, cost forty-five pund, Clydesdale mare as pulls it aint up to mich! Thirty dairy shorthorns from calves upwards like.'

'Do you want me to value the sheep for the new man?' asked Frank.

'No, we've agreed to let a fellow called Jack Spensley act as arbitrator. He'll act for both sides like and I'm tell't he does'na charge as much as you lot.'

Frank and his assistant were back at the farm a fortnight later. They had rushed through a Short Notice of Sale in the local paper, and distributed over a hundred posters throughout the district.

'Looks as if we've picked a smashing day, Mr Izzitt,' said Frank when he and Tom arrived at Grange Head. 'We'll sell all the machinery first, then the cattle, furniture last.'

'I've fixed up some hurdles in th'yard for a ring for thee,' said Cuckoo, 'and all the tinclement and hay-making tackle's laid out in t'croft.'

'Good, we've started labelling cattle at these do's with sticky lot numbers; let's take the younger end first and then the stirks followed by the cows, the bull last.'

'You'll maybe have t' watch this chap when he's in't sale ring, Mr Bowers.'

'I see you have a ring in his nose,' said Frank, 'can you hang onto him?'

'Aye,' said Cuckoo; 'I'll hev hold of a pole attached to his nose, a mate o'mine a'll be on t'other side, like, hold of a helter.'

'Sounds as if we can expect trouble,' said Frank.

'You nivver quite noo-o weer you 'ave this fella, can be as quiet as a mouse; but if owt upsets him, then you mon look out!'

'He's starting to roll his eyes and roar a bit now,' said Tom, 'doesn't like strangers, obviously.'

---

* Muck – farmyard manure.

'And paw the ground,' said Frank.

'Now don't you worry, Mr Bowers, I shall be boss of 'im as long as I hev him by t'nose. There could be one or two neighbours after him, he's gay smittle* and leaves his calves well marked.'

It was soon after Frank had started selling the cattle when Billy Sunter from the next door farm arrived at the ringside. Being small of stature he elbowed his way to the front.

He was wearing a leather jerkin over a collarless wool shirt; an oversize flat cap which drooped over each ear; he also wore a bright yellow pair of corduroy trousers, each leg tied below the knee with a piece of string. A cheerful, alert and very popular figure he was busy nodding to his various friends in the audience, accepting their return greetings, when Frank spoke to him.

'Hello, Billy, nice to see you.' He lazily accepted Frank's greeting with a nod of the head and was about to turn away to continue when Frank remarked, 'Smart pair of pants tha's wearin, do they belong to the wife?'

A huge roar of laughter rose from the assembled company, most of them if not all, fully aware of the enormous size of Fat Betty and her aptitude for displaying her undergarments at the least pretence. Billy Sunter drew himself up to his full height of five foot two inches and, quick as a flash, replied, 'Tha should know, Bowers, she tell't me tha brought her yam in that fancy motor car tha rides around in, last week.'

There was an even heartier peel of laughter, this time at Frank's expense.

'She tell't me tha had er as fast as a stuck pig on't back seeat.' The last remark was too much for young Tom Edwards, he'd dropped his notebook and was rolling about drunkenly holding his sides.

For once Frank found himself speechless. He stood there, a frozen half-smile on his face, finding it hard to realise how quickly the tables had been turned on him.

The next beast entered the ring. 'Right lads, Lot 10, heifer – two teeth; been calved a week; how much? Somebody start me at thirty-five pund, nicely into profit; get me away then, thirty pund someone surely?'

The last cow had been sold and so far the trade had been good. Suddenly Frank's audience melted away, he heard the bellow of an angry bull approaching and only then did he realise he stood on his makeshift rostrum alone. He looked round for his clerk, but already Tom sat amongst an expectant crowd of onlookers twenty yards away on top of a wall. He

---

* Smittle – fertile.

smacked his cane down heavily on the shelf in front of him, as much to let the glaring animal approaching know that he had a weapon in his hand as to reassure himself of the last line of defence he might use in case of emergency.

'Now you chicken-hearted lot,' he heard himself saying; 'as quiet as a lamb normally; bred on this farm, an extraordinarily good getter*, you've all seen his calves, how much for him?'

At this point the bull gave an extra loud bellow, flung his head in the air and left Cuckoo holding on to a staff, plus safety chain, from which dangled a copper ring. It took Frank fully two seconds longer than the two handlers to realise what had happened.

'The ring's torn out,' yelled Cuckoo as he flew past Frank for the safety of the wall. 'No way I can hang onto him now,' shouted the other handler as he disappeared equally fast in the opposite direction.

They were nicely out of the arena before the bull really felt the pain and tasted the blood from his nose. He stood stockstill in the centre of the empty yard, empty that is except for Frank, still standing on his box. Halter dangling from his face the angry bull contemplated his next move; then Fate came to Frank's assistance as it did so many times throughout

The ring's torn out

* Getter – breeder.

his long career. Firstly he realised the bull was standing on the halter shank and had not worked out as yet he was fastening himself to the ground. Secondly, he'd noticed earlier on, that the last cow to be sold was in season.

'Let that last beast back into the yard,' he bellowed, 'damned quick!' The shippon door opened and the cow reappeared; the bull spun round, sniffed, mounted and within seconds dropped back to the ground, all aggression spent.

Frank calmly walked up to him, took hold of his halter, walked him over to his wide-eyed owner and haughtily suggested the cow be taken back to her stall.

'By, that were quick thinking,' said Cuckoo as a mild burst of applause broke out from the shame-faced gallery.

'Right, lead him round on his halter.'

'Which of you fellas can bid me fifty pund for him?' he demanded. 'Come on, lads, he only wants some work!'

When finally the last stick of furniture had been sold, the two auctioneers retired to the makeshift office to cash up.

'Can I have a word with you, Mr Bowers?' the hesitant high-pitched query made Frank look up.

'Ah yes, you must be Mr Turner. Let's see, Lot 29, twenty-eight pund; nice cow that, quite a bargain, Mr Turner!'

'Aye, but I bought a geld cow like.'

'Yes,' said Frank, 'that's how she was sold.'

'Well she's now bin served like.'

'Ah, yes, I see what you mean,' said Frank calmly. 'Perhaps you ought to pay Mr Izzitt a little more for the service, but in the circumstances I'm sure he won't insist.' Frank had enjoyed the sale and was in quite a jocular frame of mind.

'No, that's not it,' said the purchaser wringing his cap in his hands. 'I didn't want her in calf just yet, then I'd hev put her to th' Hereford like, so if she'd been sold as having bin served like, I wouldn't hev bought her, so I don't really want her like.'

'These things are sent to try us,' Frank said serenely as he turned to Tom. 'All right, Mr Turner, we'll cross your name off. That cow probably saved me from getting badly hurt, I'll no doubt buy her myself. It's a fair way to shift her, but we do need a milk cow at home.'

'Thanks, Mr Bowers. That was a very brave thing you did this afternoon; not many h'auctioneers would hev stood their ground like you did.'

'That's true,' said Frank, 'you probably noticed how far back my assistant had got himself long before the bull was even in the ring.'

The very next day Frank and many of his hunting friends heard with dismay that Lord Kitchener had personally chosen an area of ground some eight miles due west of Catterick village to be an Army camp. Three or four sites had been bandied about since 1910.

'And it has to be in the middle of some of the best hunting country the Bedale possesses,' Frank moaned to Bobbie Dawson.

'Probably because it's near to the Great North Road,' said Bobbie, 'then there's all that wild land over Hipswell Moor for training.'

'Talking of the Army,' said Bobbie, 'slight compensation I think. The Royal Scots Greys Cavalry have just moved to York and the commanding officer has written to the Hunt Committee asking permission for a few days' hunting for his officers. They've agreed to extend the season and put in a few bye days hoping for a May fox.'

'These limbs of mine are getting better every day,' said Frank.

'Well, if you feel up to it, the last meet is on the seventh of May at Sessay Station. You can box old Tuffan with me overnight and we could hack over there to see how these fellows perform next day.'

'Right, you're on,' said Frank.

'Will your mother be all right on her own?' asked Bobbie.

'No! But Dick Boynton got married recently and his wife is a dab hand at looking after her, we've given them the tenancy of a cottage close by.'

Frank watched in amazement as the special train of more than thirty horse boxes drew into Sessay and unloaded its cargo of nothing but grey horses; he stopped counting at one hundred and twenty. The large station yard was suddenly full of about eighty officers in their immaculate uniforms, grooms scuttling about, taking rugs and tail bandages off.

'They've each brought two horses and about three troopers to look after 'em,' said Bobbie. 'Quite a sight though, wouldn't like to think I was a Jerry and had to fight these lads.'

The day proved disappointing. 'Too warm and too nice,' Frank said to himself. 'Funny how the best scenting days are often the coldest and wettest.'

'Nowt so queer as scent 'cept women, what Colonel?' said Frank, rather cheekily, as a senior officer ranged alongside at the side of a covert.

'Quite right young man,' chuckled the Colonel in reply to Frank's old chestnut. 'Had fairish experience myself; damned if you can tell what either of them's going to be like from day to day – take my first wife for example, know what she did to me one night when she found out I was going courtin'?'

'No, sir,' said Frank.

'Burnt me wooden leg! Eh what?'

Frank flinched as the Army officer gave his right thigh an enormous thwack with his crop. 'Lost that leg in the Boer War – grapeshot.'

'I'm sorry, sir, I had no idea,' said Frank.

'Going out with a pretty little thing, came as governess, *ménage à trois*, and all that sort of thing. Wife found out, dropped me leg in a stove – what? Curtailed my activities for a night or two till I got a replacement, I can tell you!'

'Very unfortunate, sir,' said Frank, chuckling to himself by this time.

'Wouldn't care, but she ran off with a Froggie officer a couple of months later, made me look a bloody fool around the mess.'

'Here we go, sir, holloa! far side of the cover! Follow me over this gate, there's a ride through the middle, a short cut that'll put us in front of the rest of the field.'

Halfway down the ride the two horsemen caught up with the Hunt Master running as fast as possible towards the sound of hounds in full cry. Frank alighted and with difficulty held on tight to Tuffan's bridle.

'Got caught on me feet, damn it!' puffed the Master.

'Here, sir, take mine. I'm not one hundred per cent fit; I'll find your horse and bring him on slowly.'

Fortunately hounds 'threw up' within two or three fields and although the Huntsman cast forward over the Willow beck, hounds could do no more. Frank was able to catch up with the field on the Thirsk to York main road. He exchanged horses once more with the Master.

'Much better ride than mine, Frank, want to sell him?'

'No, sir, sorry, can't see myself ever partin', he's something special; part of my life almost. I've never loaned him out to anybody else until now.'

Apart from a slow circular hunt around the Thirkelby Hall coverts nothing more could be done and the Master blew for home.

'I heard him trying to buy Tuffan off you, Frank,' said Bobbie on the way home. 'Might be wise to sell him, be a bugger if he gets commandeered by the remount lot for sixty quid.'

'I'll hang on to him some way,' said Frank, 'even if I have to turn him into a workhorse on the farm; besides we're not at war yet.'

203

Frank little knew that Colonel Jeffries, wooden leg and all, would soon be rejected for active service and placed in charge of one of the main Remount Depots for the north; and that for most of a war soon to be thrust upon them, Frank would be seconded to him as assistant.

In July, Frank found himself in Darlington. It was the Durham and North Yorkshire Agricultural Show. He was showing a good three-year-old in hand, recently bought from a Mr Albert Brown at Bedale. A crash course in deportment and manners at home, mainly carried out by Dick, paid off; the young horse beat a strong class to be placed first. In less than six weeks time he was to be commandeered by the Army and that was the last Frank saw of him.

The Hound Show, run in conjunction with the Agricultural Show, had proved an outstanding success for the Bedale. Six packs were represented – The Badsworth, The Bedale, The Cleveland, The Haydon, The Hurworth and The Zetland. Nearly all the major awards came the way of the Bedale. Frank had been collared by the Bedale Master as soon as the Hound Show was over. 'Come on, Bowers, free champagne on me! That's shown these other packs what good hounds should look like. How did you get on with your hunters?'

'Two firsts and the Championship, sir.'

'Good man, can't improve on that. Let me introduce you to Sid Macgregor from Leamington Spa, he's up here looking for a hunter or two. Been known to put one hundred and twenty livery horses out on one day with the Shire packs, perhaps you can fit him up?'

'I've a nice grey cob called Hasty Retreat to sell, seven-year-old, experienced, good sort to hire out, goes all day.'

That is how this extraordinary horse came to change hands a couple of days later for the sum of one hundred and thirty pounds; he was on his best behaviour when Dick brought him out of his box. A couple of months out at grass had put a wonderful sheen on his coat and Sid Macgregor fell for him immediately.

'Should have asked one hundred and fifty for him,' Frank confided with his foreman later.

'One of the best money-spinners I ever owned,' Sid was to confess many years later; 'Managed to keep him all through the War. Fifty shillings a day hunting with the Quorn; you could always pull him out to do five days a fortnight. Carried Royalty eventually. Finally sold him as a vanner; he went to London, pulled a cart every day, "Typhoo Tea" I think. They sent him with a packet of other horses for his rest period out on the

Essex Marshes near Foulness and be damned if he didn't take it into his head to swim out to sea.'

'I read about that in the *Horse and Hound*,' said Frank. 'No idea that was my horse.'

'Aye, struck off straight over the Maplin Sands heading south east, halfway towards Margate afore they got a boat round him.'

'Then they lassooed him,' chuckled Frank, 'and dragged him back; allus had a mind of his own, that fella.'

Back in the beer tent supplies of drink were running out.

'Here's to my predecessors,' shouted Mr Mowbray to the ever-growing band of Hunt supporters keen to share in the free supply of booze. 'The Duke of Leeds and the Belvoir draft.' The toast was drunk. 'Dexter, Villager, Vagabond and Stormer,' the Master called out, and the toast was drunk. 'Not to forget the bitches Hopeful, Verdant, Sentiment, Harebell and Rosamund.' Again glasses were raised. 'Here's to the greatest bitch of 'em all,' the Master called out, 'Belvoir Hymen 1902.'

'I'll drink to that, Maister,' some wag called out, 'not so many of them things about those days.'

As the tent erupted Frank slipped away to the secretary's office. In his usual charming fashion he persuaded the secretary's wife to let him borrow the huge rosebowl he had won. 'You'll have it back for the presentation later this afternoon,' he promised.

He scurried back to the tent. 'A bottle of sherry, a bottle of gin, half of vermouth and top it up to the brim with cider,' he ordered the bartender. 'Stir it up,' he demanded. 'Now taste it.'

'Whow!' gasped the barman. 'Fire-water, sir.'

'Good,' chortled Frank, 'now stick it in the middle of the bar, ladle it out to this lot as they need it. If you run out, same again, only next time give 'em less cider and more vermouth.'

'Whose account, sir?'

'Never mind that now,' said Frank brushing aside the very pertinent question.

'I need that rosebowl back before the Grand Parade, 'cos I've won it, and I'll pay you then.'

'Very good, sir; "this lot" h'as you refered to them 'ave 'ad an h'awful lot of champagne. I can see it'll only need a little of this to knock 'em really squiffy.'

'Good,' said Frank, 'that's the object of the exercise.'

205

18

The Great War

War commenced on the 4th August. Frank volunteered for the cavalry immediately, but a clever doctor spotted his hearing and eyesight problems and slung him straight out.

National fervour ran at a very high level and for the first month horses of all descriptions were gathered up and sent off for Army Service. Anything not too old and sound had to go.* Hunt stables were exempt for a time but all private yards were totally denuded of horseflesh.

Frank was forced to sell all but his workhorses at between forty-five and sixty-five pounds. He deliberately hid Tuffan away. His last real if tenuous hold of Charlotte's memory vanished when her grey Arab was taken. A red-hot iron brand mark was slapped on his rump.

'Forty-five pounds for that, Mr Bowers, to go as a trooper,' said the commandeering officer. 'What's this fella?'

'Four-year-old, prizewinning hunter,' said Frank.

'Sixty-eight as a charger,' said the officer. 'Mark him up, Sergeant – anything else?'

'Only six young shires, sir.'

'We could do with 'em: short of horses for gunners.'

'Far too heavy,' said Frank, 'besides we need 'em for ploughing and other jobs.'

Frank pondered hard and long for the next day or two on how to save face and at the same time hang on to Tuffan.

All his friends had signed on and disappeared overseas one by one. His close friend Arnold Cheesman arrived to say goodbye, resplendent in his uniform as an Officer of the Northamptonshire Yeomanry.

'Hard lines, Frank,' said Arnold as he was leaving, 'somebody has to stay at home and farm, otherwise we'd starve.'

---

* Over one million horses were commandeered in the first few weeks of hostilities.

'Rather be coming with you,' said Frank.

'Why not have a go with the Remount Depot – they need a clever chap like you who knows horses; we were sent a replacement lot recently with wind galls, sprains, even broken-winded horses, bought at the expense of the Army. They may call themselves patriotic, these farmers and horse-dealers, but it seems to me they've quickly caught on where to send their broken-down old nags. That main depot at York might very well do with your services. It's not far away; you can soon drive over there and continue farming, perhaps even keep the office open?'

'No, young Tom Edwards has volunteered for the Army, family tradition apparently. I intend to close the office and the Auction Mart until after the War, they all say it'll be over by Christmas. Not so sure about being seen driving around, they tell me all the London buses have been commandeered as troop carriers for the Forces; they might be after private cars next.'

'Not if you're working for the Remount Depot.'

'Mmm!' Frank said pondering, 'perhaps you're right at that.'

'There's a grand chap in charge at York, Colonel Jeffries from the Scotch Greys, sports a wooden leg.'

'I've met him,' said Frank 'great fellow, he's the chap who brought all his regimental officers hunting one day at Sessay Station.'

'Well then, what are you waiting for?' queried Arnold.

'I'll go over there tomorrow morning,' said Frank.

That is how, in spite of failing his medical, Frank was accepted as a civilian employee of the Armed Forces and, after a trial period, obtained the pay and uniform of an honorary Captain in the Veterinary Corps.

Colonel Jeffries was delighted to see Frank and had no hesitation at taking him on his staff. Both men were of the same calibre and the Colonel had already seen in Frank a younger edition of himself.

'We've a small depot just been set up at Croft near Darlington, basically to supply Catterick Camp with remounts,' said the Colonel. 'I believe you know that area.'

'Reasonably well,' Frank said.

'Well, it'll be your responsibility from now on to pull in what horses you can to that depot. I'll give you a Sergeant as assistant, plus marking irons and such like.'

'Thank you, sir.'

'You know the prices to pay for sound young horses?'

'I do indeed,' said Frank, 'having had nearly all my own horses confiscated.'

'We prefer to use the word commandeered,' said the Colonel, 'in the national interest and all that baloney eh, what?'

'Forty-five pound for troopers, sixty-five pound for gunners and sixty-eight pound for chargers.'

'Correct,' said the Colonel, 'not a penny more, nor a penny less.'

'No haggling at all?' asked Frank.

'No haggling, no argument, that's it,' said the Colonel. 'By the way, whatever happened to that good horse you loaned the Master that day?'

Frank hesitated.

'Well, man?'

'I still have him, sir! Kept him covered up when they came round and took the rest; kept him by me with this sort of job in mind.'

'Well done, quite right, never forgot your reply to the Master when he tried to buy him.'

Frank tackled his new job with enthusiasm; delighted he had found a means of helping his country. In all respects he gave every impression of being a very fit young man who really ought to have volunteered for the Armed Forces weeks ago. He was particularly pleased that he might soon be issued with a uniform.

That'll stop tongues wagging in and around the district, he thought to himself.

Frank's first task was indeed a sad one.

'Bad news, Frank,' said his C.O. in his office at Fulford Barracks. 'We've been informed that Hunt horses are not to be regarded as exempt from Army Service. Master of Foxhounds Association have been lobbying Parliament since war began but they've lost. I'm afraid you'll have to get round the various Hunt premises on our patch and get 'em commandeered, Masters' horses an' all!'

'Sorry about this, sir,' Frank was saying to Mr J.J. Mowbray the Bedale Hunt Master a few days later in the Kennels Yard near Leases Hall; 'all sixteen Hunt horses will have to go and, with your permission, sir, if I could inspect your own horses, we'll have to take them along at the same time. I'm obliged to order my Sergeant here to put the Army brand on them, not much of a price I'm afraid.'

'Perhaps just as well, Frank,' sighed the redoubtable J.J. 'Both Bill Pittaway and Fred Adamson' (Bedale Hunt whippers-in) 'told me only yesterday they've volunteered for the Yorkshire Hussars Yeomanry, not going to be much hunting until we've put Jerry in his place I'm afraid.'

Within a few weeks of his Army appointment, Frank made his first contact with the Wagoners' Reserve*; late recruits to this unique Army Unit were marched into the Cavalry Barracks at York from the station led by Major (Later Lt. Colonel) Sir Mark Sykes Bart, M.P. of Sledmere.

'There's no veterinary officer available to see these lads and their horses safely to the front line in Belgium, Frank,' he heard his C.O. saying, 'so I'm sending you, purely to look after their animals. Don't get involved in any fighting and then once you've delivered them safely come straight home.'

Frank was to learn that the first lot of 700 men were called up on the 5th August and camped out on Bradford Low Moor; they entrained for the south, picked up two heavy horses and a pole wagon each in Aldershot, drove down to Portsmouth and sailed on Sunday 15th August for Le Havre. The wagons had been securely fastened above decks and all the horses backed into stalls facing each other below. Immediately they arrived in France they entrained and went via Rouen and Amiens to Valenciennes whence, loaded with rations, they drove over the Belgian border almost to Mons.**

No sooner had they arrived, and even before a square meal had been provided, they were in full retreat along with the rest of the British Army.

On the long train journey from York to Aldershot, where the detachment were due to pick up 200 replacement horses, Frank came to know and admire a fellow officer, Captain Harry Boswell quite well. Little did Frank realise at the time what a valuable contact he was making for his dealing activities between the wars. The contacts enabled him at a later date to buy a lot of valuable horses through Boswell's Auction Sales of York. Fellow dealers were always puzzled where Frank found his quality youngsters; most came from the Wold Farms following a telephone call from Harry Boswell.

'It's my job to help to look after the wagoners, you look after the horses,' suggested Harry, 'any help you need just ask my Sergeant-Major.

---

* In 1987 the author had the pleasure of interviewing probably the oldest survivor of the Wagoners' Reserve; Mr James Stephenson, in his one hundredth year. Well cared for at the old people's home in Filey, a strong and fit man for his age with a wonderful memory; his only affliction and one not easy to live with, with total blindness. Sadly, he died just a few weeks later.

'Nivver had me boots off for eight weeks,' the author was told. 'French troops were nowhere to be seen, all guarding the wrong frontier at Alsace-Lorraine, while Jerry did a flanking movement through Belgium.'

** See Addendum (page 289).

I suggest we give 'em a careful inspection at the docks when we get to Portsmouth, no good taking unsound animals. I'll leave that to you. My orders tell me once across the channel we're to box 'em on the train at Le Havre for a depot near Arras. That's when you come home, lucky chap!!'

The Channel crossing tested Frank's resolve to the limit. Gale force cross winds in mid-channel had the ferry rolling alarmingly; most of the horses panicked. Many of the stalls and the breast bars were far too flimsy to contain these heavy draft horses. Fortunately most of the men were happy to eat and sleep with their charges; they knew how to handle them, and how to keep them reasonably calm.

Two animals who ran amok had to be put down. Frank, who had never sailed before – along with most of the men – was violently seasick; it was with some relief he saw the sanctuary of the harbour at Le Havre looming up ahead.

The journey by rail to the forward depot was something of an anti-climax. Only once at Arras could he hear the distant rumble of heavy guns; otherwise apart from a lot of troop movements there was little sign of war.

'If we don't meet again out here,' said Harry Boswell as Frank prepared to leave on the ambulance train for home, 'don't forget to look me up, call at the Sledmere Estate Office any time and ask for my place, and they'll point you in the right direction. Thanks for helping out.'

The train stopped at Lille on its way to Calais and Frank took the opportunity to exercise his aching limbs.

He watched nurses busy caring for early casualties, housed in the specially adapted box cars. One or two walking-wounded dismounted and even tried to salute Frank as he strolled past.

Suddenly he stopped dead in his tracks. A nursing sister with a wounded soldier on each arm was moving slowly towards him; in spite of her splendid uniform, her stiff white starched hat, her voluminous dark blue gown, there were the auburn curls peeping out, the beautiful green eyes.

'Sandra?' he called out hesitantly.

'Why it's Mr Frank Bowers,' she said sweetly.

'So you haven't forgotten me,' said Frank limply.

'I don't think I ever could, the only man I've ever nursed who woke up half-paralysed after being unconscious two days and made me blush by trying to kiss me.'

The two soldiers were still standing there, clutching each arm and grinning.

'Right, you two,' said Frank with authority, 'Hop it.'

'Hold on, Captain,' said Sandra sternly, 'this is a hospital train and I'm in charge of it; are you on the train as well?'

'I am indeed, ma'am, I'm in the first-class compartment up front; it would appear I'm the senior officer around here, so once more you two, hop it.'

The two men hastily did as they were told.

'What's more, Lieutenant Sandra ... what's your second name?' he queried.

'Sidebottom,' she said defiantly. Frank grinned.

'It looks well set on to me,' he quipped.

She opened her mouth to speak. 'Shh!' Frank ordered, raising his forefinger. 'Well, Lieutenant Sandra Sidebottom, I'm ordering you, as soon as your duties are through in the hospital wards, to travel up front in my compartment and so it shall be until we reach England; shh!' Frank repeated as she offered to speak. 'Then as soon as you have dispatched your duties at home, you will accompany me to London for a few days' leave; you will not, repeat not, escape me this time.'

'Yes, my handsome Captain, sir,' said Sandra, giving him a mock salute, 'But I still intend–'

'To be a doctor,' said Frank, 'and go to Africa or somewhere, not to get involved, etc., etc. I know all about that, just make sure that when you've got your charges safely to hospital that you wangle a week or ten days' leave, and spend most of it in my company – understood?'

'Yes, Frank,' said Sandra demurely.

'Queer spot for a military hospital, the Isle of Wight,' said Frank as the train carrying them sped towards London. 'Still, I suppose it's handy when you dock at Southampton. I thought we were bound for Dover when we sailed from Calais.'

'Helps to keep 'em from deserting, I've been told. That's why they've built a jail at Parkhurst; no prisoner who's ever tried to escape has made it back to the mainland as yet,' said Sandra as she snuggled even closer to her uniformed companion. 'Let's not talk, or even think, about war or prisons for the next few days,' she begged. 'Tell me what we are going to do in London.'

'To be honest I don't really know,' said Frank, 'I've never been!'

'Well, you great big softie,' said Sandra, squeezing his hand. 'I have an uncle who lives out at Finchley, and when I was a youngster he used to take me everywhere. The Zoo, The Tower, Houses of Parliament; Buckingham Palace, Piccadilly Circus; there's a nice hotel near there called The Park Lane. We sometimes used to have afternoon tea there, cucumber sandwiches, jelly, gooey cream cakes and–'

'That's where we'll go first, then,' said Frank.

'Where?'

'The Park Lane Hotel and book a nice large double room.'

Suddenly Frank felt his companion trembling; she fell silent, all the aimless chatter ceased.

'What's wrong, darling?' asked Frank.

'I guess I'm scared, I've never shared a bedroom with a man.'

'I trust sir and madam will find suite 2A to their liking,' said the portly male receptionist as he thumped the bell on the top of his desk. 'Ah, Jenkins, show Captain and Mrs Bowers to suite 2A.'

'Any more luggage, sir?' queried Jenkins as he picked up the two Army hold-alls.

'Dammit man, no,' said Frank haughtily (he was beginning to enjoy throwing his rank about), 'We're straight here from the Western Front.'

'Yes, sir, sorry, sir, they tell me it's getting a bit rough out there – follow me, sir. You see, sir,' said Jenkins as he slowly climbed the stairs, 'I have a young son out there, barely eighteen, just went off and volunteered for the London Scottish. Last letter was some time ago now from near Mons, said something about moving up and we've heard nothing since.'

'He's probably all right,' said Sandra gently, 'we have just brought a hospital train back from that area. I'm an Army nurse and saw every wounded man onto that train. There were quite a few from the London Scottish Regiment and I do recall a young lad called Jenkins, a bugler I think he said he was, with a beautiful head of blond curly hair.'

'That's him,' shouted the hall porter, 'that's sure to be him, only looks about sixteen.'

'Well, if it is him,' said Sandra, 'as soon as we get to our room I'll give you the address and telephone number of the hospital on the Isle of Wight, then you can always make enquiries.'

'Thankee, ma'am,' said Jenkins as he left the room with tears in his eyes. 'You're like an angel from heaven.'

'That's how I feel about you,' said Frank, once they were alone. They stood toe to toe in the middle of a large comfortable sitting room. 'Good job I had plenty of back pay to come to be able to afford this luxury.'

'Frank, I feel so awful,' said Sandra. 'If it is the same boy he'll never walk again, never mind write; a large piece of shrapnel had smashed his spine to smithereens right between the shoulder blades. It's only his youth that kept him alive. Blast this war,' she said vehemently, 'it's followed us into this very room.'

212

'We could go out on the town and get drunk,' suggested Frank.

'I think that's a splendid idea,' said Sandra brightening visibly. 'Let me do my face; take two minutes to unpack and then we can really make whoopee!'

As they strolled towards Piccadilly Circus from the hotel, Sandra squeezed Frank's arm extra tightly. 'How clever of you, Frank, knowing I was petrified in that bedroom.'

'You don't have to be scared, my darling, I'm not going to force you to do anything you don't want to do.'

'Oh I want to all right,' said Sandra. 'I've loved you from the moment you were brought into my ward at Northallerton. I've thought about you constantly, but I've my career to think about.'

'Shhh!' said Frank, 'we'll let nature take its course. This looks like a nice restaurant, let's go and have some supper and crack open a bottle of wine.'

'Keep talking to me,' pleaded Sandra much later as she clasped Frank's hand over the table, 'the food and the wine were superb and I'm lovely and mellow, but your voice and the way you say things, that's what makes my nerve ends tingle.'

'That's what makes my nerve ends tingle,' repeated Frank. 'Hardly "Kings English",' he chided.

'I don't care,' smiled Sandra, her beautiful eyes moist by this time, 'tell me you love me, Frank, and then take me home to bed.'

Frank bent forward as far as he could; he kissed the forefinger of his left hand and then moved it slowly and seductively across her mouth. She bit him quite hard.

'Say it,' she hissed.

'I love you, ouch!' he concluded as she bit even harder. 'I'll make you pay for that.'

'Promise?'

'Right, Sergeant,' said Frank, 'funny old job on now, apparently we've had information from some zealot that a chap called George Talbot farming north of here near Brough Hall is hanging on to half a dozen nice young horses and refusing to let 'em go.

'Apparently he's upset that both the new supply road and the railway line to Catterick Camp are going through his farm; he hasn't had a penny piece in compensation as yet and is threatening to take pot shots at any Army personnel who enter on his farm. The C.O. seems to think I can perhaps act as peacemaker, sort out his compensation claim in my capacity as valuer and auctioneer and then decide what to do with regard to his horses.'

There was quite a long drive from the main road to Brough Hill Farm.

'Hey up, sir, we've been spotted, there's a chap stood at the yard gate wi' a twelve-bore,' said the Sergeant cautiously.

Frank stopped his car at a reasonably safe distance and stepped down.

'Watch him, sir, he looks a bit trigger-happy to me.'

'I think I'll be all right, Sarge! I came in civvy clothes on purpose.'

'What's your business?' shouted a huge untidy-looking fellow.

'I'm looking for a Mr George Talbot,' replied Frank.

'That's me.'

'Can we talk? Frank Bowers is my name, the Army have sent me to investigate a claim for compensation.'

'Won't have no Army folks on this place, bugger off!' With that the enraged farmer took aim and fired a barrel over Frank's head.

He stood his ground. 'It seemed the sensible thing to do,' Frank told his C.O. when he finally got back to York.

'Just hold on, Mr Talbot,' he yelled. 'I'm a civilian, used to live at Bolton Grange, t'other side of the river.'

'Are you Richard Bowers's lad?'

'Yes.'

'Well why in heaven's name didn't tha say so?'

'You never gave me much chance, Mr Talbot,' said Frank, moving forward.

'It were that Army sergeant sittin' beside thee as put me back up. By! he didn't half dive for cover; look at little beggar,' chortled George. 'Still scared to poke his head up. What's it all about, then?' the farmer queried, 'I knew thy dad well, tha knows, bloody good farmer.'

'Slave-driver more like,' said Frank feelingly.

'Nah! I wouldn't say that. He maybe worked thee a bit hard as a lad, only for thee own good. Allus a fair man I thought; I heard as how tha were auctioneering like, down Wetherby way.'

'Tell me, Mr Talbot, this feud against the Army; what's it all about?'

'Well, that high and mighty Lord Kitchener comes up here from down south, beginning of the year like, 'as a good look round, struts about, then decides "Yes, this will do. We'll put an Army camp theer and a road and railway up the valley theer"; but nobody comes to see me and find out what I feel about that bloody lot cutting through the middle of me best land. There may be a war on now, but there weren't one on when they first

214

came sniffing around. I've had to let 'em go through like but it's not reet, not reet at all.'

'I totally agree, Mr Talbot.'

'You mon call me George, ovrybody else does.'

'Right, George, there's got to have been a mistake; I wouldn't mind betting they thought you were a tenant farmer on the Brough Hall Estate. In all probability the Army will have paid full compensation to the estate office.'

'Nivver thought o' that,' said George. 'I'll bet tha's not far off wi' that reckoning.'

'Leave it with me to sort it out,' said Frank soothingly.

'Ah will, Mr Bowers; ah will. Ah's just as patriotic as next man, but ah waint be trodden on.'

'Quite so,' said Frank, 'and that brings me to the other part of my business, horses.'

'Hosses?' echoed George.

'Yes,' said Frank producing his letter of authority. 'I'm also here as the official horse-buyer for the Army in these parts.'

'You scheming young bugger.'

'I'm afraid you'll have to let 'em go, George, otherwise they'll whisk you off to jail.'

'Ah suppose tha's reet,' said George, a resigned look on his face.

'So what have you got?' asked Frank.

'Well there's two reet grand shire mares.'

'You can keep them, workhorses are exempt; you'll find there'll be a directive soon about ploughing out more grassland for growing corn. Anything else?'

'Aye well, I've bin crossing 'em wi' a hackney stallion for three or four years now. By! there's some reet grand young hunter stores comin'on.'

'I only want three-year-olds and upwards.'

George's face brightened visibly. 'That's no so bad then,' he smiled, ' 'cos there's nobbutt yan four-year-old has ben ridden around the farm like, an' two three-year-olds nivver been touched.'

'Let's have a peep at 'em then,' said Frank.

George led the way through the farm buildings into a large straw-covered yard with a series of loose boxes on three sides.

'Ah've bin keepin' them in here like 'cos they're out of seet, an' they can exercise theirsens nicely. I lets 'em out in turn like.'

'You can have top price for those three,' said Frank, 'greatly impressed by their quality – sixty-eight pounds apiece.'

215

'By, that's a bit hard, Mr Bowers.'

'Sorry, George, I've no power to give you a penny more. Right, Sergeant, get these three branded. Now what's in this box?'

'Ah well, some'at special; two two-year-old colts both by a fancy blud hoss from Aske Hall, classic winner or some'at th' head groom tell't me.'

'I'm surprised Lordy allowed his stallion out to cover shire mares.'

'Oh no, his Lordship knows nowt about it. He allus insists his stallions get ridden out for four or five miles most days; he don't pay his staff o'er well an' yon head lad who's fancying yan o' me daughters often comes this way like.'

'So you arranged it that he came this way when one of your mares was in season?' commented Frank.

'Tha's hit nail on th' head first time,boss; two quid a time, that's what it cost like.'

Frank's eye was drawn to a particularly attractive well-grown youngster, a deep chestnut with a golden hue to his coat. He was impressed with his intelligent head, the central white star set between his large expressive eyes.

'Are you telling me this is a straight half-bred?'

'Aye, I'd heerd like, wi' a blud hoss "on top" tha sometimes gits a quality hoss wi' plenty o' bone. Spittin' image of his sire yon fella.'

'I suppose you realise that if this war lasts, this chap'll have to go next year?'

'Aye, more's the pity,' said George.

'Tell you what we'll do,' said Frank, 'sell him to me now and I'll risk whether he has to go to the Army or not. You'll lose him next year for certain at sixty-eight quid; how if I give you seventy for him now?'

'Aye, chance'd be a fine thing,' said George. 'I'll tak' ninety for 'im.'

It was fully an hour later before a deal was struck at eighty pounds, and Frank became the owner of one of the best young horses he ever bought.

The sun was setting in an orange glow to the west as Frank and his sergeant drove southwards from Catterick towards home. Over on the left the Hambleton Hills were shown up in stark relief.

'Grand young hoss, sir, the one you bought for yersen. I'll bet there's not many like him as'll survive this war.'

'Well, he'll do as a replacement horse for our job if this fighting continues, I knew I'd be able to save him whatever happens.'

'Thought of a name for him, sir?'

'I have, Sergeant; as we came over the river at Catterick Bridge with

216

those beautiful hills over there showing in the background, I decided to call him Hambleton Springs.*

A limited form of hunting was carried on during the war years. Anybody who could blow a horn reasonably well and had aspirations of tagging the initials M.F.H. behind his name could be given a chance. With the Bedale Hunt servants away on active service, willing volunteers would be co-opted as whippers-in. It's only fair to say the standards deteriorated. Nevertheless, Frank was much better placed than many of his friends to be able to grab the chance of a day when it came along.

He had long been well acquainted with the Robb family of Catton Hall near Topcliffe. Hounds were due to meet there on the 22nd March, 1916. Frank arranged that Dick Boynton would hack Tuffan through the day before; he would drive straight there on the morning of the meet from the Barracks at York.

A small field were delighted to welcome Mr Mowbray, home on leave and making a rare visit to Yorkshire from his Scottish estate. He carried the horn himself and, mainly due to an inspired cast in the early part of the hunt, gave those present one of the best day's hunting they were ever likely to have.

Hounds found in a young plantation south of Carlton Miniott known as Bamletts Whin (now part of Topcliffe Aerodrome) and ran to the Great North Road where they checked at Busby Stoop.

'Unusual name for a pub?' Frank addressed his query to Dr Carter Mitchell of nearby Topcliffe as they watched the Master casting hounds.

'Used to be a gibbet here, right on the crossroads outside the pub. Last fella to hang here was called Busby; been counterfeiting coins apparently.'

'They strung him up for that?'

'They did indeed.'

'Blood-thirsty lot. Hello, we're off again.'

Hounds were screaming away due north; with Sandhutton on the right they ran to Swale House near the junction of the River Swale and Wiske. Here the fox had apparently turned back through some 270 degrees then headed south along the banks of the Swale.

---

* Soon after the War, Frank produced Hambleton Springs to win at all the local shows. The horse was later sold to a Mrs Verrels from Melmerby Hall; a lady noted for her immaculate side-saddle turn-out, who never failed to arrive at a meet sporting a bunch of blue violets pinned to her lapel. For her he won every leading show within travelling distance, including Champion Ridden Hunter at the Royal Lancashire Show.

'He obviously doesn't fancy swimming for it,' Frank shouted across to the Master, at the same time maintaining a discreet distance to the left and behind him.

'Big greyhound of a fox, viewed him when he left cover, we could have a good hunt if he stays this side of the river,' shouted back J.J.

Once over the Thirsk to Ripon road at Skipton Bridge, the fox had run the lane to Catton Village.

'Just got tidied up and settled down for lunch,' enthused Mr Robb, Senior, later that night, 'when be damned if you weren't all back again. Never saw the fox but he must have run across the front lawn and over the ha-ha; never seen hounds going so well, straight for Bamletts Whin, eh?'

'No,' said Frank, tired but happy as he relaxed in front of a roaring fire, slowly sipping his third large whisky. 'We found him there; he swung north of Topcliffe past Salmon Hall to the Cod Beck at Dalton. That's when he took his first swim, we had to go round by the village and got a long way behind. He just followed the river all the way past Crakehill and Fawdington. I thought we were heading for those big coverts at Helperby but maybe the fox was out of his territory – they ran into him in the open and pulled him down short of Tholthorpe. An hour and forty minutes, flat out, hounds must have covered fifteen or sixteen miles. There was only Dr Mitchell, myself and the Master there at the finish.'

'Marvellous horse, that Tuffan of yours,' said Charles Robb.

'Came home nearly as fresh as when he set off,' said Frank. 'Takes everything in his stride, always give another a lead over a tricky spot. Only problem seems to be keeping him from overrunning the hounds and getting in front of Hunt staff.

'Reminds me of T.H. Hutchinson of the Manor House at Catterick, he'll be nearly eighty now. Always liked to be close up to hounds. He once said he was never too near hounds, but always so far in front of the field that he couldn't hear if he was called to order by the Master or the Huntsman.'

'Bit like a little snippit recently in the *Horse and Hound*,' chuckled Frank, 'about Will Derry, Huntsman to the Holderness in 1848. He describes how a too-forward rider was dealt with in his day. It read "that bloomin' parson sir, allus atop o' th' ounds. Whips blowed him up an he tak no notice, and I blowed 'im up an' he tak no notice, and Master blowed 'im up an' he tak no notice, so we tuk th' ounds ome".'

Still the war continued. The advent of trench warfare had resulted in a stalemate: neither the Germans nor the British and French would give way. Machine-guns mounted on fixed, intercrossing lines, and the fire power of infantry, well dug in, accounted for horrific losses of men on both sides. The accepted role of the cavalry up to that time, as shock troops behind mobile infantry battalions, no longer existed. Trenches stretched from the North Sea to Switzerland and eventually from Switzerland to Venice.

The call now on the Remount Depots became more for a heavier type of horse. A stronger type was needed to haul supplies of all sorts, ammunition and guns, to the front. Supply lines were long; successive heavy bombardments aimed at obliterating the enemy infantry from their dug-outs and destroying the endless miles of barbed wire and minefields, called for a vast tonnage of shells and armaments to be hauled from the Channel ports to the front line. Losses in horseflesh near the front were extremely high, and the wear and tear on animals pulling huge loads through the mud of Flanders resulted in an ever-increasing demand for replacements.

Vast numbers of horses were shipped over from Canada to a huge holding depot at Ormskirk, not far from the docks at Liverpool. Smaller depots were created near Darlington and eventually at Catterick camp, both of the latter within Frank's jurisdiction.

Not only had the Army in France the headache of replacing the vast losses of trained men, it was equally difficult finding enough trained horses to supply the demand.

All horse-drawn taxi cabs in Paris were commandeered and sent to the front. London's petrol-driven buses went the same way to be used as troop carriers.

Getting these vast numbers of animals to the Channel ports and on board ship with huge supplies of bulky food was a herculean task. Frank could never be persuaded to talk much of his vital part within the vast network of highly organised procuration of farming assets; during the whole of the War each truss of hay issued to the Army had a label attached to it stating whence it came. In July 1917 the Food Controller brought in rationing for horses at home; each Hunt was expected to provide a list of sound, fit horses likely to become Remounts, each animal to be allowed six pounds of corn a day up to the 1st November and ten pounds of hay per day from then to the end of the hunting season. If any horse became unfit for military purposes, the ration was withdrawn.

Frank was dismayed at the number of his friends who were being killed, one by one. Harry Rose of Spofforth had gone, so had the popular Midlands horse dealer, Harry Edwards. He heard with delight that his closest friend of all, Arnold Cheesman, had been promoted Major and he had been given a staff job, awarded a bar to his Military Cross as well as the Distinguished Service Order. His brother Jacob was not so lucky.

Frank always felt, deep down, that he should have been on active service instead of, as he put it, 'grabbing all he could by way of horseflesh and fodder for the Army'; he also felt sad at the passing of two stalwarts of the Bedale Hunt. On the 23rd November, 1916, Lt. Col. H.E. Dent, twice Master from 1878 to 1884 and 1896 to 1898, passed away at his home Menethorpe, near Malton. Also on the 24th January, 1917, Samuel the second Lord Masham died at Swinton Castle near Masham.

Frank remembered with pleasure his horse deal with the Colonel just before the outbreak of war. He had apparently bought a horse for eighty pounds and sold it to Frank straight away for one hundred and fifty. Many were the friends he told of his seventy pound profit almost overnight. Little did he know that Frank had sold the horse to Harry Edwards to go into the Quorn country, within a week, for two hundred and fifty.

Then, suddenly, the war was over and slowly life moved back to normal. Tom Edwards came home and Frank placed him in full control of the office. The Bedale Annual Hunt Ball was hastily arranged; Frank's invitation read:

The Master and the Bedale Hunt Committee have pleasure in inviting
Mr Frank Bowers and Friend
Thursday the 15th of January, 1919
at
Leases Hall, Leeming Bar.
From 9.00 p.m.   Carriages at 2.30 a.m.   R.S.V.P.

That's handy, thought Frank, I can arrange for Dick to take a couple of horses through the day before, attend the Ball and have a full day's hunting from Ainderby Steeple next morning. Only snag's a partner.

'Why don't you invite Evelyn over from Malton?' said his mother when Frank showed her the invitation; 'she can always stay here.'

'Good idea, mother,' replied Frank, not yet fully appreciative of the complexities of the adult female mind.

'And why don't you take your sister Muriel and try and find her a partner at the same time.'

'Who would you suggest?'

'Tom Edwards.'

'Really!'

220

'Muriel was saying only the other day how much she admired him. I noticed she was making eyes at him every time he came to visit when on leave. He looked very handsome in his uniform, I thought.'

Little did Mary think that her intuitive scheming would result in two marriages within six months.

Tom, it transpired, had been transferred to the Army Pay Corps soon after joining up and had enjoyed a relatively safe but boring job for most of the time. He had developed into a lively, witty companion and as the evening wore on it was obvious that Muriel, although a year or two older, was entirely smitten by her dashing escort. Within days they became engaged and almost at once wedding plans were in full swing. Frank was delighted to welcome such an efficient young man into the family and by way of a wedding present made him an equal profit-sharing partner in the auctioneering business.

Frank firmly believed all his long life that major events in one's life often come in threes.

Only a few weeks earlier he had been delighted to be asked to act as best man for his great friend, Major Arnold Cheesman, and was equally delighted that Arnold was soon to take himself off to Blackstone Manor near Oundle to learn farming.

'As soon as the hunting season is in full swing, you must come and stay, Frank; hunting with the Cottesmore and the Pytchley; Frank Freeman in control again.'

'Can't be bad,' said Frank.

And then, before he was fully aware of what was happening, he was engaged to be married himself.

'It was sort of engineered by my mother,' he later told friends.

'Your cousin Miles would be a nice choice as best man,' his mother suggested, knowing full well that if any one of her son's 'wild friends' as she called them, were asked the chances were he would probably be too drunk to perform his duties.

'But he's still in the Army out in Egypt, mother,' Frank explained.

'Then you must write and invite him over,' she said.

In the final outcome Miles had agreed to officiate. He was still single, having ditched Sarah, but at the time of writing deep in the throes of a highly charged affair with a night-club hostess in Cairo. In the event he missed his boat and with two days to spare Frank called on the services of Captain Michael Jopling to act in his place. Although Frank was never quite sure, he always blamed Jopling for the fiasco which took place on his wedding morning.

221

Following a wild bachelor night the previous evening at the Crown in Boroughbridge, Frank, his head still reeling, gingerly drove his mother over to Norton near Malton, to visit relatives. They would eventually bring her to the parish church for the midday ceremony.

Having picked up the best man on the way, the two Army friends, immaculate in dark blue dress uniform, both identical, wearing swords and spurs, retired as prearranged to the bar of the Green Man in Malton for a champagne breakfast. Most of Frank's drinking pals had been invited to what was in effect a continuance of the previous evening's festivities and it was well turned eleven-thirty before serious thought was given to 'getting to the church on time.'

Again Frank was never quite clear who it was produced a couple of donkeys, complete with saddles and bridles, but suddenly there they were in the bar.

'Right you lads, get mounted,' urged Tom Edwards. Frank's brother-in-law later vehemently denied having anything to do with it.

It transpired the donkeys had not been ridden since the previous September; to say they were frisky and anxious to divest themselves of

'Much better going back'ards way, Frank'

222

their overweight burdens must be an understatement. Michael Jopling's mount was obviously the quieter of the two and soon subjected itself to being led around the ground floor rooms of the hotel past startled early guests in the dining room, through the hall and out into the market square.

Frank's mount, introduced to him as Joey, was the biggest donkey he ever saw and certainly the most cussed. To intense merriment it had him off twice in the bar.

'*It's better going backwards!*' shouted Michael between fits of laughter as finally Frank had him under control and, surrounded by a happy cheering throng of wedding guests, the two donkeys, with their bouncing burdens, made the short trip to Norton parish church, arriving at precisely twelve-fifteen, fully ten minutes after the fuming bride.

'I'll never forgive you for this,' hissed Evelyn out of the corner of her mouth as they finally stood before the Reverend Don, a clergyman of a mild but aloof bearing, destined eventually for high office within the church.

The parson eyed the grinning groom and his swaying best man with some distaste. He winced perceptibly as Michael Jopling gave a loud uncontrollable belch, and blanched visibly as the stale smell of booze, coupled with the pungent smell of donkeys, hit him full in the face.

'Frank, you both smelt awful at the altar,' gurgled Evelyn at the reception back at the Green Man. She had soon come round to seeing the funny side of the affair. The happiness of the occasion, the surprise archway of swords outside the church and the ride through the town in a magnificent open landau pulled by two superb grey horses (borrowed from the Scots Greys, now based back at York) had all helped to mellow her initial annoyance.

Later that night, as they lay together for the first time in their honeymoon hotel bedroom on the cliffs above Scarborough, Frank thought longingly of Charlotte. Funny, he mused, such vivid memories ought to make me feel guilty. He was scarcely aware of what the new woman in his life was saying.

'Frank?'

'Yes, sweetheart.'

'Are you listening to me?'

'I think so.'

'I said, for a few awful moments waiting outside the church when they told me you hadn't arrived, I thought you must have changed your mind.'

'Not likely! For better or for worse, isn't that what I promised?'

'Yes, darling.'

'And don't forget you've promised to honour and obey.'

'I'll try not to,' said Evelyn mischievously.

Frank lay awake well into the early hours. Perhaps it had been a grave mistake to surrender his bachelor status – his mother had very cleverly organised this union; it was her way of striving to settle him down. Evelyn lay in a deep sleep beside him. She has waited for me all these years, he mused, perhaps I shall learn to love her eventually.

19

The Move to 'The Brooms'

Early in 1920, Frank successfully applied for the tenancy of the Brooms Farm near Thirsk, formerly on Lord Downs' Estate; so in April he achieved his ambition to reside in the Bedale Country. Moving the live and deadstock by road from Farrick House occupied three days and proved to be a most traumatic experience.

It had been decided to move the cattle on the first day, 'Wild West style' as Frank put it, two mounted men in front to lead the way and two behind.

'What about that bunch of Highland steers?' queried Dick Boynton, 'mad as March hares they are!'

'We'll bunch 'em up with the shorthorns,' Frank had replied, 'that'll steady 'em.'

All went well until Frank, at the head of the column, moved down the Great North Road into the centre of Boroughbridge. Suddenly a car came swiftly round the corner of his beloved Crown Inn, changed down a gear, backfired, and chaos ensued.

Frank was riding a nice young horse, recently purchased, called Goldfinch – he was in fact a very green four-year-old at the time and had only seen Frank's car in the yard at home. He shot straight up in the air and came over backwards. Miraculously, and not knowing quite how he did it, Frank slid off sideways, landed softly on his feet still clutching the reins, and had time to step aside as the horse came over onto his back, all four legs flaying the air, crashed over onto his side and then scrambled to his feet. Apart from a wound to the poll and a grazed hock, the horse was none the worse.

'I'll bet that's the last time you rear up, me lad,' Frank said aloud as he remounted, dismayed to find that the leather on the pommel of his favourite saddle had been scraped away and that the tree was broken.

'Sorry about that, young fella,' shouted the driver, 'fraid your other hoss has bolted.'

225

'Oh! It's you, squire,' said Frank curtly as the driver removed his goggles; he then noticed one of his farm men still firmly deposited on his rear in the middle of the road and his other young horse fast disappearing northwards in the direction of Ripon.

'It looks as if some of your longhorned cattle have taken orrf as well, what?' said Colonel North. 'Quite a rodeo in fact, eh?'

Meanwhile Dick Boynton, aided by the Auction Mart foreman, Tant Walmsley, were doing their best to gather up the remaining cattle.

'Christ, we need properly trained quarter horses, not inexperienced hunters,' shouted Dick, as they vainly tried to coax the Highland cattle back together.

'You'll need to give us a hand, boss! There's quite a few gone through a snicket into Horsefair and they're knockin' hell out of them stalls in the market place.'

'Excuse me, squire, I'm needed. Let's hope we meet again under different circumstances. If only you could learn to keep those cars of yours under control.'

'It's because it's a Jerry, you know, wish I'd never bought the blasted thing, always bangin' and firin', wife's forever tellin' me to buy British. Tells me she can hear me five miles orrf comin' home.'

'You only need to reduce the mixture lever on the steering column,' said Frank helpfully.

'Humm! Good idea, Bowers, never thought of it; no good myself mechanically, you know.'

'Anyhow I must go, squire, otherwise these Scottish beasts could be half way to York.'

'Let me know if there's any damage, had so many complaints, taken out an insurance policy on the blasted thing.'

'Well, I've ruined a good saddle for a start, heaven knows what else these cattle can have demolished.'

Eventually the cattle were all rounded up and coaxed into the inn yard.

'There's one of those big Highland steers missing, boss,' reported Dick.

'And my hoss,' added the young farmhand.

'Never mind th' hoss,' said Frank irritably, 'we'll surely pick him up on our way towards Baldersby; one of you stay with these cattle, the three of us had best search the town.'

They searched in vain and were returning through the Horsefair when a young gypsy urchin called out, 'Mister! Be you lookin' for a big shaggy beast?'

'We are, young fella, do you ken his whereabouts?'

226

'Well, I might.'

'Would sixpence help you remember?'

'Nah, I caint just think weer a seed 'im.'

'Here's a shilling then,' said Frank flicking the coin towards him. The youngster deftly caught the spinning coin, and checked its authenticity. 'He's fast as a thief wi' his horns in yon snicket.'

Frank dismounted and viewed his steer fast by his head in the middle of the passage.

'Now, Dick, how do you reckon we can get him out of there?' asked Frank.

'Well, we can allus prod him forward, give 'im a smart tap with your crop and see what happens.'

The beast bellowed and struggled but in spite of constant urging from behind was unable to move his head.

'Let's go round and come in the other way, boss, perhaps we can drive him out back'ards.'

Again no amount of pushing or gentle persuasion about his head had the desired effect.

'We'll have to borrow a rope and drag him for'ards,' said Frank.

As they came out of the passage there on the pavement stood the gypsy lad in his ragged clothes; this time he had a younger sister clothed in a filthy dress much too long for her and an even younger brother, equally dirty, but already trained to stick out his hand to beg for alms, clinging to his arm.

'I say, maister,' said the youth.

'Don't bother me now, sonny,' snarled Frank. 'Nip down to the Crown will you, Dick, there's sure to be a few halters somewhere about the stable yard.'

'I say, maister.'

'Oh God,' sighed Frank, 'shove off, young fella, and take those two urchins with you.'

'Theer's a butcher's shop next door,' said the lad.

'So what?' growled Frank. 'Be off with you before this beast comes charging out.'

'He wain't till you saw a lump off his horns,' said the youth.

Frank and Dick looked at each other, grinning sheepishly, and then burst out laughing.

'You're a clever lad an' no mistake,' chuckled Frank. 'Here's half a crown, now off you go and take those youngsters out of harm's way.'

Armed with a meat saw Frank and his men approached the still bellowing beast.

'Slight problem, boss,' said Tant Walmsley.

'What's that?' asked Frank.

'Well, when we free 'is head he'll come chargin' forward and tak' us wi' 'im like.'

'Ummh!' said Frank thoughtfully, 'So what do you suggest?'

'Someone's going to hev to git astride 'im from behind.'

'Right, off you go and come in from the other side; Dick and I can try and restrain him till you get aboard.'

The steer gave a great bellow as Tant vaulted onto his back. Both Frank and his foreman bolted out of the passage but the beast, struggle and plunge as he might, was still fast.

'Roared like a bloody lion,' said Frank sheepishly as he returned and handed Tant the saw.

'A couple of inches off each side should be enough, Tant, we'll wait outside at the end of the passage. Take care, think on.'

'Rather 'im than me, boss,' said Dick grinning. 'He'll come out of there wi' a hell of a rush.'

By this time a crowd of curious onlookers had gathered.

'Keep well back,' shouted Frank as he heard Tant give a 'Whoopi!', and suddenly there he was, still astride the enraged bullock clutching manfully to each magnificent horn.

'Ride 'im, cowboy,' yelled Dick as the crowd scattered.

In the middle of the Horsefair, the main thoroughfare of the town (but now long gone to make room for vehicular traffic) stood a large stone watering trough; the beast propped on all four legs two or three times as it approached the obstacle, arched his back, Tant flew through the air and landed in the middle of the trough with a huge splash.

The onlookers clapped; Dick laughingly ran to his aid; unconcerned the bullock carried on towards his companions in the stable yard.

Eventually the cavalcade moved slowly northwards once more. Frank had been expecting to find the runaway horse grazing at the roadside. Two miles further on they came across a collection of Romany caravans. 'The true "wandering people",' Frank remarked to his foreman. 'Keep your eyes peeled, that horse won't have been allowed past here.'

'Can't see any sign of him, boss.'

'Well, their own horses are pegged out down the lane there, just trot off past 'em and have a look in the copse at the end of the track.'

After a while one or two sullen-looking men and youths started to gather; their spokesman detached himself. 'Can we do anything for you, maister?'

228

'We're just looking for a riderless horse, one of my men was thrown a couple of miles back.'

'Nivver seed owt of 'im around 'ere,' replied the gypsy; 'mind I've bin asleep,' he added as he noticed Dick trotting back up the lane leading the missing animal, minus saddle and bridle.

'No sign of any tack, sir,' Dick reported, 'but he'd been tied to a tree with this old rope halter.'

Treading carefully, Frank addressed the spokesman in a loud voice, 'I wonder if any of your men picked up his saddle and bridle off the road as he galloped through here, there'll be a guinea for anyone who found them.'

A ragged-looking youth of about fifteen dived behind one of the caravans and came across to Frank carrying the missing articles. 'I fun these just down the lane theer, didn't ken as they belonged to anyone like.'

'Right lads, mount up,' Frank ordered his own men; as they moved away he tossed the gold coin into the midst of the belligerent-looking gypsies.

When they were safely on their way Frank cantered back to join Dick at the back of the column. 'Well worth a guinea to get out of there without being attacked, Dick, just look, there's one hell of a scrap going on over one little gold coin.'

20

Ruth Remembered

The hunting season of 1923–24 proved a difficult one; foot-and-mouth restrictions were in force from the end of December until mid-February. The third Lord Masham died in early January and her Ladyship, who had been in indifferent health for some time, died shortly afterwards in London at the end of May.

A niece of Lord Masham, Lady Lloyd Graeme (later Lady Cunliffe Lister) behaved in a most generous manner. Through the trustees of the Swinton Estate, in cash and kind, she gave three thousand pounds to the Hunt and lent fifteen hunters and two cobs until the end of the season.

Hounds met at Bedale on the 30th December and had taken a good fox at a fast pace from Theakston via Londonderry through Gatenby Wood down to the River Swale which he crossed. The river being in full flood most of the field galloped away to the Maunby Ferry.

Captain Frank Burrill from New Zealand, who was staying with his brother at The Greens, Masham, decided to swim his horse across. 'I shouted to warn him,' Bobbie Dawson told Frank later, 'but he was in there before I could stop him. Apparently he's been practising swimming alongside his horse in the River Ure which runs alongside his brother's property, failing to realise they're two totally different types of river.* Anyhow, his horse got into difficulties halfway across. Burrill started to swim back towards us but the current was too strong and he got swept downstream. Captain Owen of Snape and Dr Wynn Davies from Thirsk tried to help; we knotted stirrup leathers and bridles together but we failed to reach him and he just disappeared.'

It was four days later before the unfortunate Captain's body was found a couple of miles downstream.

---

* The River Swale is known to be one of the swiftest and deepest rivers for its size in England and Wales.

'Amazing the risks a fella, or for that matter a lady, will take in the heat of the chase,' said Frank philosophically.

Frank also remembered his meetings just before the war with Lord Tanfield. Although not an ardent follower of the chase, he was nevertheless a good supporter of it, and in any matter connected with the welfare of the Hunt his generosity could always be relied on. He used to ride good-looking, well-bred horses, and was always immaculately turned out. He had lost an eye in a shooting accident on the grouse moors; a Royal guest staying at the Castle some years before had committed the unpardonable sin (for him) of firing down the line of the butts; a stray pellet had lodged itself in his Lordship's right eye and a troublesome glass eye had replaced it.

Lord Tanfield was keen on cricket; the front lawn of the big house had been turned into a cricket pitch and remains so to this day. August 20th (unless it fell on a Sunday) was the traditional annual duel between the Bedale Hunt subscribers and an eleven, hand-picked, of hunting farmers.

Rather like gentlemen versus players, the subscribers were usually public school, having retained different garish hooped caps and striped blazers awarded as school colours at, say, Sedbergh or Shrewsbury, even Eton and Harrow colours would occasionally be trotted out. Whereas the farmers were solid, dependable, no-nonsense cricketers, a product of their local village side, not always immaculately turned out but usually too good for The Nobs, as they called the opposition. The quality of the cricket was sufficiently high to ensure an all-day game; an eleven-thirty start with lunch in the Castle at one-thirty, tea on the terrace at four-thirty.

Frank had never been much of a cricketer but was capable of slogging a few runs batting about number seven or eight. If asked he could bowl medium fast left arm over the wicket. A curious delivery stride with the left arm suddenly appearing from behind his head, slanting the ball across the batsman, occasionally got him a wicket or two.

His friend Arnold Cheesman had been persuaded to take on the captaincy of the farmers' team that year; a brilliant all-round sportsman, he had played for the Yorkshire County School boys' team, then the Colts.

'Frank,' he had bellowed down the phone the night before the match; he always shouted into the telephone receiver as if the recipients were deaf, Frank recalled. 'John Brown at Hutton Grange should have been playing for us tomorrow as opening fast bowler, but he's bin knocked down by his bull, not serious, just bruised. I've tried quite a few to replace him but they're too busy with harvest or whatever, so you'll have to play. I shall need you to open the bowling; get some practice in bowling at the barn doors; you can get your arm over tonight instead of your leg!'

He remembered driving slowly up the heavily rutted road from Ripon to Tanfield in glorious sunshine, arriving at about eleven o'clock, in good time to get changed. Lord Tanfield was already in the courtyard handing out glasses of sherry. Dressed in a faded blue and white striped cricket blazer, with a wide brimmed floppy white straw hat, a monocle covering his bad eye, he looked every inch a member of the landed aristocracy.

'Morning, Bowers, didn't know you were a cricketer. Here, have a snifter, only sherry I'm afraid. If you want anything stronger catch hold of Boothman, me butler, he's been given instructions to hover around you fellas all day and see you get plenty of vittals. Confounded fella should be here now doing this job, probably in the pantry helping that red-headed wife of his prepare lunch. Can't tear himself away from her side; mind you she is a smasher; could fancy her myself if I were a younger fella, eh!, what? Best housekeeper we've ever had and I took 'em on only last year, without references.'

The subscribers won the toss and elected to bat; Frank bowled badly and was taken off after four overs.

'Thanks, Frank,' shouted Arnold, 'have a rest, I reckon they've taken nearly thirty runs off you so I'll have a go myself!'

Arnold took two quick wickets and slowed down the scoring rate dramatically with his slow off-spin. Play was halted at twelve-thirty for drinks. 'Line and length, that's what it needs to bottle 'em up,' Arnold was saying to Frank as the butler, resplendent in morning suit, marched imperiously towards the players carrying a large silver salver.

'Orange juice, sir?' he said politely – as their eyes met Frank noticed a puzzled look of recognition cross the butler's face before he turned sharply away.

Frank had recognised his man straight away. The missing elder son from Nab End; his so-called redheaded wife his Lordship has taken such a shine to, just had to be Ruth from Cow Hill. Then Frank remembered with dismay his complete lack of memory of the night's activities once he returned to the pub, how Dick Boynton had gleefully handed him over into her maternal care, the smell of perfume still around his bedroom next morning, the warm glow in her eyes as she prepared his breakfast. 'Ah well, maybe I'll ask her what went on now I've found her again!'

At lunch just over forty overs had been bowled, and the subscribers' score read, 165 for 5, last man 26.

'A few quick wickets after lunch,' said Arnold in the dressing room, 'and we can beat this lot; his Lordship intends umpiring for the next session. He's noted for giving doubtful leg-before-wicket decisions, so think on you bowlers. He only has one good eye; if you hit the pads don't forget to appeal, the louder the better.'

The lunch was a splendid affair; home-made vegetable soup followed by a whole grouse each, roast potatoes, fresh vegetables from the Castle gardens, followed by Wensleydale cheese and biscuits; a delicious Medoc from Maison Dourthe Frères had been a perfect partner to the grouse (shot by his Lordship on the glorious twelfth), followed by a special vintage port from the vast cellars below the Castle.

'Bottled by Yeatman Vinhos in Oporto,' announced his Lordship, 'before I was born, decanted it myself.'

Frank was still chuckling over the incident which had taken place as the teams sat down to dine; a young fellow playing for the subscribers, straight out of public school, was heard to remark in a rather loud voice, 'Who's the old codger walking round with that daft-looking floppy hat and a big stick in his hand?'

'I happen to be Lord Tanfield, young sir and this big stick as you call it, around your neck, happens to be a bishop's crook,' came the sharp reply. 'If I pull on this you'll be on your back, probably where you belong; as my guest, young sir, I expect better manners. Think on, I shall be umpiring the rest of the match, so keep your pads out of the way of the ball,' and with a merry twinkle to his eye he'd let his suitably chastised young prisoner go.

Frank tried to catch a glimpse of Ruth Merriman during the luncheon break, to no avail. 'Maybe Boothman has said something to her,' he mused, very much aware that the butler was keeping as far away as possible.

However, as he made his way along the passage from the dining room to the quadrangle he passed the open door into the kitchen – and there she was! Frank watched her lithe movements for a few moments and then stepped quietly into the room, shutting the door behind him.

Although slightly startled she recognised him immediately.

'Ah, my young and handsome auctioneer.' She moved closer and took hold of both his hands. 'The only man who's slept with me and been unable to remember what it was like.'

Frank was about to move away when suddenly the door crashed open and there stood the butler, jealous rage oozed out of his every pore.

'I watched you sneak in here, young Mr Bowers. Ruth told me about the night you got drunk after Deepdale Sports and she looked after you,' he shouted.

'Hold on you two,' said Frank.'Calm down. You're in a very funny situation if I blow the gaff to his Lordship. I must say you're operating a bit close to home; you're wanted for theft if your father cares to prefer charges and I hate to think what Seth would do to you, madam, if he caught up with you.'

'You won't give us away, will you, Frank?' Ruth pleaded. 'We hoped if we could gain experience here we would then move away down south with suitable references. It's working out so far.'

'No skin off my nose,' said Frank, 'it seems his Lordship is well satisfied with your work. I helped your father out of a tight spot, Boothman, after you made off with his savings. He repaid me after a few months; surely you haven't spent all that cash?'

'Still got two thousand pounds left, and I've been troubled ever since.'

'Well, how would it be if you trusted me to take it back. It's in a bank, is it?'

'Yes,' they both replied simultaneously.

'Let me deliver a cheque for two thousand pounds into his hand – I'll keep mum as to where you are.'

'What a smashing young fella you are,' said Ruth lightly kissing Frank on his cheek. Her nearness, her perfume, her air of sensuality suddenly opened up memory cells within Frank's brain.

Brusquely he said, 'Let me have a cheque for two thousand before I leave tonight, Boothman, and I reckon your jobs are safe.'

He turned once more in the doorway and said slowly and softly to the beautiful woman in front of him, 'I have just remembered' – she knew exactly what he meant.

The sun continued to beat down as the afternoon session wore on; 198 for 8 with a stubborn ninth wicket partnership building up.

'Have another go, Frank,' said Arnold as he tossed him the ball. 'That different line of direction of yours might do the trick. Pitch 'em up and aim at the leg stump if you can, they'll probably try and cart you over the leg boundary, so we'll drop a man out there.'

Frank had just asked his Lordship to stand back to enable him to bowl as close as possible to the stumps when the wind played one of its tricks; a small twister caused by heat currents swept straight down the wicket, pulling up dust from inside the batting crease.

'Dammit,' cursed his Lordship, turning to face Frank, 'got some grit in me glass eye. Boothman!' he bellowed letting his monocle drop. Suddenly there was Boothman striding across the turf, a towel over one arm and carrying a silver dish full of cold water with the other. Frank watched fascinated as the offending eye was dropped neatly into the tray.

'Swill it round, man,' ordered his Lordship. 'Right, as I bend my head backwards you drop it back in.'

'Quite a nuisance, sir, this dust, extraordinary how many times we've had to give that eye an early bath.' He winked at Frank as he added, 'Could I suggest an eyepatch for his Lordship instead of the monocle for these outside functions?'

'Dammit, man, I'll decide whether I wear an eye patch or not,' shouted Lord Samuel, straightening up too soon. 'Blast it, it's come out again, where's it gone this time?'

'It's dropped down the back of my pads, sir,' said the unknown youth, the recipient of his Lordship's mock anger at lunch time.

'Hmm, it's you, young fella, well caught.'

'Go on, Boothman, fish it out, he can't retrieve it with batting gloves on.'

Once the offending eye was back in place, the butler departed at exactly the same steady pace at which he had arrived.

'Play on,' called Lord Samuel rather testily before Boothman had got half way back towards the square leg boundary. Unfortunately Frank tried to send his first ball down too fast. It was a rank long hop just outside the leg stick. The batsman, who had been in for the best part of an hour, seized on it immediately and cracked it towards the leg boundary; one screaming bounce and it hit – 'Straight up the arse' were the words Lord Samuel used on the numerous times he recounted the story to his friends. 'What a perfect butler,' he would say. 'Neither stopped or turned round, and although he staggered momentarily, not a drop of water left his dish.'

Frank took the next two wickets cheaply and the subscribers were all out for 206.

'Now lads,' said Arnold, 'we've got three hours until six-thirty minus a quarter of an hour for tea, that works out at nicely under four an over, so we want a steady start, don't get out; with plenty of wickets in hand we can always accelerate and we should beat 'em. David Hare, you can open with me; Dodds number three, Loadman number four, and the rest of you look in the score book.'

The plan seemed to be working perfectly when Frank went to the wicket with seven wickets down – Arnold Cheesman was still there having scored 90 runs out of a total of 186.

'Only twenty more runs needed, Frank,' said the skipper as they met in the middle; 'there's plenty of time, so play yourself in. I'll try and take as much of the bowling as possible; don't know much about this chap who's just come on but his first ball was far too good for Bob Broadley.'

235

Frank took guard. 'Two please, sir,' he demanded off Lord Samuel.

'Two what, Bowers?' came the reply.

'Middle and leg, if you please,' shouted Frank.

'Why didn't you say so?' came the curt reply. 'Away from you slightly, a bit more, that's two!'

Frank groaned and turned to say something to the stumper; he was slightly alarmed to find the wicketkeeper had retreated some fifteen yards – so had three slips and there were now two gulleys placed alongside them.

'Come up close,' the fielding captain was saying to Bobbie Dawson who, grinning broadly, moved to within three yards of Frank at forward short leg.

'I'll knock your block off if this chap bowls down the leg side,' boasted Frank to his great friend and rival.

'No you won't, Frank,' grinned Bobbie, 'top of the bowling averages for Yorkshire Seconds this chap! Our skipper's bin saving him in case we looked like getting beat.'

Frank looked up to find the bowler still walking away from him.

'Fastest chap in Yorkshire,' grinned Bobbie, 'needs a thirty-five yard run-up to get his true rhythm; that first ball which removed Broadley's middle stump was only a loosener.'

Frank could feel the air of expectancy around the ground; suddenly nobody was talking, everybody was watching.

Frank had time to admire his assailant running towards him, increasing his pace with every stride, then suddenly he was at the wicket, his arm came over, Frank picked up the blur of a cricket ball heading straight towards his middle stump; he lunged forward with bat and pad together and closed his eyes. Nothing happened, then he heard the thump of the ball well over to his right side and above shoulder height.

'Still rising at about ninety miles an hour when the stumper caught it,' grinned Bobbie, thoroughly relishing Frank's discomfiture.

As the bowler retraced his steps almost to the boundary, Frank had time to walk up the wicket to meet his approaching skipper.

'Fast off-cutter,' said Arnold, 'swung away off the wicket, missed your bat by six inches. Perhaps be best to let one or two go by and we'll try and score at the other end!'

Frank did as instructed; he felt quite professional as he lifted the bat over his shoulder and watched the next two balls whistle past to thud into the keeper's gloves.

What the heck, he thought to himself, I'm going to have a crack at this next ball. His wild swing turned into a perfect late cut, the ball whistled down to where a third man ought to have been stationed – four runs.

'Super shot, Frank,' enthused his captain; 'leave this last ball alone so I can have a crack at this spin bowler at the other end.'

Once more Frank did as instructed; he lifted his bat to shoulder arms without getting his front leg forward and across. This ball was not quite as quick as the others Frank had faced; he had time to watch it pitch and cut back the other way, and not only did it lift the middle stump out of the ground, it broke it in two in the process.

'Hard luck, Frank,' he vaguely heard Bobbie remark with some glee as he walked slowly back.

'If the skipper doesn't set about the slow bowler this over, I reckon we might get licked,' Frank remarked as he threw his gloves and bat into the kit bag. 'What's the score?'

'One hundred and ninety for eight, two wickets to fall; seventeen runs to win.'

Arnold Cheesman, only too aware of the danger, hit fours off the next two deliveries.

'That makes him ninety-eight; we need nine more to win,' remarked the scorer.

Arnold refused to take a single off the third ball.

'A six and a four off these next three balls, and he's got his century and we've won the match,' someone exclaimed exultantly.

Whack! Arnold hit the next ball right out of the meat of the bat.

'Six over long on,' shouted Frank jumping to his feet – then he watched horrified as the unknown young man who'd last caught Lord Tanfield's glass eye in his pads, raced round the boundary and plucked the ball out of the air one-handed, over his head.

'Brilliant catch, sir,' shouted an excited spectator jumping to his feet.

'Nonsense,' howled Frank.

'Not out,' chorused his team mates.

'His foot was over the white line when he caught it, sir!' Frank bellowed in the direction of Lord Samuel, only to notice with dismay that Arnold was walking dejectedly back towards the changing rooms. Lord Samuel, standing imperiously in the middle of the ground, had his hand raised – the forefinger pointing to the sky.

'Carried over, six runs to the farmers,' shouted another spectator.

'I'm in charge here, sir,' came his Lordship's shouted reply. 'If I say a man's out, he's out! Have a look at the score sheet after the match.'

The last man for the farmers' team took guard but he really didn't know what an arm ball was; he took a wild swipe at what he thought would be a leg break, the ball came straight on, fizzed off the wicket and clean bowled him.

'All out for one hundred and ninety-eight,' groaned Frank. 'First time the subscribers have won for ages, apparently.'

'Hard luck, skipper,' Frank said by way of commiseration later in the little private bar Lord Samuel had set up in the morning room; 'robbed of a century by that little twerp over there. He carried over, you know.'

'That little twerp, as you so rightly put it, happens to be my nephew in a round about sort of way, he's a Walmsley-Smith from Malton, staying at Leases Hall with my cousin.

Just then they were joined by Bobbie Dawson. 'Smashing game eh, fellas?'

'Nonsense,' said Frank, 'we were definitely robbed at the finish.'

'Hardly,' said Bobbie, 'another over from young Ford and he would easily have blasted the last two men out.'

'You're supposed to play *bona fide* subscribers in your team,' Frank said, 'not imported top class bowlers like that chap.'

'Well, that's just where you're wrong, Frank; he's moved into the old Coach House at Ainderby Quernhow with his parents. I heard about him and persuaded him to subscribe. He may not hunt, but he's sure as hell going to be a welcome addition to our side next year.'

After a few more drinks Frank threw discretion to the winds. He noticed Boothman the butler had disappeared and twice he had caught sight of Ruth standing in the doorway as if she wished to give him a message.

Frank slipped away down the dimly-lit passage which led to the servants' quarters; he became aware of her presence and her perfume even before she caught him by the hand and drew him quickly through the door into her private quarters. As she deliberately bolted the door Frank found himself stammering.

'I came to ask him for the cheque.'

'His Lordship's sent Neil down into Tanfield with the pony and trap to see the river bailiff; he catches trout and grayling to order. There's quite a big private dinner party here tomorrow night.'

Frank stepped back momentarily as Ruth approached him. Suddenly she was in his arms, and their lips were very close as she whispered, 'He won t be back for at least half an hour, and anyway we can hear when the pony and trap goes past the window; there's only one way in,' she added seductively, and as their lips met she mumbled,'You sure are going to remember me this time, my gorgeous young auctioneer!!'

238

21

Straying Away

Frank was really in trouble at home about this time. His mother had tried to cling on to Frank since he married Evelyn six years earlier but as she got older and more cantankerous, the two women fell out continuously. Finally she moved out and took a small flat overlooking the Stray in Harrogate.

If anything, this gave Frank more licence to please himself. The last time he'd set off on his own to the Doncaster St Leger meeting, he'd finished up in Scarborough at the Derwent Hunt Ball.

Evelyn remarked, 'Without me, and in a borrowed suit!' She continued, 'Last spring, off you went to Twickenham and the next thing I hear from you is the following Tuesday, in Paris! And where have you been this time for God's sake, dressed like that? The last time I saw you was three o'clock Saturday morning, getting undressed to come to bed. It wouldn't have been so bad if I'd been at home, but to leave me at Harry Cail's, stranded, no vehicle, with no explanation; you realise he had to run me home? – And it's now Monday evening with no word!'

Frank was standing in the kitchen looking very sorry for himself. He was still dressed in his black evening trousers, held up by bright red braces, the evening shirt was open at the neck, minus collar, but with the front stud still in place; he had Harry's tartan house slippers on his feet, and a very care-worn car coat over his shoulders.

'Frank, you look dreadful,' said Evelyn, her mood mellowing, for she never could be angry with him for long. 'You obviously haven't shaved for three days, where in the world have you been?'

'Well, darling, it's all a little bit hazy at the start; you went to bed and Harry and I had a nightcap, a double brandy as I recall, then I suddenly remembered I'd left my favourite pipe and tobacco on the bar down at the Bridge Hotel. So I nipped down in the car and there, still at the bar, was Willie Barker and quite a few more revellers. I didn't want to seem rude and walk straight out, and they sort of kept me there. Then about nine

239

o'clock somebody produced some delicious bacon and egg sandwiches, and I remembered I'd promised to go over to Barbon near Kirkby Lonsdale to the meet of the Lunesdale foxhounds at the Barbon Hotel.'

'And you went like that with your carpet slippers on?' asked Evelyn incredulously.

'Well it didn't seem to matter by then,' explained Frank. 'I got there about eleven-thirty, just as they moved off, and there was one hell of a party going on. They had masks and brushes and other trophies on the bar and so I stayed behind. It must have been teatime before the landlady, you remember Joan, and her daughter June, they came to our wedding, the daughter was about fourteen then with a mass of freckles and her hair in a long pony tail? Well, she has an Australian friend, same age, a smashing girl who's been working for them as the chef. About teatime Joan asked me could I do her a favour – "If I give you a bottle of whisky," she said, could I accompany them to Tilbury Docks to see Sue, that's the chef, off on her return home to Australia.

'I didn't like the look of her old banger so I said I'd drive them; we set off about midnight, consumed the bottle of whisky on the way and got to Tilbury about ten o'clock.'

'It's a wonder you didn't insist on taking them to church in your carpet slippers!' said Evelyn sarcastically.

'We saw Sue aboard and settled in her cabin, then Joan realised she knew the Chief Engineer who invited us to lunch with him at the Captain's table. I was ravenous by this time but we had to go through all the palaver of the pre-lunch cocktail party.'

'Poor you,' said Evelyn, 'and still dressed like that?'

'Well it was a big ship, S.S. *Aquitania* I think, amongst all those people nobody seemed to notice,' said Frank. 'There were streamers and bunting, a brass band and the girls were crying when we came ashore.'

'My heart bleeds for you, Frank, it really does,' said Evelyn.

'Then Joan wanted to visit her favourite little cafe in the West End. I vaguely remember cucumber sandwiches, muffins and some wonderful cream cakes; then of course we had to drive back to Barbon, which seemed to take all night.'

'Then what?' asked Evelyn.

'Well I snatched a few hours sleep and here I am!'

'It really is the height of irresponsibility, Frank,' she said. 'What about the firm, what about the farm?'

'Well Dick Boynton knows how to run the farm all right and Tom Edwards can run the business with his eyes closed; incidentally I'm going to sell out to him at the Walshford end, let him pay for it as he goes along and I'll concentrate here at Ripon.'

Later that evening as Frank relaxed by the fire in the snug, clean-shaven once more, Evelyn confronted him.

'I never asked you about your impromptu Paris trip and I'm not going to embarrass you by insisting, but you could have told me about the Derwent Hunt Ball.'

'Oh, I'm going to blame Bobbie Dawson for that escapade. He's well in with this racing crowd now you know, he's never looked back since he started winning all those point-to-point races a few years ago; Solitaire in 1920, Atlanta in 1921, and Sprit Sail in 1922, set him up. Now he's training these National Hunt horses, he studies form and gets to know when they're trying.

'We had a first and second backed in the big race, made out very nicely on the day; champagne party after racing and we seemed to drift in with a party of Derwent Hunt followers who invited us to their Hunt Ball at the Grand Hotel at Scarborough that night. Chap from Eberston Hall invited us back; that used to be the home of the famous Squire Osbaldeston till he lost all his estate gambling; he set us both up with a set of tails, said he'd an uncle died who used to be Sheriff of London and left him three dinner jacket suits and two sets of white tie and tails, all too big for him, but they fitted us a treat, then he took us to the do. Laughable really when we arrived, we were late as usual and there was quite a crowd at the bottom of the steps leading up into the hotel.

'They'd booked a chap with a horse called Dancing Jack to give a turn during the interval, th' hoss wore sort of felt padded boots over his hooves and could dance to piano music. Anyhow, they couldn't get the bloomin' horse to face those front steps so I borrowed a hat-pin from my host's wife, funny thing I still don't know his name; only knew him as James. Bobbie managed to get one foreleg on the bottom step and I stood off to one side and give him a slap on his arse with the pin well concealed, shot up like a bat out of hell! Two bounds and he was inside.

'Gave us a good turn though and when he'd finished, I think it was Bobbie's suggestion, not mine; it would be a good idea to see a "mare on the horse" instead of it always being t'other way round; we bumped the Mayor of Scarborough up into the saddle, trouble was he'd never learnt to ride and he got carted round the dance floor with his badge of office flapping around frightening the horse – scattered everybody seated at tables around the dance floor whilst the trumpeter played The Post-Horn Gallop, absolutely hilarious I thought.'

241

'You would, Frank,' said Evelyn. 'Did the Mayor get hurt?'

'Don't know,' said Frank. 'Th' hoss galloped out of the dance hall and I never saw either of them again.'

22

A Ringer

Frank was intrigued by a letter from the Chief Constable's office which arrived on his desk one morning, asking landowners for any information leading to the recovery of a racehorse called Flixton Grey which had vanished after winning a two-year-old race at York. 'A substantial reward' the letter read; it concluded with the information that a similar animal had been seen, being led, in the Pateley Bridge area.

It was only by a strange quirk of fortune that Frank stopped off for lunch at the Queen's Head near Summerbridge as he motored serenely up the dale on his way to Nab End. He had heard there was always a good lunch to be had and that local farmers and quite a few drovers frequented the bar, noted for serving the best ale in the district.

Hardly had he touched his first pint when in walked Seth Bailey, horse slaughterer, purchaser of fallen stock; a good customer at the market for any aged or infirm animal.

'Now Seth, good to see you. What's your poison?'

'A pint of ale for me, boss, nivver touch aught else.'

'Bit out of your territory up here, aren't you?'

'Aye, been on a bit of a queer mission like,' said Seth, 'way up into them hills to a spot called Nab End.'

'I know it,' said Frank, 'happen to be going there myself. Well?'

'I was o'er at Masham last week, big sheep sale on the square like, bought ivver say many broken-mouthed ewes for little money. Well, a very smart red-haired lass collared me after the sale, didn't say who she was, but could I go over to Nab End she says and put down a two-year-old racehorse; they'd dispose of the carcass like and there'd be thirty quid in it for me if I'd shoot it and keep me trap shut.'

'Sounds interesting,' said Frank.

'It were,' said Seth, 'but there was nowt wrong wi' th' hoss; it were a

243

four-year-old – maybe five when I looked in his gob – what's more he'd been painted a darker grey in parts. Some'at fishy, I thought, so I told th' fella as met me to keep his brass.'

'I think you did right, Seth, and unless I'm wrong this may turn out to be a serious matter. Keep it quiet, I happen to know the police are looking for a grey horse thought to be in these parts. I don't know why but I intend to find out.'

When Frank knocked at the door of Nab End, Mrs Boothman met him.

'By, am I glad to see you Mr Bowers. Come in, I were just goin' to brew up.'

'How's Ted?' he asked.

'Oh dear, you can't have heard. Buried 'im ten days ago; he were ready for off, suffered a bit towards the end like, all puffed up. I thowt as he had "new-monia", but th' doctor said it were – hang on a minute, he wrote it down for me, here you'd best read it.'

'Emphysema,' said Frank.

'Aye, that's it.'

'Air gets into the body tissue,' said Frank, 'eventually gets to the lungs and fills 'em with fluid, then the heart packs in.'

'That's just what happened, Mr Bowers, terrible to hear 'im tryin to get 'is breath; a blessin' in disguise when he passed over like.'

'So, who's at home then?'

'Just Tyrone, the youngest son and mysen.'

'And Neil?'

'He arrived for the funeral on his bike, and thanked all the folk as turned up at the wake – came back next day wi' that red-headed Ruth – her as bold as brass, calling me mum, soon sent her packing. They've bin back since, landed up wi' a smart pony and trap leading a grey thoroughbred entire horse. Out of the stables at Middleham, he said, brought it for a rest; they had a h'evil-lookin' fella with 'em an' they've hidden this hoss away up in Nannie's Nick.'

'Do you mind if I have a look at him?'

'Nah, help thysen.'

'Where's this Nannie's Nick?' asked Frank.

'Come here and I'll show thee; see that black-lookin' gill in th' fells o'er theer, well there's a grand walled paddock tucked away at this bottom end, that's where tha'll find 'im.'

When Frank arrived home later in the evening he got on the phone immediately to the local police inspector.

244

'Fred, will you be going down to the Rugby Club tonight?'*

'I will, Frank, but not too early,' said the worthy Fred Robinson. 'What's it about?'

'I understand York police are looking for a missing racehorse; I think I know where he is. Find out what it's all about.'

'I know what it's all about, but we'd better not discuss it over the phone.'

It was turned midnight before the distinctive knock announcing a member seeking admission after time, came at the bar door.

'Come in, Fred,' said Frank, allowing the burly inspector to squeeze past.

'Get yourself a drink and let's have a chat in the corner.'

'Right, Frank, it seems there was an attempted big betting coup at York racecourse recently; an untried two-year-old was substituted by a four-year-old with winning form called Flixton Grey, and he romped in at one hundred to eight, winning by about sixteen lengths.'

'Whew!' said Frank, '– a ringer!'

'Yes, but the bookies smelt a rat and refused to pay out; we know the owners of both horses and their trainers because they're all registered with Weatherby's, and we have the two-year-old; but when our officers went to the stables in Middleham, the four-year-old had been spirited away. There's quite a gang involved because at least four men and one woman slapped big sums of money, on the nose, right at the off; right down the line of bookies they went, caught 'em napping or so they thought! We have a good description of the woman –'

'Quite tall, very smart with striking red hair?' queried Frank.

'Correct, do you know her?'

'I think so, and I'm pretty certain I know where you can go to find the horse.'

'Well, let's be knowing.'

'Just let me check one or two details tomorrow morning, Fred; I'll ring you after lunch. By the way what'll happen to these folk ?'

'They will all be prosecuted when we get 'em rounded up and if found guilty, as I'm sure they will be, heavy fines – even prison!'

---

* Ripon Rugby Club was for many years the late night drinking haunt for Frank and his cronies. Thick curtains blocked out any give-away chinks of light, and with Chief Inspector Robinson, an ex-player himself, elected as President, any patrolling policeman knew to keep well away.

Frank rang Tanfield Castle early next morning.

'Sorry, sir, but Mr and Mrs Boothman left their positions here some while ago,' he was informed. 'They now live in Middleham, employed at one of the racing stables, not sure which one, but Mrs Boothman helps out behind the bar of the George and Dragon.'

It was midday as Frank elbowed his way through a noisy throng of stable lads towards the bar; he was able to stand back and have a good look at Ruth as she traded banter with her young customers. Slightly older-looking, but still damned attractive, Frank thought to himself. He had never seen her hair taken up tight to form a bun before; neck like a swan, he thought. Ruth became aware of his admiring gaze as she turned from pouring out a couple of whiskies. She gave a start and dropped one of the glasses. Suddenly there was total silence with everyone gazing curiously at this stranger within their midst.

'Why, Frank Bowers, you fairly gave me a turn you did, standin' there so sudden like – it's all right fellows,' she beamed, recovering her composure, 'a long-lost friend o' mine, he only happens to look like a plain clothes policeman.

'What's your pleasure, sir?' she said lightly. 'Apart from women and whippets.' Frank joined in the laughter around him.

'I'll break with tradition, I think, and have a Gordon's Gin with water, provided you'll join me. I don't suppose you have any Maiden's Water around these parts?'

It was Ruth's turn to join in the laughter.

'I must talk with you,' Frank said quietly as Ruth handed him his change, 'the sooner the better, preferably somewhere quiet.'

'I'll join you in the best room in ten minutes,' she replied.

Frank explained that he knew about the switching of the two grey horses, that he'd seen Flixton Grey at Nab End and knew that she was involved in the betting coup; and there were going to be prosecutions.

'But I was dragged into this by Neil,' she protested.

'I can accept all that, my sweet, but the fact remains you could be pulled in as an accessory, the net is closing fast. You must know they've already been here to the stables making enquiries and are making an extensive search for the horse. When I tell 'em where he is they're sure to be after you both. If I were you I'd go straight home, pack a bag, and disappear until this thing blows itself out. The Isle of Man, or better still Southern Ireland, could be a safe haven.'

Many weeks later following a long and costly trial in the Central Criminal Court in London which resulted in jail sentences and heavy fines, Frank received a letter from Southern Ireland addressed to 'Frank Bowers Esq., Auctioneer, Ripon, England.'

It was from Ruth, thanking him for the warning; she stated she had gone straight home and caught a boat next day. Neil had elected to stay and take his medicine; in fact he had escaped with a severe ticking off by the judge and was bound over to keep the peace.

She explained that she had been taken on as barmaid at this nice hotel in Dunloaghaire overlooking Dublin Bay and had no desire to return for some considerable time. Since Frank had already expressed his intention to Evelyn of visiting the Dublin Horse Show in the near future, he decided to file the letter away in his private drawer at the office; 'for future reference' he said aloud, as he patted the locked drawer and slipped the key into his waistcoat pocket.

23

Bedale Hunt Business

In 1926 Frank made a bad error of judgment; Mr Tommy Brennand, owner of the Baldersby Park Estate, offered him the chance to buy Brooms Farm.

'Come down and see me one evening soon,' had been the command. Frank had sold his landlord one or two good horses over the last few years and was expecting a horse deal when he drove up to the magnificent front entrance.

'My health isn't what it used to be, Frank, and those two lads of mine aren't interested in the estate, so I intend putting it up for sale; do you want to buy your farm?' Frank demurred 'Well, think it over. Would the Bedale Hunt like to buy that north whin covert?'

'I'm sure they would, sir.'

'Right, tell 'em they can have it for one hundred and fifty pounds.'

'It's got to be worth at least twice that,' said Frank.

'Never mind, that's my last contribution to the Hunt. I'm going into a nursing home in Harrogate; keeping my old "Tin Lizzie" to run around in; selling the other nine cars. There's a good Vauxhall out there, suit your firm, hardly been used, great hill climbers you know. Let's have a whisky, only thing as keeps me going these days.' Tommy took down a couple of large cut glasses from a corner cupboard and proceeded to fill them to the brim from one of two nine-gallon barrels set up on a small gantry in the corner of the study.

'With the price of whisky going up steadily nowadays, I decided to buy in bulk,' said Tommy, 'ordered a nine-galloner from a distillery in Scotland and damn me if they haven't made a mistake and sent two; only charged for one so they can't realise I've got it. Don't quite know what to do about it.'

'Best end for it would be to sup it,' grinned Frank.

Meanwhile, the Hunt committee were having slight problems with the Master; they had been asked to take over the 'Litter, Find and Stop' money as he found this item came to a great deal more than he expected. They were unable to comply, but increased the amount of his guarantee by one hundred pounds a year.

In January 1927 they received a letter from Major Burdon stating that he could not continue to hunt the country on the sum at present guaranteed; that the cost of the lowest estimate was twelve hundred pounds a day, or three thousand six hundred a year for the three days a week; and that he was unable to provide more than twelve hundred pounds a year towards this amount.

The committee fully discussed the matter and then called a General Meeting on the 27th January at Jervaulx Abbey, on the eve of the Hunt Ball. It was decided that the Master's guarantee should be raised to two thousand four hundred for the following season. Needless to say the rates of subscription were raised to twenty, thirty, forty and sixty-five pounds; at the same time it was decided that the number of officers from Catterick camp to come out with hounds should be limited to twenty-five on any one day.

Frank and Evelyn had travelled through to Jervaulx by bus. This was a new venture inaugurated by a garage proprietor from Masham, by the name of Todd, running from Ripon to Leyburn. A special bus had been laid on to take revellers home in the early hours and, as Frank so aptly put it, 'You can drink till it comes out of your ears, lads; as long as the driver remains sober we should get home safely.'

(What he failed to tell them, of course, was that he'd pranged his car a few days earlier by running into the market cross in Bedale High Street around midnight. He was returning from a meet at Patrick Brompton, after high jinks in the Green Tree Inn afterwards.

'I've been this way many times before in daylight,' Frank was heard to say to the Sergeant as he recovered in the local police station. 'I allus thought that monument was in the centre of the road. Of course it were pitch black and those lights aren't much use. I aimed off left handed and ran straight into the blooming thing.')

It had been snowing on and off all day and a blizzard was raging when the bus finally set off down the valley for Masham, at the end of the Hunt Ball.

'At least the snow will cushion the jolts from those solid rubber tyres,' remarked Evelyn. 'Never travelled in such a bone-shaker.'

About two miles out of Masham the driver decided to try and charge a snow-drift, and stuck fast; the bus remained there for the next three weeks! Frank volunteered to fetch help. Quite fortuitously the first big house he came to on the outskirts of the town belonged to a family of brewers who were keen to organise sledges and a plentiful supply of rum and brandy. They were able to offer accommodation in three public houses they owned in the town; it was not until three days later that Frank and his wife were able to set off home.

'Just think,' he said as a reserve bus slithered and bounced along the single track cut through drifts as high as the roof, 'we used to go to these functions in horse-drawn vehicles and could always get back. And they call this progress!'

In 1927 Frank's hunting diary records another memorable Hunt. It started not far from Catterick camp.

'Remember, Harry, how we thought this camp would ruin hunting in these parts for good, when they started building just before the war?' He was addressing his remarks to Harry Cail of Scorton (father of Nancy, who as Nancy Staveley later became Joint Master of the West of Yore and probably the most proficient Lady Huntsman in the country).

They were wearily returning from Reeth in Upper Swaledale after a fast run of nine miles. Hounds had found almost immediately in Park Wood at Hipswell. The meet had been at the officers' mess in the centre of the camp. (This was the first occasion Frank used a trailer. He had seen it advertised in *Horse and Hound*, a cumbersome heavy wooden structure, to take one horse only, but what a godsend! It brought all sorts of distant meets within reach.) The fox had run to Colburn Banks, then back from there through Park Wood and West Wood over by Throstle Gill to the south side of Badger Gill and thence to Hudswell Grange. From there he went on over to Downholme across Stainton Moor by Hag's Hill, past the priory known as Ellerton Abbey; having crossed the Swale they turned back off Marrick Moor at a point one and a half miles north east of Reeth.

Frank was on a young horse called Sugar Loaf who was to win the Bedale Open point-to-point for him a few seasons later and went on to qualify for the Grand National. The horse only had one eye – 'same as me' he often quipped – and Frank always maintained that when knocked over at the second to last fence in the National he looked like winning but failed to see danger coming up on his blind side. Frank had pulled up Sugar Loaf on the road overlooking the river Swale; it was easily fordable but he felt the horse had done enough. He had been walking him up and down the road for ten minutes to cool off when Harry Cail joined him.

'My fella's about cooked,' Harry said. 'Which way have they gone, Frank?'

'They've crossed here and gone up onto the moor, but I'll swear I could hear 'em coming back.'

'You're going to be right,' said Harry, 'because there's a very tired fox, look, other side of the river. What do we do now?'

'Pretend we haven't seen him and keep quiet,' said Frank.

Wearily the fox entered Spring Wood within view of the two friends. Hounds came along slowly, still just touching the line, and marked to ground in a large pile of rocks in the middle of the wood.

'He deserved to get away,' said Frank as they started the hack home. 'Even more pleasurable we weren't called on to give him away; had we shouted when he went past he could have gone anywhere and probably been caught.'

Harry Cail was a tireless worker for the Bedale Hunt; he had followed Frank's example and built a stick heap. Frank had two on his land near the river; they were built from substantial logs in such a way that there was a perfectly dry centre where a fox could find sanctuary and nothing of much size could get in. Hounds certainly were barred access, but a terrier could always be put in to try and bolt an inmate when required.

In 1928 the Bedale Hunt committee had for some time been trying to find a suitable site for a new Gorse Covert in the Friday country somewhere north of Kiplin and Scorton. Many sites were looked at, but it was Harry who found the ideal site on the east side of some old nurseries; this became the renowned Scorton Whin.

October brought sad news to all connected with the Bedale Hunt. The formidable J.J. Mowbray died on the 21st at his Scottish home, Naemoor. A short memorial service was held in Bedale parish church and in his address Major Burdon, the Master, described him as 'one of the best friends to foxhunting the Bedale Country has ever had; his solicitude for the welfare of the country was in the extreme and his unostentatious generosity unbounded. He will be sorely missed.'

'Amen,' said Frank aloud. 'He is nae moor.'

24

Change of Sex

It was autumn in the year 1929. Frank was delighted that the hunting season was once more upon him; it promised to be the best ever. Mr David Green had earlier in the year started a small pack of hounds with kennels at Nidd Hall near Harrogate. He informed Frank that Major Burden had agreed to lend him a portion of the Bedale country on its south and south west boundary, roughly from Dishforth, via Sharow, to Ripon and Studley Royal. This brought a lot of land only sparsely hunted before within easy hacking distance of the Brooms; hunting would be on Tuesdays and Saturdays. Since the Bedale hunted Mondays, Wednesdays and Fridays it meant that if the office could spare him it might be possible to hunt almost every day of the week. But the office could not spare him entirely.

'I'd like your assistance and advice, Frank.' Tom Edwards was on the phone one morning soon after Frank returned from morning exercise.

'Young fella called Jim Anderson in all sorts of trouble up on the Wilstrop Hall Estate. If you remember, we let him Hall Bank Farm a couple of years ago. He's had a bad attack of abortion in his dairy cows and mumbled something about family troubles, his wife has changed sex, or so he would have me believe. He's way behind with his rent, so we can go for possession, but there are extenuating circumstances. I haven't been up there yet but he tells me the cowhouse roof has caved in and the water supply has all but dried up, a job for you to sort out if you don't mind.'

Frank drove himself there the next day. He remembered a very bad approach road and wisely left his car at the Estate Office. The track was much worse than he anticipated, heavy winter rains followed by an unusually intense summer storm had virtually washed away any top covering.

'I wish these tenants would look after their approach, like the Boothman's at the head of Nidderdale, he said to himself. He remembered with pleasure the look of uninhibited joy on the faces of Mr and Mrs

252

Boothman as, many years before, he had called and handed them a cheque for two thousand pounds.

'I met your wayward son by chance recently, Ted,' he told him. 'I've sworn to keep his whereabouts secret, but he asked me to give you this; he asks your forgiveness and intends to let you have the balance as soon as possible.'

'By, Mr Bowers, but you're like a guardian angel to us two,' Mrs Boothman had managed to get out, her emotions almost choking her.

Hall Bank seemed to be deserted; his knock on the door to the farmhouse brought no response. He stood back and looked up, only to catch sight of the frightened faces of two children at one of the bedroom windows, as they dodged back out of sight. He knocked again and once again nothing happened.

Then he heard the sound of digging followed by a muttered curse in the cowhouse just across the yard. As he entered he could see just one cow tied up by the neck in her stall. A man was furiously wielding a pickaxe in quite a large hole immediately behind her, and laid out in the 'group' was a dead calf.

'Mr Anderson,' Frank called out as the fellow straightened up. 'Frank Bowers, land agent; called to see how you're making out.'

'Hello, Mr Bowers, don't often see thee around here nowadays,' said a tall, athletic young man in his late twenties. 'Don't think I've sin thee since th' interview when tha let me 'ave this spot.'

'What's going on?' asked Frank, nodding at the hole in the floor.

'This cow picked her calf afore her time like and as'm doin' what me faather allus did, buryin it on its back, now it's stiff, wi' its legs straight up.'

'What's that supposed to do?' queried Frank.

'Well it means she waren't do it agin, wards off disease like.'

'But surely she won't abort again because she'll become immune?' asked Frank.

'Nah, we keeps her in like for a couple of days and then makes sure we allus milks her in this stall. We've lost nearly every calf this time and as you'll see, cows 'as no milk at 'em.'

'And have they all been buried here?' asked Frank.

'Aye, just about every yan of them flagstones 'as been up. Disease waaren't have come from watter supply neither, 'cos we have none. Wife's away with a schoolteacher lass 'as helps her – fetchin' watter in milk churns from next door.'

'Well, finish your task,' said Frank, 'then we'll have a chat about the

253

rent arrears and other matters. I was informed the shippon roof had collapsed?'

'Aye, it 'as, next door – that bad storm a few weeks back, as washed out farm road like, well lightnin' struck a h'old h'oak round t'back and a ruddy great branch came down. Good job all th' cows was out to grass.'

'Sounds like an estate job,' said Frank. 'And what's wrong with the water supply?'

'Them old iron pipes is gunged up wi' red ochre and there's a burst or two every back end as soon as there's ony frost.'

'I'll look into that for you,' promised Frank.

By this time the two men were sitting in what Jim Anderson called his front parlour.

'Anything else gone wrong?' queried Frank, keen to hear about his tenant's marital problems.

'Aye, lots,' said Jim reaching into a cupboard and pouring out two large glasses of neat whisky.

'Ah didn't h'ask if you'd be wantin' a drink, Mr Bowers, 'cos ah've heard as how you're h'inclined to tak' a drop now and agin. Aye! Nivver know'd sic a time. H'awful lambin' time this spring; there's a big pit back o' th' house here full o' dead ewes and lambs, terrible time it were.'

'That's a bad do,' said Frank.

'Aye, lost a good dog only last week; these daft women left th' hoss and cart outside like when they came in for a cup o' tay, then I seed 'em come out to set off for some watter, laughin' and gigglin'! Afore ah could shout a warnin' th' waggon wheel went reet o'er 'im, kill't 'im stain dead; then there's them bairns upsteers.'

'Yes,' said Frank eagerly, 'I saw two children at the window when I arrived.'

'Little buggers were playin' wi' some fancy matches that daft school lass bought 'em for Christmas an' they set fire to me haystack. We couldn't put it out 'cos we had no watter.'

'What about insurance?' ventured Frank.

'Nivver bother wi' it,' said Jim truculently. 'Cain't be bothered wi' sic fellas comin' round selling politics.'

'Anything else?' queried Frank. 'I can well see why you're having difficulty finding the rent.' I've heard a similar tale to this before, he thought to himself.

'Aye, wife wairn't have nought to do wi' me.'

Just then the sound of a horse and cart could be heard entering the farmyard. As both men looked out of the window Frank's eye, as usual, was caught by a tall, striking blonde girl striding out across the yard towards the house. 'Beautiful, what a mover.' Frank failed to realise he was speaking aloud.

'Aye, she's half th' trouble,' said Jim. 'That's the school ma'am I was tellin' thee about. She'll go straight upsteers to see if the bairns are all reet; treats 'em as if they were her own.'

'I don't quite understand,' said Frank.

'They 'ave 'em locked in a bedroom so's I cairn't touch 'em. They've booted me out like.'

'So who's the farm man lumping the milk churns off the cart?'

'That's no farm man, that's me missus,' said Jim.

Frank took another look.

'Aye,' said Jim, 'dresses like a fella, shaves every day, does all the farm work.'

'And yet she's mother to two children?' queried Frank.

'Just so,' said Jim.

'I still don't understand,' said Frank.

'Nor does onyone else,' Jim said, ' 'cept maybe the doctor. We was both virgins like when we married, nivver tried that sex lark afore, and it was allus a bit difficult for me to penetrate like. There's a seven-year-old lad upstairs as was born in th' first year. Wife seemed to change then like. When young lass was dropped, that were it! No way in like. That's when she started a growin' whiskers and havin' to shave.

'Doctor had a good look at her and took her off to see a solicitor like. That's when she changed her name from Anne to Alan. She went off yan neet to th' village dance an landed back wi' this lass, an' they've lived togither ivver since.'

'So that means you're the tenant in name only, Mr Anderson. Not only does the landlord have power to repossess for non-payment of rent, but he can also turn you off for indirectly subletting without permission.'

'I suppose tha's reet,' said Jim listlessly; 'ah can see th' job goin' from bad to worse. There's only yon schoolteacher's wages as keeps us goin' like. If you'll excuse me a second, I'll nip out an tell th' wife tha's here.'

As Jim moved out into the central dimly-lit passage he met the schoolteacher at the foot of the stairs; unaware of Frank's hidden gaze and not understanding his desperate attempt to keep her away, she put her arms around his neck and seductively melted her body against his at the same time lifting her pouted lips for a kiss.

'Darling, I've missed you,' she whispered. Then she caught sight of Frank standing in the middle of the parlour and hastily drew back.

255

Up to that moment Frank had been lending a sympathetic ear to this family's problems.

'Nearly taken for a ride,' he said grimly to himself, as Jim Anderson clumsily introduced his companion.

'This is Miss Richardson what lives here, Mr Bowers and helps out. Thelma – this is Mr Bowers, our land agent.

'Obviously a girl of many talents,' said Frank disarmingly, desperately trying to hide his feeling of admiration for such a magnificent specimen of the female gender.

'Jim tells me you reside here with Mrs ... or is it now the other Mr Anderson?' The girl blushed a bright pink, but said nothing. 'I think I'd better have a word with your wife, or whatever else you refer to her as, if you don't mind, Mr Anderson. Does she know about you two?' he asked bluntly.

'No, sir!' said Jim desperately, 'and I hope for the sake of the children she nivver does.'

'I'll do a bargain with you then,' said Frank. 'What you do in your private lives hereafter is up to you, and if you, young lady, wish to keep two Mr Andersons happy then I think that's great, but you, sir, will have to give up the tenancy, quietly! Arrange your farm sale as soon as it becomes convenient and allow me to repossess the farm. Otherwise I shall give you notice to quit for non-payment of rent; even if you scrape that together, I shall go for you on the grounds of subletting. Then all these, and I hesitate to use the word "sordid" details, but so they would appear in an arbitration court, would come out, and all the family, but especially the innocent children, would suffer. I hate to think what would happen if one or two of the London newspapers got hold of a story like this. I leave you to sort this out with your "wife" after I've gone.'

25

Early 1930s

Trying to make a living out of farming in the 1930s was a fairly hazardous occupation. An almost total loss of confidence in the industry from the banks and financial institutions resulted in a complete absence of working capital. Prices for any sort of produce were completely on the floor, particularly livestock; average sheep prices were down to ten shillings a head from around sixteen shillings in 1918. Cattle prices had fallen to about fifteen pounds per head, wool was down from a shilling a pound to threepence (maybe sixpence for good quality) and, to complicate matters, there was a sequence of particularly harsh winters.

An auctioneer's lot was not a happy one around this time. Bidding at the market or at a farm sale had become desultory and Frank always maintained that had he been forced to rely on farming alone, he would, like so many others, have gone to the wall.

'The sale of hunters kept me going,' he often said, 'even better than the Auction Mart. Times were so hard my neighbours even resorted to sticking anything that died in a big tin bath, and then sold maggots at threepence a tin to fishermen who came down to the River Swale on a Sunday morning.'

Fox-hunting seemed to flourish, however. Even though Mr David Lycett-Green's venture of his own pack based at Nidd Hall had come to a premature end, in 1930 Mr W.E. Burrill at The Greens, Masham, had started a small pack of hounds at his home, to hunt all the Bedale country south and west of the River Yore. Wooden kennels were built to house the hounds and so a new Hunt – The West of Yore – was formed. Frank hoped this new pack would live up to the brilliance of forerunners, but it was never to be. 'A fun pack to be with,' but the hounds were never good enough, a 'scratch pack, too many cast-offs,' Frank had written in his diary.

The first 'heathen' pack (as Frank often referred to it) to hunt this country had been started by Mr Simon Conyers Scrope at Danby-On-Yore in the early 1900s. (He was long remembered in connection with point-to-point racing about that time, winning the Bedale Members' Race in 1898, 1899 and 1901 on his old white horse Moses.) Frank was twenty when Mr Simon, as he was affectionately known throughout the area, died on the 16th June, 1910. The obituary read: 'His death removes from our midst in Yorkshire one of the largest hearted, purest minded, honest gentlemen and noblest sportsman that ever lived. He has left a very worthy successor, in his brother Mr Henry Scrope.'

Frank never forgot his day with Mr Henry, as this entry in his diary shows:

23rd March, 1912. Found in Spennithorne Wood at two-fifteen, ran across to Danby, then on the south side of Thornton Steward to Kilgram Bridge, turned south west from here through the Park at Jervaulx past Mr Maughan's house to Ellingstring village and on to the north east end of Agra Plantation; halfway between which two points, there was a short check. From Agra the fox ran by the north west end of Birk Gill, by Farmory Mire and Jenny Bank's moss to East Scrafton; on by Agglethorpe, Middleham High Moor and Capple Bank plantation, over the Yore by Lord Bolton's private bridge into the grounds of Bolton Hall, where he holed up in the coal-house at five o'clock. As hounds ran, the distance was twenty miles. Her Ladyship came out when she heard the commotion and demanded that since the fox had travelled all that distance we 'leave him be'.

Mr Scrope, the Huntsman and three other riders apart from myself saw the end of this fine run.

The run was very straight and fast up to Kilgram Bridge. The fox twisted about a good deal over the moor from Birk Gill to East Scrafton but from there to Bolton Hall the line was quite straight.

Needless to say, Frank was mounted on Tuffan.

Exactly twenty years later, in March 1932, Frank made his customary early morning visit to the stable yard. Dick Boynton was leaning against the open door to Tuffan's box. Instinctively Frank knew the worst. He hurried over.

'Stone cold when I fun 'im, boss – died in his sleep, I reckon.' Dick had tears in his eyes.

Funny, thought Frank, never seen Dick cry before.

'Still, he nivver suffered, nivver sick nor sorry – like losing a close friend, there'll nivver be another like 'im.'

'Almost a freak, Dick, he was so good. All that work and not a mark on him; legs still as clean as a whistle. Funny he should be my first horse; there's huntin' men search a lifetime for a horse not nearly as good and never find him.'

Frank moved over to Tuffan, bent down and tweaked an ear, as he had done so often when he was alive.

'Goodbye, old friend,' he said, the emotion welling up inside him. 'We'll bury you here on the farm. Get the men to dig a grave down by the bottom covert, overlooking the river, Dick; you'll be able to take him down there on a sledge. Who knows, he may still be able to twitch those beautiful big lugs when they come round cub-hunting. He'll certainly be able to hear the horn when they move off from Topcliffe Station and hunt around Guy Robb's coverts.'

Following early morning mist, the 12th August, 1932, turned out to be a brilliantly hot sunny day. Frank had arranged for a shooting party of ten guns (including himself) for the opening day. He never professed to be anything but an average shot and invariably found grouse far too fast. Provided he tried to take them early, head on, or take them late, going directly away from the butts, he usually managed to kill a few birds.

The moor above Wilstrop Hall had steadily been improved over the years. Tweet Umpleby, now nearing retirement, had skilfully first of all destroyed the vermin, then reduced the numbers of other predators; grouse numbers had increased year by year; the shooting butts had been improved and two extra lines added. It was now possible to hold six drives a day.

The thrill of being amongst the heather; the anticipation as the first birds from each drive came whizzing through; then the silence, broken only by the crack of shotguns further down the line; the pleasant company of kindred spirits; the picnic luncheon party and all the other aspects of this unique British tradition all added up to a most memorable and joyous occasion for Frank.

Following a very severe winter, spring had been unusually mild and dry; Tweet reckoned bird numbers were up fifty per cent on previous years.

'Twenty-five brace, boss,' Tweet reported to Frank following the first drive. 'I reckon that's more than we shot in ony one day when we first started this caper.'

'That's all thanks to you and the Almighty,' said Frank.

'Don't see wheer th' Almighty comes into it,' remarked Tweet. 'He'd had th' moor for mony a year to hi'sen afore thou set me agait. I reckon as how he'd made a bit of a cock-up, if yer h'ask me.'

'Steady, Tweet, keep your voice down, that gentleman just over there out of butt number three is a retired bishop.'

'Aye! Tha wouldn't hev thowt so, way he were cussing old Pilkington in number two fer pickin' up yan of his birds.'

'That's perhaps why he's continuing to search back there with his two spaniels,' ventured Frank.

'Aye! Maybe it's th' only bugger he shot,' chortled Tweet.

Frank issued fresh butt numbers for the next drive and escorted his guests to their new positions. He soon realised the heated argument between the bishop and the Captain had not subsided; strong words, some quite unprintable, could be heard wafting on the breeze.

Frank approached the Captain in an effort to make peace; suddenly following a shouted curse in German the old man raised the gun to his shoulder and fired straight at the butt alongside. Turf flew off the front parapet wall as the bishop and his loader dived for cover; a second shot followed in quick succession, showering the inmates with peat.

The Captain was struggling to reload with trembling hands as Frank gently took his gun away from him; next door, the loader, having retained his sense of humour, raised a thumb-stick bearing a white handkerchief.

'I will not be called "Fritz" or "German bastard".'

'Quite so,' murmured Frank; he was alarmed to find the Captain appeared to have lost all self-control, was slavering into his beard and shaking from head to toe.

'I'll arrange for Umpleby to take you back down to the Hall on the pannier-horse, Captain. Perhaps you might like to apologise to the bishop.'

'Certainly I will not. Never!' and with a second Bavarian curse directed towards the bishop, who by this time was sheepishly emerging from cover, he haughtily turned on his heel and allowed Frank to lead him away.

The rest of the day proceeded without incident and with a total bag of over eighty brace everyone agreed it had been a highly successful and record first day.

'I don't think it u'd be wise to tak yon bishop in th' pub when tha gets back home, boss,' counselled Tweet as he led his horse down from the fells with its laden panniers, at the end of the day. 'Th'owd bugger refused to be tacken 'ome tha knows, goon boozin'– still be theer for sure.'

260

'Thanks, Tweet, I don't suppose the bishop will be a drinking man. I'll make sure he gets on his way. I suppose you'll be calling in?'

'You bet – I'll hang this lot up in th' game larder first, then I's gang t' murder a pint or two.'

Frank had no sooner entered the Wheatsheaf than he was sprinting for his car and speeding off down the valley to the doctor with Captain Pilkington aboard, blood pouring from his head. As he walked in he'd caught sight of the flustered landlord pointing towards a gently swaying Captain Pilkington atop one of the bar tables, peering closely at the flagged floor below him.

'The sea,' he heard him say, 'the sea, full of tiny fishes,' and with that he launched himself off, head first.

'He'll have quite a headache for a day or two, even after the hangover wears off, Mr Bowers. Get him to stay in bed for a few days. I've put twelve stitches in that bad cut on his forehead. I don't think there's any serious damage. I'll nip up to the Hall in about ten days time to take the stitches out.'

'I hardly expected you back tonight, dear,' Evelyn had whispered as Frank had slipped quietly into bed, 'but then I suddenly remembered you'll be cub-hunting at six-thirty at Baldersby North Whin; I knew you wouldn't want to miss that!'

Little did Frank know as he recounted to Evelyn the shooting incident, followed by the extraordinary happenings in the bar, that a double tragedy was happening in the same hotel even as he spoke.

One of the guests, down from Scotland, staying at the Wheatsheaf was a certain Captain Ian Spencer, Scots Guards, close relative of Major Marmaduke. 'Young enough and daft enough,' as Frank remarked later, 'to attempt to show off his prowess as a whisky drinker.'

'He sort of challenged the landlord to a drinking bout,' remarked a witness at the inquest. 'I remember him saying, "A wee dram from every bottle of whisky right along the top shelf of the bar, and a double from every bottle coming back." They were still at it when everybody left or went to bed.'

It was eleven-thirty before Frank returned from cub-hunting. 'Would you ring Tom at the office immediately,' Evelyn urged him, 'seems your tenant at the Wheatsheaf and a shooting guest were both found dead in the well of the staircase early this morning. Tom has the details.'

'Looks as if Charles Hallam was carrying the Major's nephew up to bed, probably over his shoulder, up to the second floor; they over balanced, crashed through the bannisters and when the chef came downstairs to open up the kitchen he found 'em both laid out, stone cold. Must have been dead for about five hours.'

'Christ, what a mess!' said Frank. 'I'll drive up there right away and sort things out. I'll try and persuade Christine, his wife, to stay on, I think she's been running the place behind the scenes anyway. I don't suppose they've been informed at the Hall, probably still in bed: hardly relish dodging those two new German guard dogs just to tell the Major his favourite nephew has been killed.'

It was the first week of June 1934, and Frank was in Upper Wharfedale. For many years past he had visited farms in Langstrothdale, usually twice a year, buying hardy feeding cattle in the spring, and store lambs to fatten during the winter months in September to early October. His main supplier, Benjamin Moorhouse, who farmed near Yockenthwaite, had written to inform Frank he was retiring and that Tom Taylor, auctioneer from Skipton, would be selling his livestock on the farm on the Wednesday.

Frank always stayed at the Racehorses Hotel in Kettlewell when he was on these trips and over the years had become firm friends with the landlord, George Mangles. He wrote to the hotel reserving a room for the Wednesday night and to Benjamin Moorhouse saying how sorry he was to hear of his impending retirement, but that he hoped to attend the sale. He did so and was very impressed with the good humour and skill of the auctioneer, who soon had an active trade going at prices way beyond Frank's reach.

'Bought nowt, Ben,' said Frank later in the huge farm kitchen, as his host poured out a liberal supply of whisky into Frank's proffered glass. 'I think you've had a wonderful trade, far and away too much brass for me to pay and then have to cart 'em over to Ripon. You won't know what to do with yourself when you wake up in the morning and there's no stock to look after.'

'We have one daughter, Frank, living in America; we've always promised oursens a trip o'er there like, nivver seed the two grandchildren. We've got bookings to sail on a cruise ship; what's name o' that ship, mother?'

'*Mauritania*,' his wife replied, her eyes lighting up at the thought of the adventure ahead.

'Aye, its last voyage, shipping agent tell't us, an' we've nobbut seen th' sea yance, church outing to Morecambe.'

'I know that ship,' said Frank, 'she was an armed cruiser during the war; escorted us back home from the Middle East in 1918. She was sort of dazzle-painted with a fancy criss-cross pattern. She had four large funnels and was built for speed; apparently she could leave most warships for dead and had twice the speed of the enemy U-boats. Sister ship to the *Lusitania* who blew up off the Irish Coast in 1915, after she was hit by a torpedo. Apart from sixteen hundred neutral passengers, she was carrying a contraband cargo of shells, ammunition and explosives. It was said that the Germans were waiting for her. Twelve hundred souls perished that day.'

'Glory be,' remarked Mrs Moorhouse.

'Aye, well. this'ns a cruise ship now,' said Benny, 'all gleaming white. We're going second class like to New York; then she goes off cruising in the Carry-bean, weer ivver that is, for a month or two, and then we shall get back on board like, in New York. When do we come home, mother?'

'End of September, dear.'

'Aye, she's sailing back then to be broken up.'

By the time Frank arrived at the Racehorses Hotel the taproom was crowded. George was delighted to see his old friend. He was quite partial to a late-night drinking session himself and he knew once Frank arrived, however much his wife might disapprove, his old chum would be good for, say, a three o'clock finish, if not an all-night thrash.

'You seem to be very busy tonight, George!'

'Aye, they've been picking the May Queen and dancin' around the maypole and sich like.'

'But it's June now,' protested Frank.

'Aye, it's second go. Th' heavens opened up on reet day, usually second Saturday in May. Ony how there's a hoss show and kiddies fancy dress tomorrow and when I knew you were comin' I tell't committee as how you'd be a good man to judge leading rein class.'

'That's great, George, thanks very much; seeing as how I've never done it before, and haven't much idea how to go about it.'

'It's easy, Frank, we get different judges every year, allus a male, 'cos these daft women can never make up their minds. I tell 'em to go for th' handler: best-lookin' mother. Do that and tha won't go far wrong. Th' missus has a special supper for thee; there's a nice bowl of broth simmering yonder and some tasty belly pork wi' a fresh cauliflower. Get that down thee, it'll act as blotting paper, and I'll tell th' locals tha'll be through directly to give 'em a turn.'

'What?'

'Tha knows, supping a pint of beer wi' no hands.'

It was much later that evening before Frank was persuaded to do his party trick. Following many hours of practice he'd realised that it was extremely difficult to get the pint down at one go when sober; once he'd had a few drinks and felt entirely relaxed he found it easy.

'Right you lot, clear the way,' George shouted.

'Leave the corner of the room free, my friend Frank Bowers, who I'm sure is well known to you all, will now take a pint of beer, place the full glass on his head, drink its contents without using his hands and will replace the empty glass back on the bar.'

Total silence ensued; balancing the glass of beer on his head Frank slowly moved to the corner of the room, keeping his hands in full view behind him. Inch by inch, the full glass pressed firmly into the angle of the wall, slid first past his forehead, then his nose, then his chin, came within reach of his lips; two gulps and Frank was able to grasp the rim of the glass in his teeth; tilting his head back he drained the glass without pausing for breath; then to tumultuous applause reversed the procedure until he was able to walk carefully back towards his host and still not using his hands slip the empty glass from his head onto the bar in front of him.

Amidst cheers George called out, 'Anyone wishing to emulate my friend here is free to try, but not only will they have to pay for the ale, I shall demand a deposit of sixpence a glass to cover the cost of any broken in the process.'

Two brave souls had a go and both finished up with half the ale down their front and the rest on the floor amidst a pile of shattered glass.

'You need to have a pointed chin like mine to hang onto the glass before you get it in your gob,' Frank confided in George. 'If it slips, then you've had it. Took me hours at home with a glass half full of water before I cracked it.'

Next morning Frank found himself in a small square field on the banks of the River Wharfe with neat stone walls on three sides; there he reported to a small tent bearing a hand-painted sign at the entrance, which simply read: Secretary.

'Here you are, Mr Bowers,' said the prim, bespectacled lady secretary, 'Mr Mangles told me you had agreed to judge the leading rein class. We have ten entries; they all get a rosette, here they are in this box. The first prize gets this special red rosette and a riding crop. Here's your rosette,' which says Judge, it's bright pink – I hope you don't mind.'

She moved closer and pinned the rosette on his lapel. Frank looked down into a perfectly oval face. What a beautiful complexion, he thought, as his eyes locked on to hers; she gave an involuntary shudder and took a pace backwards. (Unerringly and unknowingly, Frank usually had this

264

effect, as a younger man, on any vibrant young female who came too close.) He noticed how quickly she blushed and how a red flush had appeared on either side of her graceful neck.

Realising they were alone, Frank moved quickly. 'Excuse me, but do I detect a pair of beautiful eyes behind these glasses?' She froze as Frank gently removed them. 'Indeed I do, and all this thick auburn hair piled up here, what happens if I remove these pins?'

'No! No! You musn't,' she pleaded and turned away totally confused.

'You're at least ten years younger than I thought you were,' said Frank. 'Why all this severe get-up?' he asked.

'That's my business,' she replied. 'If you must know I happen to be the only schoolteacher for miles around and these Godfearing folk expect a school ma'am to look the part.'

'Well, Miss . . . er, I don't know your name.'

'Mary Lancaster.'

'Well, Miss Lancaster,' said Frank formally, as a very portly gentleman squeezed his way into the tent, 'do I get a lunch out of this?'

'Yes, we have a special luncheon at twelve-thirty for officials and judges at the Red Lion. Could I introduce you to our treasurer Mr Peter Parker from the Yorkshire Penny Bank? This is Mr Frank Bowers from Ripon who has kindly agreed to judge the leading rein class.'

'Pleased to meet you, Bowers, heard about you from Benny Moorhouse; he banks with me. I heard he had a good sale.'

'Far too dear for me,' said Frank. 'I'm sorry he's retiring. I understand he and his wife intend sailing to America; quite an adventure for them.'

'Aye, especially since they've only been out of this valley about twice in a whole lifetime.'

'Now, if you'll excuse me,' said Frank, 'I'd better go out and face the wrath of the losing parents. They all think that little Alice or Fred or whatever should have had first prize. You'll save me a seat at lunch, Miss Lancaster?'

Frank took a long time getting the ponies in the right order of merit. When he'd finished, the advice of George Mangles seemed to be a complete reversal of what had happened. At the top of the line was a smart grey Welsh pony ridden by a plain tubby youth with a superior look on his face. Probably used to winning, thought Frank. Then he took another good look at the handler: What a thoroughly ugly female, thought Frank, and why wear tight-fitting breeches with an arse like that?

Frank had asked each handler to walk the pony towards him following his initial selection; and to trot away from him back into line. The last to

265

go was an ancient little shaggy black Shetland ridden by an angelic-looking girl child with a long blonde pigtail tied with a bright red ribbon; she was doing a very rapid rising trot in perfect time with the pony. Mum's quite a smasher, he thought to himself as he watched a very tall blonde girl trotting alongside sporting an identical pigtail.

Frank was scratching his head, wondering if he'd got them right, when he caught sight of George Mangles leaning on a ringside post with a huge grin on his face. George stealthily made a semicircular cross-over motion with both index fingers. Christ, Frank thought to himself, he thinks I should reverse the placings! Just then fate took a hand. Some child in the crowd let go of a balloon; a stiffish breeze sent it bobbing along the ground parallel to the line of ponies and about three feet in front of them. The Welsh pony went straight up in the air depositing its startled young rider on the ground; most of the others backed away or swung round. The Shetland never moved a muscle. Seen it all before, said Frank to himself, a perfect kiddies' pony. He immediately waved to the tall blonde girl to bring her daughter into first place.

The incredulous look on the fat lady's face inwardly amused Frank and for devilment he moved them down four places.

'Nice pony, but far too skittish,' he murmured as he fixed a Highly Commended rosette to the Welsh pony's bridle.

'I shall be complaining to the show committee,' the fat lady hissed. 'This pony has been first at every show we've been to this year.'

'But not today, dear,' said Frank gently as he moved further down the line.

The Red Lion was almost directly opposite the Racehorses; Frank looked at his watch; just time for a pint of Guinness with George, he thought.

'Have that with me,' said George. 'Glad to see you took my advice and put that smart lass at the top.'

'Damned attractive girl,' said Frank, 'does she hail from these parts?'

'Oh, I thought perhaps you knew her; Colonel Webber's daughter; Show President. There's two of 'em – identical twins – both unmarried, both six footers, nobody's quite sure which o' 'em's th' mother to that bairn, let alone who's th' father. They moved into Litton Hall over in Littondale last year, both cracking good hosswomen. They come here regular like, they'll be 'ere tonight, dining wi' their parents.'

'No wonder that fat piece was hopping mad,' chortled Frank, 'I had no idea I was placing the Show President's grandchild first.'

Frank bustled across to the Red Lion, where the show officials were gathered in the cocktail bar.

'Hello, Miss Lancaster,' Frank called out, 'you've made a quick change.'

She turned, startled, and coloured up immediately. Gone was the drab woollen dress, replaced by an attractive figure-hugging cocktail dress. Her naturally thick, wavy hair fell about her shoulders; gone were the glasses, her eyes had been beautifully made up and her sensuous mouth carried a discreet touch of lipstick.

'Oh, I'm sorry,' said Frank disarmingly, 'you can't possible be the Miss Lancaster I met this morning.' They both laughed as he pretended to turn away.

'Let me introduce you to the Show President, he's asked to meet you; you've made his day placing his granddaughter first. If only you'd seen her pretty little face when she came into his tent wearing that large red rosette and carrying the riding crop, the Colonel had tears in his eyes.'

He shook the Colonel by the hand. 'A perfect first pony in my opinion, sir, steady as a rock; and if these kiddies are to go on they must never lose their confidence.'

'Couldn't agree more, Bowers – by the way, my gals are entered for the Yorkshire Show, both riding sidesaddle. We only moved up here from Oxfordshire last back end so this'll be their first big show in the north. Perhaps you'll make it in your way to look after them.'

'I'll try my best, sir,' said Frank meaningfully. 'I'm staying across the road at the Racehorses Inn; would you care to have a drink with me after the show?'

'Are you, by gad! Tell you what, better still, we're all dining there tonight; you come and join our table. Be my guest, then you can tell the gals what's what, eh!'

Later as Frank sat next to Mary at the crowded luncheon table he had a sudden idea. 'My friend George Mangles across at the Racehorses tells me he can't make it to Appleby Fair. I shall be driving over there tomorrow, would you like to come?'

She hesitated. 'Well, the children are still on holiday, but I wouldn't like to be seen!'

'We shall leave very early and it'll probably be dark before we get back.'

'All right, then,' she said quietly.

Frank was driving his new Vauxhall car. The one feature he didn't like was the circular temperature gauge mounted over the front of the bonnet, which left no room for his beloved fox mascot. As arranged, he'd picked up Mary at her little cottage on the outskirts of the village at seven-thirty in the morning. Only the milkman was to be seen as they sped northwards through Buckden towards Appleby.

Everything was on Frank's side that day. It was a superb June morning, early mist had rolled down the valley revealing a cloudless sky, the canvas hood to the cab was neatly folded back. He glanced across at his companion; she smiled enquiringly back at him

'Definitely not the same girl I met yesterday in that Secretary's tent,' he remarked.

She laughed as she clutched his arm and pressed her cheek to his shoulder. 'Don't know when I last felt so happy,' she replied taking in a series of deep breaths. 'What beautiful fresh mountain air. Oh, I'm so glad you asked me to accompany you today. I was secretly hoping you might have asked me out last night, until that beastly Colonel invited you to dine with his daughters.'

'Funny – I'd had the same idea,' said Frank.

'He perhaps thought you were unmarried and might take one of them off his hands.'

'If you're trying to find out whether I'm single or not, I'm afraid it's "not". No, what puzzles me is why two such attractive girls, who must be nearly thirty...'

'Twenty-eight actually.'

'Why two such eminently suitable girls have never married.'

'Do you mean you really don't know?' asked Mary incredulously. 'I thought you were a man of the world?'

'Yes, well maybe!'

'I suppose it takes a woman to spot these things.'

'I'm still not with you,' said Frank.

'They're identical twins, silly, they do everything together, sleep together and, you know!'

'Know what?'

'Oh, Frank! Do I have to spell it out?'

'Pardon?'

'Ever heard the word lesbian?'

'Yes, but I've never come across one. Besides one of 'em has a child.'

'So what; you've heard the word bisexual, haven't you?'

'Aah!' said Frank, 'I'm with you. Had a tenant's wife change sex a little while ago over at Givendale,' he grinned. 'I don't suppose that's quite the same?'

'No, that's not the same,' said Mary, giggling.

Long before they got to Appleby the road was becoming blocked by richly painted gypsy caravans pulled by sturdy piebald horses, often with another loosely tied behind. Every spare piece of ground within miles of the town had been taken over as a parking place. Hundreds of horses and ponies were tethered wherever grass grew on the roadside.

'This ranks with Barnaby Fair at Boroughbridge as one of the largest Horse Fairs in the land,' Frank explained. 'I don't think it's the oldest; that could be Topcliffe Fair, held only a few miles from my farm.'

Frank turned left off the main road, crossed the bridge over the River Eden and was able to park comfortably in the small town square.

'Hello, they've moved 'em out to Fair Hill again; that's a big field just down the road. The gypsies make such a mess here, and get drinking, fighting and smashing the place up. What are you grinning at?'

'I was born here, Frank! See that lovely red sandstone house at the top of the square? I still have a widowed aunt living there. I went to school here, this is my home town.'

'And I thought you were seeing something new!'

'I am, Frank – you are brand new; the marvellous way you're looking after me, the way you talk, that's all new; I feel like a wonderful new person.'

'Come,' she took him by the hand, 'let's walk back to the bridge and watch the horses being washed in the river. I used to stand there for hours as a young girl and watch the gypsy boys riding bareback and showing off.'

'Well, being a schoolteacher, you probably know much more about this fair than I do,' said Frank despondently.

'I know that by law the gypsies can only stay here for seven days and that they've been coming here in the first week of June since the seventeenth century; James II granted Appleby a charter for the trade of horses, sheep and cattle but gradually the gypsies took over and made it into their own.'

The mile walk to what used to be known as Gallows Hill was full of incident; there was a constant traffic of horses to and from the river; entire Romany families were still arriving, lurchers and yapping terriers were everywhere.

'One wonders how they manage to bring order to such a scene of chaos,' Mary remarked.

The scene at Fair Hill never ceased to impress Frank; they were immediately accosted by ragged-looking youngsters selling lucky charms or

269

simply begging. Avenues of stalls were selling china, harness, horse brasses and countless other trinkets. He counted eight booths occupied by fortune-tellers, three of them claiming to be daughters of Gypsy Rose Lee. A makeshift sale ring was already in action at the bottom of the hill with horses being trotted out for closer inspection. All sales were negotiated privately; long, heated haggling sessions were taking place on all sides. Hundreds of horses and ponies were tethered to any convenient anchorage point; the main bulk, those with any size (Frank wasn't interested in anything much under sixteen hands) had for convenience been tethered to the railway fence.

The loop line happened to be in a cutting and seldom used. Frank was certain no one on the ground had ever given the slightest thought to what might happen if a train came along. Suddenly clouds of white smoke were billowing up in front of the horses and enveloping them. In slow motion as a train approached Frank witnessed every animal plunge and rear backwards, either breaking the halter or taking a lump of fence with it. Loose horses were galloping everywhere.

'Keep still and don't move even if a horse gallops straight at us,' ordered Frank drawing his companion towards him and putting his arms around her.

'This is nice,' Mary murmured looking up at him.

'They'll always swerve past if you keep still,' Frank said, hesitantly looking down as a mischievous grin spread across her face.

'I'm finding that very hard to do,' she murmured, pressing her lithe body even closer against him.

Then as the smoke surrounded them he bent down and kissed her for the first time.

'My toes are still tingling,' Mary whispered as they sat holding hands at the very top of Gallows Hill, looking down on the colourful scene below. 'Just think, I feel so happy, and yet once upon a time unhappy wretches would be brought up here after the quarterly assizes and strung up on the gallows.'

'I heard the gypsies were not against doing the same to their own kind if they were found guilty of serious crime; they even buried 'em up here!' said Frank.

She shivered. 'Let's go back into town, we'll call on my aunt at the Red House and arrange some lunch. She's quite old and slightly deaf but very understanding; she's sure to ask us to stay.'

Mary took Frank by both hands and slipped inside his arms. She reached up and kissed him lightly on the cheek. 'After the festivities in the market place this evening, if you like, we could always stay the night – separate rooms of course – but it will be just like having the house to ourselves!'

Frank had an annual assignation thereafter in the first week of June. Eventually the old lady died and Mary inherited the house. She moved in and contrived to secure a teaching post in the town in time for the next Appleby Fair.

Having been introduced to the delights of fishing with fly or minnow for game fish whilst still at school, Frank had, when the few chances came along over the years, improved his technique until he was now quite proficient. He remembered how, before the war, it had been possible to catch the occasional salmon in both the Swale and the Ure; but gradually pollution of the river in the lower reaches around York and beyond ended all that.

The invitation from his cousin to fish the River Esk for a few days in mid-July had come as a very welcome surprise. He travelled by train to be met at Egton Bridge by the estate coachman with a pony and trap.

'Hello, sir,' he remarked as Frank alighted, 'I'm Johnny Wright, come to tak' thee luggage round to th' Shoe.'

'Ah yes,' said Frank, 'by th' Shoe I suppose you mean the 3 Horseshoes Hotel.'

'Aye, that's reet,' he said giving Frank a funny look.

'Well, I'll walk,' said Frank. 'I just want to call at the Catholic church and then look at the river.'

Frank stood for a long time outside the church remembering Charlotte. He thought of the dreadful time when her body had been brought here on a horse-drawn sledge. He marvelled at the contrast in the weather; the dappled sunlight at his feet; the song of birds; the raucous sounds of a rookery close by.

The large entrance doors swung silently back revealing the magnificent interior, and he moved inside. A priest was to be seen busying himself replacing lighted candles at a shrine of the Virgin Mary; he turned round, smiled at Frank, and continued with his daily tasks.

Overcome with emotion Frank sat in one of the pews. He was alarmed to find as the occasional tear ran down his cheeks, how vividly he remembered his last visit; the long intimate journey on horseback into these parts so many years ago. The dreadful moment as he saw Charlotte disappear over the falls and the thud as her body hit the rocks below.

A slight sound at the door brought him out of his reverie, it was Miles.

271

'I thought I might find you here, Frank,' he said gently as they walked towards the river. 'That girl obviously meant a lot to you.'

'The only one I've ever truly loved,' said Frank wistfully. They reached the river. 'So what about this fishing, there doesn't seem to be much water.'

'No, when I wrote there was quite a spate and a lot of early salmon came through. It hasn't rained since and I'm afraid the water level's dropped as quickly as it came up. We had a Scotsman down here for a day recently and he annoyed one or two folk by calling it "a mucky wee burn".'

'I read recently,' Frank said, 'where a Scots gillie giving evidence before "The Lords" at a Salmon Commission enquiry is reported as saying "it's a well kenned fac' in oor country mi Lords, where there's na watter, there's na fush", and I must say it looks a bit like that here.'

'How do you like our new bridge?' asked Miles.

'I thought something was different,' Frank said. 'Wasn't there a lovely old stone bridge here?'

'Until two years ago,' said Miles. 'Then we had a monstrous flood, a huge tree blocked the main arch, debris piled up and the entire bridge got swept away – parts are still to be seen at the bottom of the pool when it's clear. It backed up enough to flood the 3 Horseshoes above the depth of the bar; barrels of ale were floating about in the cellar and the tale goes that when the floods subsided, a ten pound salmon got left behind. Johnny Wright, who you just met, took a horse and cart to the front of the hotel and got guests out of the bedroom windows by means of a ladder.'

'He seems to be quite a character,' remarked Frank.

'Likes a drink, loves a gamble on the horses, and he's a great romancer. He often repeats himself when he gets excited and one rough old stormy night last winter he'd gone into the bar dripping wet and told 'em such a tale. "Nearly caught sike a big un, seed 'im wi' me lantern, sike a big un! I got clip (home-made gaff) intiv him, but he were sike a big un, I couldn't lug him oot." "So what did you do, Johnny," one of his friends asked. "I louped astride him wi' sike a bump, aye sike a bump that me clogs struck fire as I flashed through under yon new brig on him!"'

'Very clever,' laughed Frank, 'at least it shows a vivid imagination.' (It was Johnny who years later sat in the bar of the 3 Horseshoes on the evening following the American landing on the moon. When asked what he thought about it, was heard to remark, 'I'll tell thee what I think, I think if they're not careful they'll "lake" on wi' bugger till they hev it down!')

'I heard him telling a lovely story about one of his neighbours the other day,' said Miles. 'Apparently old Tommy Noble who rented one of the estate farms had been to see the doctor for the first time in his life. "He were havin' trouble wi' his back passage," Johnny said, "bunch of cherries!" – obviously piles,' laughed Miles. ' "Ony how," said Johnny, 'th' old doctor had gin him a box of supposaries and tell't him to insert yan in his rectum neet and mornin; when he'd gotten 'ome his wife had tell't him they hadn't yan; so he'd come over th' fields like and I heard my missus tellin im as how we hadn't yan either. I kept out of it but I heered her sayin, "I think we did have one, Tommy, but I'm certain he sell't it," then amidst hearty laughter Johnny went on: "So he went 'ome and his missus made him swallow yan neet and mornin for a week; then he went back to th' doctor who h'esked if he'd cured him. "Naw, Doctor" Tommy said, "I've swallowed ruddy lot, and for all th' good they've done me I might as well 'av stuffed 'em up me arse!" '. Incidentally,' grinned Miles, 'that same doctor driving across a water splash where it runs across Butter Beck just up the road from here, felt one hell of a bump and when he stopped at the other side to investigate he found he'd run over a sixteen-pound hen sea trout.'

'So how am I going to catch a fish like that?' asked Frank.

'Well I suggest you leave the river alone until this evening and then work a fly down through the Sawmill pond and the sheepwash, a Jock Scot, or later on Teal and Silver; then tomorrow I'll take you up river spinning; being low water you'll have to fish deep. We can start off at Dead Man's Pool, if there are any big fish about that's where they'll be.'

'Looks to be a good morning, Frank, stiffish breeze and not too much sun, you could be lucky today.'

The two cousins were following a well-worn track through Arncliffe Woods some distance from the river.

'This is another of those monks' paths, Frank; you can follow these sandstone flags all the way back to Whitby Abbey. Nearly all of them were worn concave over a few hundred years by the hooves of packhorses; it gradually drops down to the river and that's where we'll find this famous holding pool.'

'Why famous?' asked Frank.

'Well, because it's very deep, quite eerie, with high trees all around. All the record-weighted fish for the whole river have been caught here: a thirty-pounder in October 1882, a twenty-nine and a half pounds one in 1912, then a twenty-four-pounder during the war. Here we are, this is Dead Man's Pool, so deep you never see the bottom.'

'How did it get its name?' asked Frank.

'Oh, from way back,' said Miles. 'Long before the Association was formed in 1864.* They'd be fishing for sea trout in those days, I suppose, because until the 1870s by some quirk of nature, salmon never ran this river; they had to be introduced. The story goes, one of the locals came here poaching and noticed a fishing bag on the bank; then he saw a rod floating on the surface in the deepest part, there, look; where the main current slowly revolves back on itself. Then to his horror he saw a man he knew well from the village also moving slowly around with the current about a foot under the surface with his eyes wide open, staring at him. "Like he were stood to attention," he'd told the coroner at the inquest, "held up wi' t'h'air in 'is clothes I 'spect, horrible look on his face, sir, just horrible, caint sleep at neet no more."'

'I'm not surprised,' said Frank.

'Turned him into a drunk so they say, he finished up a quivering wreck,' Miles added.

'Fancy a chap catching a thirty-pound fish here,' Frank remarked, 'Wonder it didn't pull him in!'

'It was a fellow called Hawson,' said Miles, 'who came from Pickering; after the railway line opened in about 1887 he could get here easily; apparently he walked down the other bank from Glaisdale station, half a mile that's all, assembled his rod, put on a nice juicy bunch of fresh worms and on his third cast was into this "leviathan".

'Fortunately I suppose the fish elected to stay in the pool; a young lad of twelve watched the struggle from this bank here with some awe. Apparently Mr Hawson, who sported a long red beard down to his belly and had huge eyebrows of the same colour, was a frightening sight in himself to a lad of that age. Eventually the youngster was persuaded to run upriver where he crossed over and came to Mr Hawson's assistance. There is no account of what the youngster, by the name of Brown, was doing on
the

---

* August 20th, 1864. At a meeting held at the Angel Hotel, Whitby, the following resolutions were carried unanimously:
Proposed by C.W. Strickland Esq., and seconded by C. Richardson Esq., 'That an association to be formed for the improvement and maintenance of the River Esk and for the maintenance of fish ladders and passes, and that the most noble the Marquis of Normanby be patron of the Association.'
Following which a committee was formed under the Chairmanship of Mr Charles Bagnall. A Secretary and Treasurer were also appointed and the rate of subscription fixed. This meeting was ultimately to bring salmon to the River Esk thus helping to bring thousands of pounds annually to the Whitby Sea Fishermen and thousands of pleasant days and memories to future members of the Association.

river bank at the time when he should have been at school, but it appears he was quite skilled in the use of the gaff and was able to drag this huge fish onto the bank for a very tired Mr Hawson about an hour later.

'Apparently Red Beard then retired to the Anglers Rest pub in the village to wet the fish's head, recounting his story several times over for any newcomer who cared to listen; until he passed out, and had to be carried a few hundred yards to the station to be put on the train for home.

'In the meantime, young master Brown, for a small consideration, had been persuaded to take the fish down river to Grosmont to be weighed; a cord having been passed through the fish's gills, he got it over his shoulders, the fish hanging down his back with the tail trailing on the ground, and carried it over four miles to the weighing scales at Grosmont Station.

'The story of this monster duly appeared in the *Fishing Gazette,*' said Miles, 'because up to that time the best salmon reported in the Esk had weighed a mere ten pounds, caught by a Reverend Philpot. By a strange quirk of fate, both gentlemen were featured again in the same magazine almost three years later, more or less to the day,' chuckled Miles. 'I have a copy in the office dated 10th October 1895, headed "Stoning Pools in the Esk"; it recounts how the reverend gentleman, noted as having caught the first salmon on the Esk, on the fly, and described as a "fly purist", came across Mr Hawson of Pickering quietly worming the Bridge Pool at Grosmont. It goes on to point out he was apparently a great contrast to the thin figure of the preacher.

'The article then recounts how the reverend gentleman came down to the river and after fishing over the neck of the pool with his fly, laid down his rod and deliberately took stones and threw them into the pool one after the other close by Mr Hawson. That gentleman, it goes on to tell us, on enquiring why these tender attentions, was told that "every pool would be stoned where beastly worms were being used!"

'Whereupon righteous wrath stirred in the bosom of the fully paid-up member, Red Beard; apparently his Reverence hadn't even paid his subs,' grinned Miles. 'He arose, seizing many cobbles and heaved them with force at his Reverence, adding thereto such a volley of language that the holy man fled and the red-bearded one after him, pelting him and telling him what he thought of him and his ancestors along the whole length of the Toll Road, well-nigh to Egton Bridge, where the slim one outran him and Red Beard returned to his worms and quiet fishing.'

Frank fished hard for the next two days and failed to land a fish; he tried every trick he knew. 'I had a good fish take a prawn,' he told Miles over supper at the end of his first full day, 'but it simply took off downstream. I couldn't possibly keep up; the line wrapped around a couple of big rocks in the middle and "twang", the line broke and he was gone.'

The highlight of his second blank day occurred as he approached the weir above Glaisdale. Frank was moving upstream on a broad track some height above the river when he heard shouting. It soon became clear from his vantage point that a gentleman above the weir was into a good fish and he was asking a fellow angler to allow him access to the pool below to play his capture (this being the etiquette at the time). The gentleman below refused to budge because he was also into a fish. As the heated words continued Frank was the only one to realise they both had hold of the same fish.

He watched fascinated as a beautiful silver salmon tumbled slowly down the weir, twisting the lines together as he fell into the pool below. Suddenly he flashed into the air only yards away from Frank's gaze, the twisted lines clearly showing he was caught by a spinning device in the mouth, but with snatching gear in the tail. Obviously the indignity of the situation had got to the fish, and he straightened out as he hit the water with a mighty splash and was gone leaving two very angry anglers on the far bank remonstrating and arguing as they tried to untangle their slack lines.

It was Johnny Wright who saved the situation. Frank, waiting for his train for home on the morning of the fourth day, having caught nothing, was suddenly presented with a fresh run salmon of twelve pounds carefully wrapped in brown paper.

'I heard as how you were having a bad time of it, Mr Bowers, so last neet when that gong sounded in th' Hall an they all sat down for dinner like, ah nipped down to that private pool they keep to th' sens. 'Ad this fella inside five minutes; you mont let on like?'

'I won't let on, Johnny,' said Frank, 'but how did you catch the fish so quickly?'

'We has ways and means, sir,' said Johnny, giving a knowing wink, gratefully pocketing the two pound notes Frank held out for him. 'Once that gong sounds at neet there's usually a race on between us staff, keepers an' all, as to who can catch fust en. I usually win like.'

26

A Brush With the Law

It was the middle of July, 1938, and Frank was about to find himself in two separate courtrooms inside fourteen days. In the first case he was to appear as a prosecution witness, having apprehended a burglar in his own home. In the second case the boot was on the other foot – he was due to appear at Northallerton County Court accused of 'Driving under the influence of Alcohol and Resisting Arrest'.

He had been summoned to appear at Ripon Magistrates' Court, close by the Cathedral at ten o'clock in the morning

'Merely committal proceedings, Mr Bowers, the Crown Prosecutor informed him; 'since you are the only witness and it's such a straightforward case, all you are asked to do is corroborate, under oath, the statement you made to the police when you apprehended one of the accused; shouldn't take long. Have you recovered from your injuries?'

Frank felt the remains of the scar on the back of his head. 'Still a little tender, but thank you, I feel well and have stopped having dizzy spells.'

He'd come home from the Auction Mart early one afternoon. It was a glorious sunny day and with most of the farmers busy in the hay fields, there had only been a light show of stock forward for sale.

He'd dropped Evelyn off at the station in the morning where she'd joined other members of the Women's Institute (she was President of the local branch) for a day trip to Scarborough, promising to pick her up on her return in the evening.

Frank, much to his wife's delight, had recently purchased a newly-built detached house about a hundred yards away from the entrance to the Brooms. It was close to the main road, but surrounded by lawns and a pleasant garden.

'Time we had a place of our own, Frank, not living in rented farmhouses as we have done since we married – it'll be twenty years come next

March,' she'd hinted, hoping for once Frank might remember his wedding anniversary.

He'd paid scant attention to a scruffy-looking van parked by his garden fence thirty yards away from the drive entrance, and was still blissfully unaware there was anything unusual as he fumbled for his back door key. The constant tooting of the horn of the van on the main road and the fact that the small window beside the door was wide open failed to alert him to what happened next.

Frank heard a scuffle as he stepped into the hall; there above him were two men, even more startled than himself. They were halfway down the stairs with his safe. It was quite small but extremely heavy, as Frank was only too well aware, having helped haul the thing upstairs only recently.

They had it teetering on the second landing, obviously contemplating dropping it through the bannisters, as Frank walked in; before he knew what was happening, it came crashing through the uprights.

'Lucky to be alive, Sergeant,' he was to tell the police when they finally arrived, summoned by Frank's rather garbled telephone message. 'Could have flattened me,' he said, holding a blood-stained rag to his head. 'Split me head open, as you can see, but luckily must have bounced off my shoulder. It's bruised but I can still move it all right.'

'The doctor's on his way, sir. Looks as if this chap could do with some medical attention at the same time, do you know who he is?'

'No idea, at least two have got away. Wouldn't be surprised if there isn't somebody local mixed up in this, knowing the house would be empty; I'm usually at the Auction Mart much later than this.'

'Yes, sir; if I may be so bold your – what should we say – slightly erratic? style of driving home on market days has been noted and reported to my desk on numerous occasions! How did this chap come to get injured?'

'That safe knocked me flying, as you can imagine, Sergeant. I was a bit dazed but I sort of came to as two fellas dashed out of the front door. I caught this chap with a rugby tackle; I think his head struck the gatepost because he was out cold when I tied his hands behind his back.'

'We'll soon trace the van if that number you gave us is correct. Let's hope this is the small gang we've been seeking for some time; sure to help next week, when I see you are due to appear in court at Northallerton. I was in that bus you ran into at Easter; it was our divisional football team, you know!'

'I had heard,' said Frank, 'nivver ever been in trouble with you fellas, and I have to run into a bus a mile from home with thirty-five rozzers

278

A Brush with the Law

aboard; wouldn't care but you were all three parts cut, and that bus smelt like a brewery!'

'I have to admit the driver pulled up in a hurry; if you hadn't come round to his cab threatening to knock his bleeding block off, or words to that effect, then resisted arrest, it might have been all right.'

'I heard you'd won the league and had been celebrating in every pub in the district,' said Frank.

'True,' said the Sergeant, 'but you were well away.'

'Deserved to be,' said Frank, 'put young Archie Tomlinson up on a four-year-old I bred; first time out, took him to Otley Show and my old mate Gunner Welburn made him Hunter Champion. We didn't half wet his head afterwards.'

Within days Frank was back in court, this time at Northallerton, accused of driving without due care and attention, and also disorderly conduct under the influence of drink, swearing at the police and resisting arrest. Frank dutifully rose to his feet alongside his solicitor as three magistrates entered the court; he knew them well. The presiding magistrate was Major Hubert De Butts Cowgill, a local landowner, nicknamed Cow Girl by his hunting friends; Frank had known him for many years. His florid complexion and his pitted bulbous nose bore proof of his addiction to whisky.

279

'Th head man allus drinks trebles,' Frank murmured out of the side of his mouth to his advocate.

The Major was flanked by two associates; one was Tom Lister who farmed near Sandhutton and regularly sold Frank a good unbroken hunter; they usually contrived to do a deal in the early evening and then retire to the Busby Stoop for a drink or two to clinch it. Tom had winked at Frank as he sat down.

'That wink's a good sign,' said Frank to his solicitor, 'I think we should change the plea to guilty.'

The third magistrate was the only one Frank wasn't sure of. He was a corn merchant of some repute, a Methodist lay preacher and a pillar of the local community.

The Major cleared this throat: 'Will the accused please stand.' Frank rose to his feet. 'Are you John Francis Bowers of The Brooms in the parish of Baldesby St James near the township of Thirsk in the county of York?'

'Yes, sir.'

'You are accused that on the third day of April 1938, you did recklessly without due care and attention at seven-thirty in the evening drive your motor car into the rear of a stationary constabulary bus near Howefield crossroads, causing extensive damage to police property; and did then threaten the driver with physical violence by suggesting he climb down from his cab so that you, and here I quote, "would knock his bleeding head off", and that furthermore did resist arrest when numerous policemen tried to remonstrate with you and were forcibly taken into custody. Do you plead guilty or not guilty?'

Frank turned to his solicitor who rose to his feet: 'May it please the court my client wishes to take up as little of your time as possible; and whereas we officially notified you that the plea would be not guilty, in view of the fact, as your worships are no doubt aware, the accused is under some strain following his heroic action only a few days ago in apprehending a member of a gang who have been pillaging the district and have since been rounded up; at which time I must add my client was quite seriously injured in protecting his own property; I am advised by my client he now wishes to plead guilty.'

Major Hubert looked down over his glasses, smiled and said, 'You may sit down, Frank.'

After a whispered conversation the Major bent forward and spoke to the Clerk of the Court below him. 'Please rise,' intoned this worthy gentleman, 'the court will recess!'

'We sit here and wait, Mr Bowers,' said his young advocate, 'they seem to be kindly disposed towards you.'

'I'm not sure about that corn merchant fella, name of Greensit, Greenshite I call him – praying mantis, that's what he is. Fit me up last year with a lousy sample of grass seed, followed that up with some sugar beet which barely germinated. I had a lot of complaints at the market so I banned him from trading there; shouldn't wonder he'll try and get his own back.'

The magistrates returned some twenty minutes later. 'Please rise,' intoned the clerk. 'Will the accused please step forward and remain standing.'

Frank took a quick glance at all three magistrates as they sat down; Major Hubert was bent forward peering at his notes; Tom Lister gave an apologetic shrug of his shoulders; Bill Greensit had a triumphant glint in his eyes.

The Major once again cleared his throat. 'John Francis Bower, we have given due consideration to the serious charges brought against you to which you have pleaded guilty and in arriving at our verdict have taken into account your brave action recently, leading to the arrest of dangerous criminals. We have also carefully studied the letter you submitted earlier to the court as a plea of mitigation and are fully aware of the importance you place on the continued use of your motor car for business purposes.

'We have decided to be lenient in this case but must issue a warning that any repetition of this sort of behaviour will be dealt with most severely.

'You are to be fined thirty pounds and banned from driving for six months; please leave your driving licence with the clerk as you leave the court.'

Frank was stunned. The indignity of having to use a bicycle, or to go to market on horseback, or to have someone drive him around on valuations, was too much. He raised his arm, pointing at Bill Greensit. 'I'll knock that smirk off your ugly...'

'Take it easy, sir,' his young advocate said as he spun him around, 'you'll be done for contempt of court next; come, "least said, soonest mended".'

'Aye, you're right lad, my old mum always used to say that, rest her soul; I'm glad she's not around to hear about this carry on.'

Frank should have appeared in the Divorce Court in Leeds only days later. He had scurried along to see his solicitor in Boroughbridge as soon as the bombshell had dropped through his letter box.

'Right, Frank, let's take it calmly,' said his solicitor. 'I gather from this

281

letter you are being accused of committing adultery with the Honourable Lady Webber of Litton Hall and Colonel Webber is suing his wife for divorce on the grounds that he found you together in a compromising situation on a date to be specified; evidence will also be forthcoming that adultery had occurred between you on numerous occasions both prior to that date and since. Is this true?'

'Well, er – yes! I suppose so.'

'How do you mean, you suppose so?' demanded Mr Fitzgerald. 'We've known each other a long time, Frank, and I know you can't refuse a pretty face. Has the Colonel got a case?'

'Only if Miranda has blown the gaff and I don't think she has. Old Webber was threatening her with divorce last time we met, but she confirmed that, apart from the time he caught us in the stables, he knew nothing about our other meetings and if he went ahead she felt obliged to contest it.'

'We are going to need a very clever barrister to get you out of this hole, Frank; they don't come cheap. Simon Bernstein is by far the best; he has chambers in Leeds. I'll write to him outlining the case and if he'll take it on, you and I can motor over there together.'

Ten days later they were both shown into Mr Bernstein's office. A short, heavily-built young man with jet black hair and bushy eyebrows held out a flabby hand. 'Sit down, Mr Bowers, you here in front; Mr Fitzgerald could perhaps sit on the couch at the rear. Now sir, I have the bare outline of this case. Can I please have your side of the story from the beginning. When did you first meet this lady?'

'We first met in June about four years ago.'

'Sorry to interrupt, Mr Bowers, "about" won't do, I want to know exactly.'

'Yes, well it was the first week of June 1934. I judged at a small horse show in Upper Wharfedale, gave her granddaughter first prize in a lead rein class and dined with the family that night. Funnily enough I didn't pay too much attention to her Ladyship at the time; I can remember how refined she was, in a class of her own compared to everyone else there; much younger than the Colonel, married at eighteen and produced twin daughters when she was twenty; two of the most attractive girls you could ever wish to see; they were twenty-eight then. The Yorkshire Show was at Bradford that year; the Colonel had asked me to look after them and mother came as chaperone. I was asked to judge the breeding classes, and when I'd finished that's when I took Lady Webber to the members' bar. We had quite a long session; I remember she drank nothing but neat brandy as fast as it came and never turned a hair.

'We discovered we had the same birthday. She's very keen on the signs of the zodiac you know; anyhow she made me feel about eight foot tall and kept repeating how grateful she was about me finding livery for her girls and their hunters for the coming season. I think she'd mistaken gratitude for love by the end of the afternoon – I've seen a few women do that,' said Frank, rambling on.

'Quite so,' said the barrister, 'do go on.'

'Well, I remember that evening she sent the girls home with the horse box; there were quite a few coming onto the market at that time, and before I knew it we were sharing a hotel bedroom. Twice as passionate as her daughters!'

'I beg your pardon?' said Simon Bernstein sitting bolt upright.

'Ah, yes, well, you wanted to know everything.'

'Indeed. Do proceed, sir.'

'Yes, well. The daughters, Zoe and Abigail, both built like Greek goddesses I might add, started hunting two or three days a week with the Bedale that winter, and as I've said I fixed them up with livery at Melmerby Hall. If they'd had a hard day they'd stop over ready for the next week; that's when I got to know them better!'

'Do you mean you became intimate?' asked Simon.

'There didn't seem to be any harm.'

'With both of them?'

'Yes,' said Frank, 'but never at the same time.'

'Thank God for small mercies,' sighed the barrister.

'Never in the same league as Mummy.' It was Frank's turn to sigh.

'I'd been warned they could be lesbians,' said Frank, 'Must be because they were identical twins, both very frigid, you know.'

'No, I wouldn't know, Mr Bowers,' said Simon Bernstein. 'Tell me, did you continue to see the Lady Miranda regularly after that?'

'Oh yes,' grinned Frank, 'she came over here as often as she could get away.'

'*Habit adulter*,' sighed Simon.

'I beg your pardon?' said Frank.

'Oh nothing, it's the Latin term for one who habitually commits an act of adultery,' said the barrister. I don't really see how I can make out a case for the defence of your client, Mr Fitzgerald.'

'Hang on a minute, I'm only telling you the truth,' said Frank, 'The Colonel knows nowt about this, nor does anybody else apart from us three and the lady in question. He's basing his case on supposition, after that evening he sort of surprised us in the stables.'

'Tell me about that, Mr Bowers,' said Simon Bernstein with a resigned look on his face.

'Well her Ladyship had sent me a letter, addressed to the Auction Mart, asking if I could break my rule not to visit the Hall because she was having problems with a young horse who the vet thought could be a rig.'

'Pardon me, what's a rig?'

'Oh, a rig is an entire horse that has not been properly castrated and still retains his full male characteristics; he's inclined to get a bit naughty if he gets near any females.'

'Rather akin to yourself,' said Simon, grinning broadly in the direction of Mr Fitzgerald at the rear of the room.

Frank ignored the remark; he was having difficulty sizing this barrister fellow up. Rather acts like an adversary than an adviser, he thought to himself, but at least he seems to have a sense of humour.

'Kindly proceed,' said Simon.

'Well, when I got there, apart from the old family butler, everyone else was either away or had been given a couple of days off; the Colonel was salmon fishing in Scotland and the twins were away down in Oxfordshire visiting relatives.'

'Very handy,' smirked Simon, 'very handy indeed.'

'Well, yes,' said Frank.

'A finely baited trap,' Simon quipped, 'and you fell for it?'

'I suppose so.'

'And that was the one and only time you ever went to the Hall?'

'Yes.'

'Good, perhaps we might have a chance after all. Do continue.'

'There's no doubt this horse was a rig and proving very difficult to manage – he'd recently been backed.'

'Pardon?' said Simon.

'Broken in,' said Frank, 'would at least allow someone to sit in the saddle.'

'Right.'

'I tried to make some sense of him but he was fighting the bit all the time and wouldn't respond to the aids.'

'Are you saying he was difficult to ride?'

'Yes,' said Frank, 'almost impossible – very nappy.'

'Pardon me,' said Simon, 'A nappy to me is a cloth you put around a baby's bottom.'

'Sorry,' said Frank, 'He would rather go backwards or sideways instead of forwards when you asked him.'

'I see, so the lady had a genuine reason to ask you to call because,' here he paused, 'because you are a recognised authority on all matters relating to the riding and breaking of the horse.'

'That's right,' said Frank, 'having performed the duties of a top show judge for close on twenty years,' he added.

'Excellent,' said Simon triumphantly, hastily scribbling it all down. 'We may have a defence after all; interesting case, Fitzgerald, you warned me it might be. Then what?'

'I'd had quite a tussle with the horse, prancing and rearing; I could see from the saddle he was flashing his male organ about from side to side, about as long as my arm.'

'Quite so, Mr Bowers, quite so, but I don't think we could introduce evidence of that sort into a Divorce Court.'

'Don't see why not, that's what happened, and I could tell by the flush on her face it had got her Ladyship going. As I led the horse back to his box she was clinging on to me afraid to let go. "I've gone at the knees," she gasped in my ear as I held her up with my free arm. Then when the horse bit her shoulder and ripped her dress that excited her even more. She was pulling me across into an empty stall full of straw before I could even get the saddle off. What could I do? There was this beautiful cultured woman moaning and gasping as she whipped off her torn dress; no man in his right mind could resist.

'Anyhow, I was fully dressed and had taken the saddle and bridle off the horse and was rubbing him down when we heard the car. Miranda was laid half asleep wrapped up in the cow gown. By the time the Colonel burst in she was entirely composed and looking radiant and beautiful wearing the blasted thing.'

'Excuse me, Frank, but what is a cow gown?' asked the barrister.

'Sorry, I though you would know. It's a big rough ugly smock that farm hands wear at milking time, bit like a great big hessian sack; it was hanging on the wall and seemed a handy sort of thing to lie on as I got dragged down.'

'So it's really his word against the two of you?' said Simon thoughtfully.

'Yep.'

'And it really is the case that the horse was difficult and needed an expert to sort him out?'

'Yep.'

'And it genuinely tore the lady's dress and she donned the cow gown to cover up her confusion?'

'Yep.'

'Good, looks like his word against yours, leave it with me. I'll sort out what questions I shall put to you in court and tie in our defence with Lady Miranda's lawyers. Best if we are seen to be acting separately, but we shall really be acting in tandem, hope you understand?'

'I do indeed,' said Frank.

'Well, there we are, Mr Fitzgerald,' said the barrister, 'as long as it stays two to one and there's no surprise evidence of a liaison between her Ladyship and our client here, we might get him off!'

'What does Evelyn think about all this, Frank?' asked Mr Fitzgerald on the way home.

'Haven't told her yet.'

'Well she'll have to know sooner or later, it's bound to hit the headlines.'

In the final event the case against the beautiful Lady Miranda never came to court. It transpired that Simon Bernstein, having prepared his brief, had travelled to London, to Lincoln's Inn Fields and met the barrister acting for the Colonel over a cosy lunch. He had eventually convinced him that they really had no case; it was all based on circumstantial evidence.

So the whole thing was hushed over. Evelyn never got to know; Frank breathed a huge sigh of relief and willingly paid his substantial legal fees; the twins never spoke to Frank again, and her Ladyship continued to see him whenever possible. She bought Frank's mother's flat overlooking the Stray in Harrogate where they enjoyed many a secretive candlelit dinner; as their arms interlocked across the table and glasses clinked, the toast would always be 'to the cow gown'.

27

The Second World War

It is, of course, well chronicled how ill-prepared the British Armies had become when hostilities began in 1939; little seemed to have changed since 1919. It was still felt that the horse had a major role to play in the struggle.

Early in 1940 it had been decided horses should go with an expeditionary force to Norway. Frank, as a civilian this time, but with the same powers as in the 1914–18 conflict, was asked to gather up eighty horses on his farm near Thirsk.

'Funnily enough,' recalled Frank, 'the price remained unaltered.' He had been asked to get his charges to be ready to board ship at Newcastle in the last week of May. He asked Jim Ruddick to help.

There were horses aplenty to be commandeered but many a heated argument on the farm over the inadequate price structure. Eventually sixty animals were ready to leave The Brooms for their long journey to Norway; the other twenty were to be delivered personally by their owners ready to be boxed on board the train waiting in a siding at Thirsk Station.

With little traffic about, the road journey was uneventful. Frank was congratulating himself as the main body of horses trotted onto the bridge over the main Edinburgh to London line when a London express flashed past underneath and enveloped the whole bridge in a dense pall of white smoke. Total chaos ensued. Half the animals stampeded back past Frank and his helpers, the other half galloped flat out the other way past the racecourse to the outskirts of the town; pandemonium had been so sudden and complete that one wretched animal, blinded by smoke, had jumped the parapet and lay badly injured across the main Up line.

The station master, who had seen the approaching herd of horses and turned out all his staff to help pen them prior to loading, stood transfixed.

'There's another express due any minute,' he shouted up at Frank. 'If he hits that horse, it'll bring him off the rails.'

'Well, stop it then!' Frank shouted back.

'The signal box is up yonder,' he shouted, pointing further up the line, 'and he wain't be able to ken what's happened – phone's dead – lines are down!'

Without hesitation Frank turned his horse, galloped around the side of the bridge and put him at a large, heavily padlocked, L.M.S. gate which blocked his way.

'The horse was too startled to do aught but jump it,' chuckled Frank afterwards. 'Don't know who was most surprised, him or me. Anyhow I galloped up to the box, the signalman had the sense to come out on his little platform, he pulled the lever to stop the train with seconds to spare. The driver told me the signal changed from green to red as they flashed towards it; he'd pulled up fifty yards short before I got back to the bridge. There must have been two or three hundred folk on that train and they fairly motor through Thirsk station, eighty or ninety miles an hour at least.'

'There's no doubt about it,' said the station master, 'quick thinking saved us from a major disaster. I'll make sure the Company know about your part in this, Mr Bowers.'

Indeed, when Frank returned from his trip to Newcastle there was a splendid letter of thanks from the London Midland Scottish head office.

At the time Frank was unaware how lucky he was to be returning from Newcastle at all. It had been expected that he would accompany the horses all the way, but the weather was pretty foul for the time of the year and knowing how badly horses travel below decks in a heaving, rolling ship, he persuaded Jim Ruddick to volunteer to go in his place. It was a few weeks later when Frank heard the news; the ship carrying the horses had been dive-bombed off the coast of Norway – there were no survivors. The horses went down with her, still in their stalls.

He could imagine poor old Jim down in the hold trying to quieten his charges following the explosion. Later reports confirmed that the ship sank stern first within a few minutes of being hit, so at least the end was pretty swift.

'There but for the grace of God go I,' Frank muttered to himself.

ADDENDUM

Frank was to live a full and interesting life for the next forty four years. He died peacefully in his own bed on the 28th February, 1984.

The opening paragraph of a letter dated the same day from his solicitor to one of his trustees says it all. It reads:

Dear Mr Robb,
I was very sad indeed to learn of Mr Bower's death. He was such a kind friend to me, especially after my father's death (his saviour in the divorce case Webber v. Webber), and he was always such an entertaining person to speak with. Few people will be more sadly missed in this area as he had such a wide circle of friends who thought very highly of him.

I am enclosing a copy of the Will, etc.

On his deathbed the last whispered message for his housekeeper, barely audible, was that he be buried alongside his wife around eleven-thirty the following Wednesday morning.

'Hounds are at Topcliffe Station, they musn't cancel; happen th' hounds will be in full cry round Guy Robb's coverts when they drop me in ...' He then turned on his side, gave one last sigh and breathed his last.

That is exactly what happened; as the author, along with so many bare-headed friends and representatives of the organisations and firms Frank had dealings with, watched his coffin being lowered slowly into the ground. The Bedale hounds in full cry, encouraged by a series of rapid blasts on the Master's horn, could clearly be heard just a few hundred yards away on the other side of the River Swale.

One would like to think that his wonderful old horse Tuffan, as Frank had suggested to his trusted friend and servant Dick Boynton so many years previously when they buried him overlooking the river, was listening at the same time.

Waggoner's Reserve

The poem from the Sledmere monument. Many years of weathering makes the odd word unreadable:

There remains a noble tale to tell
Of what men do when war befell
And in that fourteen eighteen tide
A call for lads went far and wide
To help to save the world from wrong
To shield the weak and bind the strong.

When from the Wolds XII hundred men
Came from the field and fold and pen
Law of might to labour and to dee for right
And to save the world from wrong
To shield the weak and bind the strong.

The simple lads knew nowt of War
They only knew that GODS OWN LAW
Which SATAN'S Will controls must fall
Unless men then did heed the call
To Gan to save the world from wrong
To shield the weak and bind the strong.

Ere Britain's hopes were dashed or planned
The lads who joined this homely band
To Normandy had passed o'er sea
Where some were maimed and some did dee
And all to save the world from wrong
To shield the weak and bind the strong.

Good lads and game our Ridings pride
These steans are put by this roadside
This tale your children and bairns to tell
On what ye did when war befell
To help to save the world from wrong
To shield the weak and bind the strong.

The photographs of the Memorial and the Poem thereon are published with the kind permission of the Curator of the Sledmere Memorial Museum, Sledmere Estates, Driffield, East Yorkshire.